LATTICE THEORY

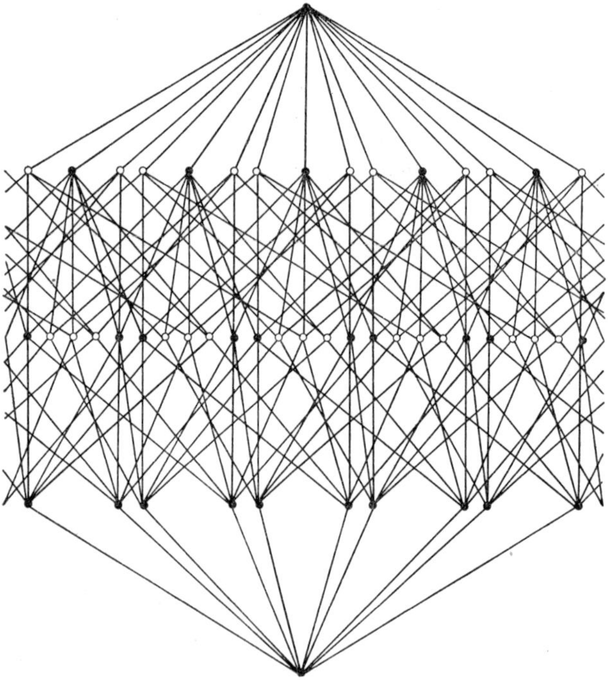

(Frontispiece) Lattice of the partitions of a set of five objects.

LATTICE THEORY

by

THOMAS DONNELLAN

PERGAMON PRESS

OXFORD · LONDON · EDINBURGH · NEW YORK

TORONTO · SYDNEY · PARIS · BRAUNSCHWEIG

Pergamon Press Ltd., Headington Hill Hall, Oxford
4 & 5 Fitzroy Square, London W.1

Pergamon Press (Scotland) Ltd., 2 & 3 Teviot Place, Edinburgh 1

Pergamon Press Inc., 44–01 21st Street, Long Island City, New York 11101

Pergamon of Canada Ltd., 207 Queen's Quay West, Toronto 1

Pergamon Press (Aust.) Pty. Ltd., Rushcutters Bay,
Sydney, New South Wales

Pergamon Press S.A.R.L., 24 rue des Écoles, Paris 5e

Vieweg & Sohn GmbH, Burgplatz 1, Braunschweig

First edition 1968

Library of Congress Catalog Card No. 67–28661

---

08 103416 4 (flexicover)

08 203416 8 (hard cover)

TO THE MEMORY OF MY FATHER

CONTENTS

PREFACE

THIS book gives a strictly elementary account of an important branch of contemporary mathematics, and requires no previous knowledge at all of the new algebra and very little of the old. It is based on the few books and the many papers devoted to lattice theory in the last 35 years; it is appropriate that a first introduction should be entirely derivative, but unusual features include the presentation and exploitation of partitions of a finite set, the thoroughgoing definition without finitary restriction of a semi-modular lattice, the approach to the free Boolean algebra by way of partitions, the emphasis put on irreducibles, and the original treatment of logic, intuitionist and classical, where a tangible and determinate lattice is obtained. A notable exclusion is that of infinite operations and hence of Moore and Galois closure; as a consequence there are no examples with a topological flavour. In accordance with the dictum of Gauss that notions matter more than notations, a least upper bound has been set to the variety of symbols used; for instance, juxtaposition and the plus sign have generally been preferred to $\cap$ and $\cup$ (see Author's Note, p. xi).

College and university students of mathematics, logic and such new technologies as communication engineering will find here easy access to a vast abstract theory; I have had in mind particularly the needs of the solitary student. I should like to recommend the topic of lattices to those teachers who are currently preoccupied with modernization of school mathematics, and who wish to impart a unified and serious intellectual formation rather than to toss to young students a few fashionable gobbets of information.

I must thank friends for their assistance and encouragement, especially the former colleague who designed the Frontispiece and Mr. John Costello, who inundated me with all references in all languages to all recent work in lattice theory; also the Headquarters Staff of the Lancashire County Library for their unfailing help, and the officials of Pergamon Press for their forbearance and courteous efficiency; also my son Peter, who has assisted me in many ways, not least in computing 115,975 partitions at the age of 12. Lastly, I express here my indebtedness to the late Dr. D. A. Steele, of Fordham University, who first flung open the magic casements.

T. DONNELLAN

AUTHOR'S NOTE

A LATTICE is a system of elements with two basic operations: formation of meet and formation of join. For these, different authors have different notations; here is a list:

Meet of elements a, b	Join of elements a, b
$a \cap b$	$a \cup b$
$a \wedge b$	$a \vee b$
$a \cdot b$ or ab	$a + b$

The first symbols are much used, especially when the elements are sets, but they are difficult to read, easy to confuse and lack standard verbal equivalents. The writer would suggest reading "*a* et *b*" for $a \cap b$ and "*a* vel *b*" for $a \cup b$; the Latin monosyllables are genuine connectives, could not be shorter and exactly characterize meet and join of elements in propositional logic.

The second notation is much the same as the first but, curiously enough, is easier to read; it has recently been favoured by Birkhoff and MacLane.

The third notation has all the advantages of simplicity and familiarity; for example,

$$a\,(b + c) = ab + ac$$

is much more perspicuous than

$$a \cap (b \cup c) = (a \cap b) \cup (a \cap c).$$

But this distributive formula implies

$$a \cup (b \cap c) = (a \cup b) \cap (a \cup c)$$

which, written

$$a + bc = (a + b)(a + c),$$

might appear bizarre to the unwary student. A further difficulty is that some lattices, namely Boolean algebras, are also rings and therefore Abelian groups, which have a pre-emptive claim on the plus sign for the group operation. Finally, the most abstract of algebraists occasionally needs to refer to the ordinary addition of natural numbers or integers!

The present writer believes that the advantage of ease of reading outweighs all other considerations when it is a matter of a book where only passing reference is made to ring addition, and has therefore generally preferred the simple notation of juxtaposition and plus sign. In this he follows the recommendation (on p.133) of the authors of *Some Lessons in Mathematics: A Handbook on the Teaching of "Modern" Mathematics*, ed. T. J. Fletcher, Cambridge, 1964.

A word of caution is needed about the meet of two relations. In this book, if P, Q are relations in a set S with elements x, y, z,

$$xPQy \quad \text{means} \quad \text{that } xPy \text{ and } xQy.$$

This meet or intersection of P and Q must not be confused with their product, written $P; Q$ by Tarski and Jónsson but denoted by juxtaposition in, for instance, Szász. For the last named

$$xPQy \quad \text{means} \quad \text{that } xPz \text{ and } zQy \text{ for some } z \text{ in } S.$$

The concept of relative product is not used in this book.

CHAPTER 1

SETS AND RELATIONS

1. Sets

Modern mathematics—and lattice theory is here no exception—is much concerned with sets of elements, and with relations between elements or between sets. In this first chapter we consider sets in general, then the important set of the natural numbers, next relations and operations, then the relation of equivalence, and finally the relation of congruence. These topics either are fundamental to what follows or else provide useful illustrative matter; and in point of fact they reflect the chronological order in which the concepts of lattice theory took shape.

We take for granted the notion of set, of a set containing elements, of elements belonging to a set, of elements being members of a set; and as an immediate example we take the set of four objects $\{a, b, c, d\}$. We say that two sets S, T are equal, writing $S = T$, if and only if they contain precisely the same elements. A set T is said to be a subset of a set S if every member of T is a member of S; we may also say that T is included in S or contained in S and we write $T \leqq S$. Thus the set $\{a, b, c\}$ is a subset of $\{a, b, c, d\}$. If $T \leqq S$ and $S \leqq T$, then the two sets have exactly the same members and $S = T$. If $T \leqq S$ and S contains one or more elements not in T, we say that T is a proper subset of S and may write $T < S$. $S \geqq T$ means $T \leqq S$, $S > T$ means $T < S$. A vertical stroke marks negation: $T \neq S$ means that T and S are not equal.

George Boole (1815–64), an English schoolmaster of great originality, devised a system of calculation with sets. In its modern form this has two basic concepts. First, given two sets S and T, we call the set of elements they have in common their intersection, written ST or $S \cdot T$ like a product in elementary algebra with or without a dot. Thus the intersection of the set $\{a, b, c\}$ and the set $\{b, c, d\}$ is the set $\{b, c\}$. Note that $ST \leqq S$, $ST \leqq T$ for all S, T.

The question at once arises: what if S and T are disjoint, that is, have no elements in common? In this case we do not say that S and T have no intersection, but that their intersection is empty. Indeed, we find it convenient to go further and envisage a unique set having no members—the empty set or void set or null set, which we shall denote by O. Thus if S is the set $\{a, b\}$ and T the set $\{c, d\}$, we may write $ST = O$. The empty set is a subset of every set, $O \leqq S$ for every S, since the requirements of the definition of subset are satisfied vacuously. Also $O \cdot S = O$ for every S.

Secondly, we have the concept of union: given two sets S, T, we call the set of elements which belong to at least one of S, T, their union, writing $S + T$. For instance, the union of the set $\{a, b\}$ and the set $\{b, c\}$ is the set $\{a, b, c\}$. Note that if an element occurs in both sets, it does not occur twice in their union. Clearly we have $S \leqq S + T$, $T \leqq S + T$ for all S, T; $S + O = S$ for all S.

It is clear that the concepts of intersection and union can be applied to three or more sets.

We now select four useful formulae, valid for any sets R, S, T, to be proved from the definitions given:

$$S(S + T) = S. \tag{1}$$

$$S + ST = S. \tag{2}$$

$$R(S + T) = RS + RT. \tag{3}$$

$$R + ST = (R + S)(R + T). \tag{4}$$

To prove these equalities we have to show that all members of the left-hand set in each case are contained in the right-hand set, and conversely. To prove (1) we observe that if x belongs to S and $S + T$, it certainly belongs to S; conversely, since the union of S and T contains the whole of S, the intersection of S and $S + T$ is S, and if x belongs to S, it belongs to $S(S + T)$. Formula (2) is proved from similar considerations. To prove (3): if x belongs to R and $S + T$, then x belongs to R and S, or to R and T, or to R, S and T; that is, x belongs to RS, or to RT, or to both RS and RT; in any case x belongs to at least one of RS, RT; that is, x belongs to $RS + RT$. Conversely if x belongs to $RS + RT$, then x belongs to at least one of RS, RT, hence certainly to R and to at least one of S, T; but this is the same as belonging to $R(S + T)$. The proof of (4) is similar.

Exercises

1. Show that $SS = S + S = S$ for any set S.
2. Prove that $ST \leqq S + T$, for all sets S, T.
3. Prove that if $ST = S + T$, then $S = T$.
4. Show that $ST(S + T) = ST$, for all sets S, T.
5. Show that $ST + S + T = S + T$, for the same.
6. Prove formulae (2) and (4).
7. Prove that $(RS)T = R(ST)$; $(R + S) + T = R + (S + T)$.

2. The Natural Numbers

If the members of two sets S, T can be paired off in a one-to-one correspondence so that to each member of S there corresponds just one member of T and to each member of T there corresponds just one member of S, we say that S and T are equivalent, writing $S \sim T$. If a set S is equivalent to a proper subset of itself, S is said to be infinite; otherwise S is said to be finite.

An infinite set of the greatest importance in mathematics is that of the natural numbers. These are the familiar numbers used in counting

$$1, \quad 2, \quad 3, \ldots,$$

and in fact any set which is equivalent to the set of natural numbers is said to be countable. The essential feature of the set of natural numbers is that there is a first member followed by a succession of members that can be continued as far as we please, each member having a unique immediate successor.

We say two natural numbers a, b are equal, writing $a = b$, if and only if they are identical. We know that any two natural numbers can be related to a third by addition; for instance, the sum of 2 and 3 is 5, in symbols $2 + 3 = 5$. If a, b, c are natural numbers such that $a + c = b$, we say that a is less than b or that b is greater than a, writing $a < b$ or $b > a$. (c is termed the difference of b and a, written $c = b - a$.) If a, b are any natural numbers, it is clear that there must hold just one of the relations $a < b, a = b, a > b$; if either the first or the second of these holds, we write $a \leqq b$, if either the second or the third, $a \geqq b$. We now define min (a, b) to mean a if $a \leqq b$, b if $a > b$; similarly we define max (a, b) to mean a if $a \geqq b$, b if $a < b$; and we establish the following useful results for any natural numbers a, b, c:

$$\min\,[a, \max\,(a, b)] = a. \tag{5}$$

$$\max\,[a, \min\,(a, b)] = a. \tag{6}$$

$$\min\,[a, \max\,(b, c)] = \max\,[\min\,(a, b), \min\,(a, c)]. \tag{7}$$

$$\max\,[a, \min\,(b, c)] = \min\,[\max\,(a, b), \max\,(a, c)]. \tag{8}$$

We prove (5).

$$\text{If } a < b, \quad \min\,[a, \max\,(a, b)] = \min\,(a, b) = a;$$

whereas

$$\text{if } a \geqq b, \quad \min\,[a, \max\,(a, b)] = \min\,(a, a) = a.$$

The proof of (6) is similar. To prove (7) we observe that:

$$\text{if } a > \max\,(b, c), \quad \min\,[a, \max\,(b, c)] = \max\,(b, c)$$

$$\text{and} \qquad \max\,[\min\,(a, b), \min\,(a, c)] = \max\,(b, c);$$

if $\quad \min(b, c) < a \leqq \max(b, c), \quad \min[a, \max(b, c)] = a$

and $\quad \max[\min(a, b), \min(a, c)] = \max[a, \min(b, c)] = a;$

if $\quad a \leqq \min(b, c) \leqq \max(b, c), \quad \min[a, \max(b, c)] = a$

and $$\max[\min(a, b), \min(a, c)] = \max(a, a) = a.$$

Formula (8) may be proved in similar fashion.

Again, we know that any two natural numbers can be related to a third by multiplication; for instance, the product of 2 and 3 is 6, in symbols $2 \times 3 = 6$. If a, b, c are natural numbers such that $a \times c = b$, we say that a and c are factors of b, b is a multiple of a and of c, a and c divide b, b is divisible by a and by c; and we write $a|b$, $c|b$. If a number > 1 has only the trivial factors 1 and itself, it is said to be prime; if it has other, non-trivial, factors, it is said to be composite. It is a major theorem in the theory of natural numbers that every natural number greater than 1 is a product of a unique set of prime factors.

We now define inductively exponents (or indices) of powers of natural numbers. We lay down that for any natural number a, $a^1 = a$, $a^n = a^{n-1} \times a$, n being a natural number not less than 2; a^n is called the nth power of a, n its exponent or index. It will be convenient to adjoin to the natural numbers used as exponents a special symbol 0 called zero, being by definition such that $a^0 = 1$ for any natural number a and $\min(0, a) = 0$, $\max(0, a) = a$, for any a natural number or zero. Then relying on the theorem quoted above we assert that any natural number $a > 1$ is a product of powers of distinct prime factors $p_1, \ldots, p_s$; that is to say

$$a = p_1^{\alpha_1} \times p_2^{\alpha_2} \times \cdots \times p_s^{\alpha_s}$$

or

$$a = \prod_{i=1}^{s} p_i^{\alpha_i}.$$

for some fixed natural number s, where the α_i are natural numbers. Thus $600 = 2^3 \times 3^1 \times 5^2$. Also we may set $1 = p^0$ for any prime p.

We know that any two natural numbers a, b have associated with them two natural numbers termed their highest common factor (h.c.f.) and least common multiple (l.c.m.) respectively. We will denote the former by $\varphi(a, b)$ and the latter by $\mu(a, b)$. Let $p_1, \ldots, p_t$ be the first t primes to occur in the sequence 1, 2, 3, ..., where p_t is the greatest prime factor appearing in the factorizations of a and b. Then if

$$a = \prod_{j=1}^{t} p_j^{\alpha_j} \quad \text{and} \quad b = \prod_{j=1}^{t} p_j^{\beta_j}$$

where some of the exponents α_j, β_j may be zero, we have

$$\varphi(a, b) = \prod p_j^{\min(\alpha_j, \beta_j)}, \quad \mu(a, b) = \prod p_j^{\max(\alpha_j, \beta_j)}.$$

For example, let $a = 18 = 2 \times 3^2$, $b = 600 = 2^3 \times 3 \times 5^2$; then we can compute as follows:

$$a = 2^1 \times 3^2 \times 5^0,$$

$$b = 2^3 \times 3^1 \times 5^2,$$

$$\varphi(a, b) = 2^1 \times 3^1 \times 5^0 = 6,$$

$$\mu(a, b) = 2^3 \times 3^2 \times 5^2 = 1800.$$

We may now establish another set of four formulae that will be useful later:

$$\varphi[a, \mu(a, b)] = a. \tag{9}$$

$$\mu[a, \varphi(a, b)] = a. \tag{10}$$

$$\varphi[a, \mu(b, c)] = \mu[\varphi(a, b), \varphi(a, c)]. \tag{11}$$

$$\mu[a, \varphi(b, c)] = \varphi[\mu(a, b), \mu(a, c)]. \tag{12}$$

To prove (9).

$$\varphi\,[a, \mu\,(a, b)] = \prod p_j^{\min[\alpha_j,\, \max(\alpha_j, \beta_j)]}$$
$$= \prod p_j^{\alpha_j} \qquad \text{by formula (5)}$$
$$= a.$$

The proof of (10) uses formula (6) in a similar way.

To prove (11). Let $p_1, \ldots, p_t$ now be the first t primes, where p_t is the greatest prime occurring in the factorizations of a, b and c. Let a and b have the same product forms as above, and let

$$c = \prod_{j=1}^{t} p_j^{\gamma_j}.$$

Then

$$\mu\,(b, c) = \prod p_j^{\max(\beta_j, \gamma_j)}$$

and hence

$$\varphi\,[a, \mu\,(b, c)] = \prod p_j^{\min[\alpha_j,\, \max(\beta_j, \gamma_j)]} \tag{i}$$

whilst

$$\varphi\,(a, b) = \prod p_j^{\min(\alpha_j, \beta_j)} \quad \text{and} \quad \varphi\,(a, c) = \prod p_j^{\min(\alpha_j, \gamma_j)}$$

whence

$$\mu\,[\varphi\,(a, b), \varphi\,(a, c)] = \prod p_j^{\max[\min(\alpha_j, \beta_j),\, \min(\alpha_j, \gamma_j)]}. \tag{ii}$$

But by formula (7) the typical exponents in expressions (i) and (ii) are identical; and the theorem is proved. To prove (12) use formula (8) in the same way.

Let us illustrate (11) with $a = 30$, $b = 28$, $c = 27$; then

$$\varphi\,[30, \mu\,(28, 27)] = \varphi\,(30, 756) = 6,$$

whilst

$$\mu\,[\varphi\,(30, 28), \varphi\,(30, 27)] = \mu\,(2, 3) = 6.$$

With the same numbers (12) gives

$$\mu\,[30, \varphi\,(28, 27)] = \mu\,(30, 1) = 30,$$

whilst

$$\varphi\,[\mu\,(30, 28), \mu\,(30, 27)] = \varphi\,(420, 270) = 30.$$

Exercises

8. By pairing off a with $2a$, show that the set of the natural numbers is infinite.
9. Prove that min $[a, \min(b, c)] = \min[\min(a, b), c]$; prove the corresponding formula for max.
10. Prove formulae (6) and (8).
11. Let the natural number

$$a = \prod_{i=1}^{s} p_i^{\alpha_i},$$

as above. Show that the number of (trivial and non-trivial) factors of a is

$$\prod_{i=1}^{s} (\alpha_i + 1).$$

12. If h, k are h.c.f. and l.c.m. respectively of natural numbers a, b, prove that $h \times k = a \times b$.
13. Use the results of Exercise 9 to prove that

$$\varphi[a, \varphi(b, c)] = \varphi[\varphi(a, b), c]$$

and that

$$\mu[a, \mu(b, c)] = \mu[\mu(a, b), c].$$

14. Prove formulae (10) and (12).

3. Relations and Operations

We begin now to number definitions, theorems and some examples for convenience of reference.

Definition 1. A finite sequence is a set of n elements placed in one-to-one correspondence with the set of natural numbers $\{1, \ldots, n\}$ where these are arranged in their basic order of succession. An ordered pair is a sequence of two elements.

Definition 2. Given a set S of elements $a, b, \ldots$, let us suppose that we have determined in some precise way a set R of ordered pairs (x, y) with x, y in S; such a set R of ordered pairs we call a dyadic relation in S. If the ordered pair (a, b) belongs to R we may write

aRb and say "a is in the relation R to b" or "the relation R holds between a and b"; a is said to be the antecedent to b, b the consequent to a in the relation. If every member of S appears as antecedent, R is said to be over S. For example, the ordered pairs of natural numbers (1, 2), (2, 3), ..., $(n, n + 1)$, ... define a relation R where aRb means that a is the immediate predecessor of b; R is over the set of the natural numbers.

Definition 3. Given a set S, let us suppose that we have formed sequences $s_n = (x_1, \ldots, x_n)$ of n elements of S, for some fixed n, and that to each of these sequences we have allocated just one element y of S; then the set P of ordered pairs (s_n, y) is called a finitary operation in S; for $n = 1, 2, 3$, P is said to unary, binary, ternary, and for general n, n-ary. It is clear that P is a dyadic relation where s_nPy holds, the antecedent being a sequence of n elements and the consequent a single element. If $n = 1$, the unary operation P is the same as a dyadic relation between single elements; if $n = 2$ (as often occurs), the binary operation P is a dyadic relation between an ordered pair as antecedent and a single element as consequent. If an n-ary operation P is given such that s_nPy holds, we may use the notation $P(x_1, \ldots, x_n) = y$; often a special symbolism is used.

Example 1. Let S be the set of the natural numbers. To each number a we allocate a number $\bar{a}$ as follows:

$$\text{if } a = 1,\ \bar{a} = 1; \quad \text{if } a = \prod_{i=1}^{s} p_i^{\alpha_i},\ \bar{a} = \prod_{i=1}^{s} p_i;$$

thus if $a = 5880 = 2^3 \times 3 \times 5 \times 7^2$, $\bar{a} = 2 \times 3 \times 5 \times 7 = 210$. Then the set of ordered pairs $(a, \bar{a})$ is a unary operation in S. Binary operations in S are numerous: to the ordered pair (a, b) we may allocate their sum (addition) and if $a = b + c$ their difference (subtraction), min (a, b) and max (a, b), their product (multiplication) and if $a = b \times c$ their quotient (division), their h.c.f. and l.c.m., and the power a^b (exponentiation). Notations vary: we have $2 + 3 = 5$, $\min(2, 3) = 2$, $2^3 = 8$.

Definition 4. Let binary operations P and Q be defined in a set S of elements $a, b, c, \ldots$.

(i) If $P[a, P(b, c)] = P[P(a, b), c]$ for all a, b, c, P is said to be associative. Thus

$$9 + (5 + 3) = (9 + 5) + 3$$

but

$$9 - (5 - 3) \neq (9 - 5) - 3.$$

(ii) If $P(a, b) = P(b, a)$ for all a, b, P is said to be commutative. Thus

$$2 \times 3 = 3 \times 2$$

but

$$2^3 \neq 3^2.$$

(iii) If P is commutative and $P[a, Q(b, c)] = Q[P(a, b), P(a, c)]$ for all a, b, c, P is said to be distributive with respect to Q. Thus

$$3 \times (5 + 7) = (3 \times 5) + (3 \times 7)$$

but

$$3 + (5 \times 7) \neq (3 + 5) \times (3 + 7).$$

Definition 5. If in a set A an n-ary operation P is defined for every sequence s_n of n elements of A, the set A is said to be closed with respect to the operation P. A set closed with respect to one or more specified finitary operations is called an algebra. The natural numbers with the binary operations of addition and multiplication form an algebra. A subalgebra is a subset of an algebra A which is self-contained with respect to the operations of A. Thus the even numbers form a subalgebra of the algebra of natural numbers just mentioned; but the odd numbers do not, for the sum of two odd numbers is even.

Example 2. Let A be any subset of a finite set U; let A' be the set of elements of U not in A. Then the set of ordered pairs (A, A') is the unary operation of complementation, and A' is called the complement of A. For $U = \{a, b, c, d\}$, $A = \{a, b, c\}$, we have $A' = \{d\}$. The formation of intersection AB and of union $A + B$ for any subsets A, B of U provides two binary operations in the set S of all subsets of U, both of them associative and commutative, each distributive with respect to the other. The subsets of U then, with complementation, formation of intersection and formation of union, constitute an algebra. If $U = \{a, b, c, d\}$, there are sixteen subsets to serve as elements of the algebra (including the empty set O and U itself); there are fifteen subalgebras, one of two elements, seven of four elements, six of eight elements and one of sixteen. As an example take the four subsets $O, \{d\}, \{a, b, c\}, U$; this set contains the complement of each of its members and the intersection and union of every pair, and hence is a subalgebra.

Example 3. Let S be the set of all ordered pairs (a, b) of natural numbers. Define two binary operations "inf" and "sup" in S as follows:

$$\inf\,[(a_1, b_1), (a_2, b_2)] = [\min\,(a_1, a_2), \min\,(b_1, b_2)];$$

$$\sup\,[(a_1, b_1), (a_2, b_2)] = [\max\,(a_1, a_2), \max\,(b_1, b_2)].$$

These cumbersome definitions describe simple operations; for instance, inf $[(3, 5), (7, 4)] = (3, 4)$, sup $[(3, 5), (7, 4)] = (7, 5)$. With these two associative and commutative operations the ordered pairs of natural numbers form an algebra; ordered pairs of the type $(a, 1)$ clearly form a subalgebra. We may show that, for any elements of the algebra:

$$\inf\{(a_1, b_1), \sup[(a_1, b_1), (a_2, b_2)]\} = (a_1, b_1); \tag{13}$$

$$\sup\{(a_1, b_1), \inf[(a_1, b_1), (a_2, b_2)]\} = (a_1, b_1), \tag{14}$$

and that each operation is distributive with respect to the other:

$$\inf\{(a_1, b_1), \sup[(a_2, b_2), (a_3, b_3)]\}$$

$$= \sup\{\inf[(a_1, b_1), (a_2, b_2)], \inf[(a_1, b_1), (a_3, b_3)]\}, \tag{15}$$

$$\sup\{(a_1, b_1), \inf[(a_2, b_2), (a_3, b_3)]\}$$

$$= \inf\{\sup[(a_1, b_1), (a_2, b_2)], \sup[(a_1, b_1), (a_3, b_3)]\}. \tag{16}$$

To prove (13), (14), (15), (16) we need in turn formulae (5), (6), (7), (8).

Exercises

15. Show multiplication of natural numbers to be distributive with respect to formation of h.c.f. and to that of l.c.m.
16. Let a, b, c be natural numbers, and let X be the binary operation of exponentiation $X(a, b) = a^b$. Prove X distributive with respect to formation of min and to that of max; that is, prove that $X[a, M(b, c)] = M[X(a, b), X(a, c)]$ where M stands for min or max.
17. Verify the details of Example 2.
18. Show that the operations of Example 3 are associative and commutative.
19. Prove formulae (13) and (15), and deduce (14) and (16) by symmetry.
20. Let A be the set of factors x of the natural number

$$\bar{a} = \prod_{i=1}^{s} p_i.$$

Show that A has 2^s elements (see Exercise 11). Define the complement x' of x by $\varphi(x, x') = 1$; show that x' is unique in the set. With this complementation and binary operations φ and μ show A to be an algebra. Exemplify with $\bar{a} = 210$, and compare the 16-element algebra of Example 2.

4. Equivalence Relations

We now study a relation of particular importance in modern mathematics.

Definition 6. Given a set S of elements $a, b, c, \ldots$, we define an equivalence relation E over S as any dyadic relation over S which is:

(i) reflexive: for every a in S, aEa;
(ii) symmetric: if aEb, then bEa;
(iii) transitive: if aEb and bEc, then aEc.

Example 4. Let S be the set of natural numbers, where aEb if and only if $a + b$ is even. Conditions (i) and (ii) are clearly fulfilled; as to (iii), if $a + b$ and $b + c$ are divisible by 2, then $a + (b + b) + c$ and hence $a + c$ are so divisible. In this equivalence all the odd numbers are equivalent, and so are all the even.

Example 5. Let S be a set of four objects $\{a, b, c, d\}$; let xEy if x and y belong to the subset $\{a, b\}$ or if they belong to the subset $\{c, d\}$. Here we have really laid down that a and b are equivalent to one another and to themselves, and so are c and d.

Example 6. Let S be the set of natural numbers considered as products of powers of primes. For $1 = a$, define $\bar{a}$ as 1; for $1 < a = \prod p_i^{\alpha_i}$, define $\bar{a}$ as $\prod p_i$; thus if $a = 360 = 2^3 \times 3^2 \times 5$, then $\bar{a}$

$= 2 \times 3 \times 5 = 30$. Then let aEb if and only if $\bar{a} = \bar{b}$. Here all numbers having the same prime factors are equivalent.

THEOREM 1. Any equivalence relation E over a non-empty set S induces a partition of S into disjoint non-empty subsets, which contain all the members of S.

Proof. Let subsets of S be formed by the following rule: If aEb, put a and b in the same subset. Since aEa for every a in S by reflexivity (Def. 6 (i)), every element a of S is in some subset, even if it is the only member of that subset. Further, if a and b were in one subset, and b and c in another, then we would have aEb and bEc, whence by transitivity (Def. 6 (iii)) aEc, and a and c would be in the same subset, contrary to the supposition just made; hence the subsets are disjoint.

Definition 7. The subsets of Th. 1 are called equivalence classes or the blocks of the partition.

In Example 5 the equivalence relation is actually defined by a partition of the sort described in Th. 1; in Example 4 the natural numbers are partitioned into two infinite classes 1, 3, 5, ... and 2, 4, 6, ...; in Example 6 we have 1 in a class by itself, all other natural numbers being classified according to the variety of their distinct prime factors, one class, for instance, containing all numbers of the form 2^r, another all those of form $2^r \times 3^s$, etc.

THEOREM 2 (Converse of Theorem 1). Any partition of a set S into disjoint blocks or subsets such that every member of S is in some block and no member of S is in more than one block induces an equivalence relation E over S.

Proof. For a, b elements of S define a relation E over S by aEb if and only if a and b belong to the same block of the partition. We must show that E is an equivalence relation. Clearly E is reflexive and symmetric; as to transitivity, if a and b belong to the same block, and likewise b and c, and if b can appear in only one block, then there is only one block in question, to which a, b, c all belong, and hence aEc.

Of the possible partitions of a set two should be specially noted: the partition in which each block contains just one element—this we call the zero partition; and the partition with only one block, which contains all the elements of the set—this we call the unity partition. In the first each element is equivalent to itself and to no other; in the second all elements are equivalent. We also note the partitions in which at most one block contains more than one element—these we shall call singular; partitions in which this condition is not fulfilled will be called non-singular.

The number $p(n)$ of possible partitions of a finite set of n elements is obviously finite; for n small, the actual partitions can be enumerated.

Example 7. There are 15 partitions of a set of four objects $\{a, b, c, d\}$. We denote them as follows:

U $(abcd)$,

R_1 (ab/cd), R_2 (ac/bd), R_3 (ad/bc),

Q_1 (abc/d), Q_2 (acd/b), Q_3 (bcd/a), Q_4 (abd/c),

P_1 $(ab/c/d)$, P_2 $(cd/a/b)$, P_3 $(ac/b/d)$,

P_4 $(bd/a/c)$, P_5 $(bc/a/d)$, P_6 $(ad/b/c)$,

O $(a/b/c/d)$.

O is the zero partition, U the unity partition; R_1, R_2, R_3 are the only non-singular partitions.

We can arrive at a formula for the number $p(n)$ if we assume that the number of ways of selecting r things from n is

$$\frac{n \times (n-1) \times \cdots \times (n-r+1)}{1 \times 2 \times \cdots \times r},$$

written ${}^nC_r$ or $\binom{n}{r}$. It will be convenient to use the symbol 0, with $0 < 1$, adjoined to the natural numbers as in § 2; by convention we set $\binom{n}{0} = 1$ and also $p(0) = 1$. Clearly $p(1) = 1$; hence we may concern ourselves with a set of $n + 1$ elements, for n any natural number. We select one element a; from the n remaining elements we choose r elements to put with a to form a block of $r + 1$ elements containing a; we can make this choice in $\binom{n}{r}$ ways, for every r, $0 \leqq r \leqq n$; each time that we make this choice, we have $n - r$ elements left over, to be partitioned in $p(n - r)$ ways. Thus we have

$$p(n+1) = \binom{n}{0} p(n) + \binom{n}{1} p(n-1) + \cdots + \binom{n}{n} p(0)$$

$$= \sum_{r=0}^{n} \binom{n}{r} p(n-r).$$

The values of $p(n)$ rise steeply with n; for instance, $p(10) = 115{,}975$. Further statistical information on partitions will be found in Chapter 2, § 9.

We remind the reader that α implies β, where α and β are statements, means that if α is true, then β must be true; or again, α is true only if β is true. If E_X, E_Y are equivalence relations over a set S, and if aE_Xb implies aE_Yb, we say that E_X is contained in E_Y, E_Y contains E_X, writing $E_X \leqq E_Y$. Thus in Example 7 $E_{P_1} \leqq E_{R_1}$ but $E_{P_1} \not\leqq E_{R_2}$, for $aE_{P_1}b$ is true, $aE_{R_2}b$ is false. Two equivalence relations are equal, $E_X = E_Y$, if each is contained in the other.

If X, Y are the partitions corresponding to E_X, E_Y, and $E_X \leqq E_Y$, each block of X must be wholly contained in some block of Y: for if a, b were in the same block of X but in different blocks of Y, aE_Xb would be true and aE_Yb false, contrary to hypothesis. When the blocks of X are thus subsets of the blocks of Y, we say the partition X is contained in the partition Y, Y contains X, writing $X \leqq Y$. We also say that X is a refinement of Y. Two partitions are equal, $X = Y$, if each is contained in the other.

We now introduce two binary operations on equivalence relations and on the associated partitions. If E_L, E_M are equivalence relations over a set S, we define as their meet the relation E_LE_M where aE_LE_Mb if and only if aE_Lb and aE_Mb. It is easy to prove E_LE_M reflexive, symmetric and transitive, and hence an equivalence relation; and it is easy to extend the definition to any finite number of relations. Clearly $E_LE_M \leqq E_L$, $E_LE_M \leqq E_M$.

Before proceeding further, we make the restriction that S is finite, to avoid certain difficulties that arise with partitions of infinite sets. If L and M are the partitions corresponding to E_L, E_M, form the set of all the non-empty intersections of all the blocks of L and M, and denote this set by LM. Since any element a of S appears in just one block of L and in just one block of M, it can appear in only one intersection in LM, and must so appear; therefore LM is a partition in the sense of Theorem 2, and clearly is the partition corresponding to E_LE_M. LM is called the meet of the partitions L, M; the definition is extended in an obvious way to any finite number of partitions. From the definition of intersection of sets in § 1 we have immediately $LM \leqq L$, $LM \leqq M$. As an illustration we take partitions P_1, Q_1, R_1 from Example 7.

Q_1	R_1	Intersection
a, b, c	a, b	a, b
a, b, c	c, d	c
d	a, b	empty
d	c, d	d

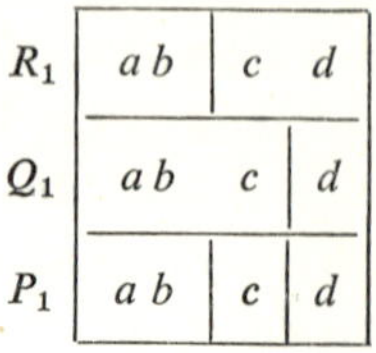

The meet of (abc/d) and (ab/cd) is $(ab/c/d)$, or $P_1 = Q_1R_1$.

The join $E_L + E_M$ of two equivalence relations E_L, E_M is defined as the meet of all relations E_X containing both E_L and E_M, that is, the meet of all relations E_X such that aE_Lb implies aE_Xb and at the same time cE_Md implies cE_Xd. By definition of meet $E_L + E_M$ is an equivalence relation. It is obvious how the definition may be extended to any finite number of relations, and that $E_L \leqq E_L + E_M$, $E_M \leqq E_L + E_M$. We will form the join of E_{P_1} and E_{P_2} from Example 7.

E_{P_1} is contained in E_{P_1}, E_{Q_1}, E_{R_1}, E_{Q_4}, E_U;

E_{P_2} is contained in E_{P_2}, E_{Q_2}, E_{R_1}, E_{Q_3}, E_U.

Only E_{R_1} and E_U contain both E_{P_1} and E_{P_2}; whence $E_{P_1} + E_{P_2} = E_{R_1}E_U = E_{R_1}$.

Let $L + M$ be the partition corresponding to $E_L + E_M$. If X is a partition containing partitions L and M, then every block A of L must be wholly contained in some block C of X, and likewise every block B of M in some block D of X. If aE_Lb and bE_Mc, then aE_Xb and bE_Xc and by transitivity aE_Xc; hence if block A of L overlaps block B of M, their union $A + B$ is wholly contained in a single block C of X; in the same way, if X' is another partition containing L and M, $A + B$ is wholly contained in a single block C' of X'. Therefore $A + B$ is wholly contained in the intersection CC'; and hence from the definition (as a meet) of $E_L + E_M$, the overlapping blocks of L and M are wholly contained in a single block of $L + M$.

Let Y be *any* partition having this property that overlapping blocks of L and M are wholly contained in just one of its blocks; since from the nature of the partitions every block of L must overlap at least one block of M and vice versa, the blocks of L and M must lie entirely within blocks of Y; that is, Y is one of the partitions X containing L and M, and $L + M \leqq Y$. Hence $L + M$ is characterized as the most refined partition having the property that overlapping blocks of L and M are wholly contained in just one of its blocks. As illustration we take the partitions corresponding to the relations in

U	$a\ b\ c\ d$
R_1	$a\ b \mid c\ d$
P_2	$a \mid b \mid c\ d$
P_1	$a\ b \mid c \mid d$

the last example. R_1 and U are the only partitions of the set which contain in single blocks the overlapping blocks of P_1, P_2; R_1 is a refinement of U; hence we have: $P_1 + P_2 = R_1$.

It is clear from a scrutiny of the definitions that both formation of meet and of join of equivalence relations or partitions of a set S are commutative operations; before proving associativity:

$$E_L\,(E_M E_N) = (E_L E_M)\,E_N, \tag{17}$$

$$L\,(MN) = (LM)\,N, \tag{17'}$$

$$E_L + (E_M + E_N) = (E_L + E_M) + E_N, \tag{18}$$

$$L + (M + N) = (L + M) + N, \tag{18'}$$

we establish two theorems.

We prove that if $E_V \leqq E_X$ and $E_W \leqq E_Y$, then (i) $E_V E_W \leqq E_X E_Y$ and (ii) $E_V + E_W \leqq E_X + E_Y$.

(i) By hypothesis aE_Vb implies aE_Xb and aE_Wb implies aE_Yb. Now aE_VE_Wb implies aE_Vb and aE_Wb; these imply aE_Xb and aE_Yb; and these last imply aE_XE_Yb; implication being a transitive relation, it follows that aE_VE_Wb implies aE_XE_Yb, or $E_VE_W \leqq E_XE_Y$.

(ii) $E_V \leqq E_X \leqq E_X + E_Y$ and $E_W \leqq E_Y \leqq E_X + E_Y$. Hence $E_X + E_Y$ contains both E_V and E_W; therefore by definition of join (of equivalence relations E_V, E_W) $E_V + E_W \leqq E_X + E_Y$.

We observe further that (iii) $E_X \leqq E_X$, (iv) $E_XE_X = E_X$, (v) $E_X + E_X = E_X$ follow immediately from the definitions.

To prove (17):

$E_LE_M \leqq E_M$ and $E_N \leqq E_N$;	$E_L \leqq E_L$ and $E_ME_N \leqq E_M$;
then by (i) $(E_LE_M)\,E_N \leqq E_ME_N$.	then by (i) $E_L(E_ME_N) \leqq E_LE_M$.
Also $(E_LE_M)\,E_N \leqq E_LE_M \leqq E_L$;	Also $E_L(E_ME_N) \leqq E_ME_N \leqq E_N$;
hence by (i)	hence by (i)
$[(E_LE_M)\,E_N]\,[(E_LE_M)\,E_N]$	$[E_L(E_ME_N)]\,[E_L(E_ME_N)]$
$\leqq E_L(E_ME_N)$,	$\leqq (E_LE_M)\,E_N$,
and by (iv)	and by (iv)
$(E_LE_M)\,E_N \leqq E_L(E_ME_N)$.	$E_L(E_ME_N) \leqq (E_LE_M)\,E_N$.

Each side of (17) is contained in the other, whence the equality.

If in this proof we replace all meets by joins, use (ii) and (v) instead of (i) and (iv) and reverse all "inequality" signs, we obtain (18); (17′) and (18′) are corollaries, or may be proved directly in terms of partitions.

Other useful formulae are the following:

$$E_L\,(E_L + E_M) = E_L; \tag{19}$$

$$L\,(L + M) = L; \tag{19'}$$

$$E_L + E_L E_M = E_L; \tag{20}$$

$$L + LM = L. \tag{20'}$$

To prove (19): In (i) above put $E_V = E_X = E_W = E_L$, and $E_Y = E_L + E_M$. Then $E_L E_L = E_L \leqq E_L(E_L + E_M)$. But $E_L(E_L + E_M) \leqq E_L$ by definition of meet. Hence the equality in (19).

To prove (20): In (ii) above put $E_V = E_X = E_Y = E_L$ and $E_W = E_L E_M$. Then $E_L + E_L E_M \leqq E_L + E_L = E_L$. But $E_L \leqq E_L + E_L E_M$ by definition of join. Hence the equality in (20).

Formulae (19′) and (20′) are immediate corollaries, or may be proved directly.

The reader may test the validity of these formulae with partitions chosen from those of Example 7. Thus we have:

$$P_3(Q_1R_1) = P_3P_1 = O, \qquad P_1 + (P_2 + P_6) = P_1 + Q_2 = U,$$

$$(P_3Q_1)R_1 = P_3R_1 = O, \qquad (P_1 + P_2) + P_6 = R_1 + P_6 = U,$$

$$P_1(P_1 + P_2) = P_1R_1 = P_1,$$

$$Q_1 + Q_1R_1 = Q_1 + P_1 = Q_1.$$

Exercises

21. Prove $S \sim T$ as defined for sets S, T at the beginning of § 2 to be an equivalence relation.
22. Let U be a finite set of n elements; let the number of subsets of U (including the empty set and U itself) be denoted by $s(n)$. By using the binomial theorem

$$(a + b)^n = \sum_{r=0}^{n} \binom{n}{r} a^{n-r} b^r$$

or otherwise, show that $s(n) = 2^n$. Cf. Exercise 20.
23. Show that $p(1) = 1$, $p(2) = 2$, $p(3) = 5$, $p(4) = 15$, and find $p(5)$.
24. Show that α implies β where α and β are statements is not an equivalence relation.
25. Prove that $E_L E_M$ is an equivalence relation.
26. Show that LM is the least refined partition contained in L and M.

27. Show that if E_L, E_M are equivalence relations (over a finite set S) $E_L + E_M$ may be defined as the relation where

    $a\ (E_L + E_M)\ b$ if and only if there can be found a finite sequence $x_1, \ldots, x_{2n-1}$ of elements of S such that $aE_Lx_1, x_1E_Mx_2, x_2E_Lx_3, \ldots, x_{2n-1}E_Mb$.

    Hint: If $E =$ join as defined in text, $E' =$ join as defined here, first show E' to be an equivalence relation, then that $E \leqq E'$ and $E' \leqq E$.
28. Prove formulae (19′) and (20′) directly in terms of partitions.
29. If K, L, M are singular partitions of a finite set and $K \geqq M$, prove that $K(L + M) \geqq KL + KM = KL + M$.
30. Select three partitions from Example 7 to prove that formation of meet of partitions need not be distributive with respect to formation of join nor join with respect to meet.

5. Congruence Relations

In this section we regard the natural numbers as an algebra with two binary operations, addition and multiplication; here but not elsewhere we shall write ab for $a \times b$, where a, b are natural numbers.

Let us take again the equivalence relation between natural numbers of Example 4, where aEb if and only if $a + b$ is even. If a_1Eb_1 and a_2Eb_2, then $(a_1 + b_1) + (a_2 + b_2) = (a_1 + a_2) + (b_1 + b_2)$ is even; therefore we have $(a_1 + a_2)\,E\,(b_1 + b_2)$. We see that if in a sum the summands are replaced by equivalent elements the class of the sum is undisturbed; the class of the sum depends upon the classes to which the summands belong and not upon the summands themselves. Again, since

$$a_1a_2 + b_1b_2 = (a_1 + b_1)\,a_2 + b_1(a_2 + b_2) - 2b_1a_2,$$

which is clearly even, we have $a_1a_2Eb_1b_2$. Thus factors can be replaced by equivalent numbers without disturbance of the class of the product; the class of the product depends only upon the classes of the factors and not upon the factors themselves. The equivalence classes here are the two sets of the odd and even natural numbers; an instance of what we have proved is that the sum of *any* even number and *any* odd number is always odd, the product always even. The relation E thus provides rules for combining the equivalence classes themselves, making of them a two-element algebra with binary operations of addition and multiplication:

(i) the sum of the class containing a and the class containing b is the class containing $a + b$;
(ii) the product of the class containing a and the class containing b is the class containing ab.

Definition 8. Let A be an algebra with one or more finitary operations such as P with $P(a_1, \ldots, a_n) = y_1$, $P(b_1, \ldots, b_n) = y_2$; let C be an equivalence relation defined over A such that (in each finitary operation P) $a_1Cb_1, a_2Cb_2, \ldots, a_nCb_n$ jointly imply y_1Cy_2; then C is called a congruence relation over A.

THEOREM 3. To any congruence relation C over an algebra A there corresponds an algebra A/C, the elements of which are the equivalence classes into which C partitions A, and which possesses finitary operations on the classes corresponding in number and kind to the finitary operations of A.

Proof. C is an equivalence relation and therefore partitions A into equivalence classes by Theorem 1. C is a congruence relation and therefore by Definition 8 the class of the result of any finitary operation depends only upon the classes of the elements of A operated upon; hence to each finitary operation $P(x_1, \ldots, x_n) = y$ in A there corresponds a finitary operation Q on the equivalence classes, defined by $Q(X_1, \ldots, X_n) = Y$ where $X_1, \ldots, X_n, Y$ denote the classes containing $x_1, \ldots, x_n, y$ respectively.

Definition 9. The algebra A/C of Theorem 3 is called a quotient algebra.

Example 8. Consider the set of all ordered pairs of natural numbers; we make this set into an algebra A by defining two binary operations for all ordered pairs (a, b), (c, d):

(i) $(a, b) + (c, d) = (a + c, b + d)$;
(ii) $(a, b) \times (c, d) = (ac + bd, ad + bc)$.

Thus $(7, 2) + (5, 8) = (12, 10)$; $(7, 2) \times (5, 8) = (51, 66)$.

Next we define a relation C over A by the rule:

(iii) $(a, b)\ C\ (c, d)$ if and only if $a + d = b + c$.

For instance, $(7, 2)\ C\ (9, 4)$. C is clearly reflexive and symmetric; if $(a, b)\ C\ (c, d)$ and $(c, d)\ C\ (e, f)$, then $a + d = b + c, c + f = d + e$, which give $a + d + c + f = b + c + d + e$, whence $a + f = b + e$, $(a, b)\ C\ (e, f)$, and C is transitive; therefore C is an equivalence relation. We now show that C is a congruence relation.

Let $(a_1, b_1)\ C\ (a_2, b_2)$ and $(c_1, d_1)\ C\ (c_2, d_2)$; then by (iii) we have

(iv) $a_1 + b_2 = a_2 + b_1,\ c_1 + d_2 = c_2 + d_1$.

If

$$(a_1, b_1) + (c_1, d_1) = (a_1 + c_1, b_1 + d_1)$$

and

$$(a_2, b_2) + (c_2, d_2) = (a_2 + c_2, b_2 + d_2),$$

then

$$\begin{aligned} a_1 + c_1 + b_2 + d_2 &= (a_1 + b_2) + (c_1 + d_2) \\ &= (a_2 + b_1) + (c_2 + d_1) \quad \text{by (iv)} \\ &= a_2 + c_2 + b_1 + d_1; \end{aligned}$$

hence $(a_1 + c_1, b_1 + d_1)\ C\ (a_2 + c_2, b_2 + d_2)$.

Again, let

$$(a_1, b_1) \times (c_1, d_1) = (a_1c_1 + b_1d_1, a_1d_1 + b_1c_1) = (u_1, v_1),$$

say, and

$$(a_2, b_2) \times (c_2, d_2) = (a_2c_2 + b_2d_2, a_2d_2 + b_2c_2) = (u_2, v_2),$$

say; let also

$$p = a_1 + b_2, \quad q = a_2 + b_1,$$

$$r = c_1 + d_2, \quad s = c_2 + d_1.$$

By (iv) $p = q$, $r = s$.
Then $pc_1 + qd_1 + ra_2 + sb_2 = qc_1 + pd_1 + sa_2 + rb_2$.

Multiplying out and cancelling, we are left with

$$a_1c_1 + b_1d_1 + a_2d_2 + b_2c_2 = a_2c_2 + b_2d_2 + a_1d_1 + b_1c_1$$

or

$$u_1 + v_2 = u_2 + v_1;$$

whence

$$(u_1, v_1)\, C\, (u_2, v_2).$$

Therefore C is a congruence relation over A, and by Th. 3 yields a quotient algebra A/C. The elements of A/C are the classes V, W, X, Y, ... of equivalent ordered pairs, and there are two binary operations defined as follows:

$X + Y = V$ if (a, b) belongs to X, (c, d) to Y,

$(a + c, b + d)$ to V;

$XY = W$ if (a, b) belongs to X, (c, d) to Y,

$(ac + bd, ad + bc)$ to W.

Let a, b be any natural numbers such that $a > b$; then $a + a \neq b + b$ and (a, b), (b, a) are in distinct equivalence classes, but $a + b = a + b$ and (a, a), (b, b) are in the same class. Since $a > b$, the difference $a - b = n$ exists; from

$$a + 1 = b + (a - b) + 1 = b + (n + 1)$$

we have $(a, b)\,C(n + 1, 1)$ and $(b, a)\,C(1, n + 1)$. In view of these congruences the equivalence class containing (a, b) is denoted by $+n$ and called a positive integer; the class containing (b, a) is denoted by $-n$ and called a negative integer. So from the examples above of operations on ordered pairs of A:

$$(7, 2) + (5, 8) = (12, 10), \qquad (7, 2) \times (5, 8) = (51, 66),$$

we derive the operations on classes in A/C:

$$\{\text{Class containing } (7, 2)\} + \{\text{class containing } (5, 8)\}$$
$$= \{\text{class containing } (12, 10)\},$$

$$\{\text{Class containing } (7, 2)\} \times \{\text{class containing } (5, 8)\}$$
$$= \{\text{class containing } (51, 66)\};$$

these operations we call addition and multiplication of integers and we write them in the much more familiar form:

$$5 + (-3) = 2, \qquad 5 \times (-3) = -15,$$

the positive sign being commonly omitted.

We note that $(a, a)\,C(1, 1)$, that $(a, b) + (1, 1) = (a + 1, b + 1)$ which is congruent with (a, b) and that $(a, b) \times (1, 1) = (a + b, a + b)$ which is congruent with $(1, 1)$; therefore we denote the class containing $(1, 1)$ by 0 and call it zero. Thus $(5, 8) + (9, 9) = (14, 17)$ and $(5, 8) \times (9, 9) = (117, 117)$ in A yield in A/C $(-3) + 0 = -3$ and $(-3) \times 0 = 0$.

Example 9. We now define a relation C_j over the integers

$$\ldots, \quad -3, \quad -2, \quad -1, \quad 0, \quad 1, \quad 2, \quad 3, \ldots.$$

Let a, b, c, j be integers where j is positive; we lay down that aC_jb if and only if $a - b$ is divisible by j. Obviously aC_ja; aC_jb implies bC_ja; if aC_jb and bC_jc, then

$$(a - b) + (b - c) = a - c$$

is divisible by j and aC_jc; hence C_j is an equivalence relation. aC_jb is usually written $a \equiv b \pmod{j}$. The associated partition of the integers is into j blocks, all members of the same block leaving the same remainder upon division by j; the blocks are usually called residue classes and denoted by the remainders. Further, if $a_1C_ja_2$ and $b_1C_jb_2$, j divides $a_1 - a_2$ and $b_1 - b_2$ and hence $(a_1 + b_1) - (a_2 + b_2)$; therefore $(a_1 + b_1)\, C_j\, (a_2 + b_2)$; also (multiplication signs being suppressed) j divides $b_1(a_1 - a_2) + a_2(b_1 - b_2) = a_1b_1 - a_2b_2$, whence $(a_1b_1)\, C_j (a_2b_2)$; therefore C_j is a congruence relation over the algebra of the integers, yielding a quotient algebra of j residue classes. For every positive integer j we have a congruence relation C_j. Applying the concepts of § 4 we say $C_j \leqq C_k$ if and only if j is a multiple of k; $C_jC_k = C_m$ where m is the l.c.m. of j, k; and $C_j + C_k = C_f$ where f is their h.c.f.

Example 10. (In this example the multiplication sign between integers is again suppressed.) Let (a, b), (c, d) denote ordered pairs of integers with b, d not zero; we construct an algebra A from all such pairs by defining two binary operations:

(i) $(a, b) + (c, d) = (ad + bc, bd)$;
(ii) $(a, b) \times (c, d) = (ac, bd)$.

Thus $(7, 2) + (5, 8) = (66, 16)$; $(7, 2) \times (5, 8) = (35, 16)$. We now define a relation C over A by the rule:

(iii) $(a, b)\, C\, (c, d)$ if and only if $ad = bc$.

Thus $(7, 2) = (21, 6)$. C is clearly reflexive and symmetric; transitivity is readily proved, for if $(a, b)\, C(c, d)$ and $(c, d)\, C(e, f)$, $ad = bc$ and $cf = de$, $adf = bcf = bde$, hence $af = be$ and $(a, b)\, C\, (e, f)$; therefore C is an equivalence relation. Let $(a_1, b_1)\, C\, (a_2, b_2)$ and $(c_1, d_1)\, C\, (c_2, d_2)$; hence

(iv) $a_1 b_2 = a_2 b_1 \quad \text{and} \quad c_1 d_2 = c_2 d_1.$

Then $a_1 b_2 d_1 d_2 + c_1 d_2 b_1 b_2 = a_2 b_1 d_1 d_2 + c_2 d_1 b_1 b_2$ from (iv)

or
$$(a_1 d_1 + b_1 c_1)\, b_2 d_2 = (a_2 d_2 + b_2 c_2)\, b_1 d_1;$$

hence sums of equivalent pairs are equivalent. As for products, we have

$$a_1 c_1 b_2 d_2 = (a_1 b_2)(c_1 d_2) = (a_2 b_1)(c_2 d_1) = a_2 c_2 b_1 d_1,$$

using (iv); hence products are equivalent. Therefore C is a congruence relation, yielding a quotient algebra A/C; the elements of A/C are the classes of equivalent ordered pairs of integers, and the two binary operations of A/C are class addition and class multiplication as derived from (i) and (ii). The element (a, b) of A is called a fraction and written

$$\frac{a}{b};$$

the class of A/C containing (a, b) is called a rational number and is denoted by any of the fractions it contains; each class (apart from such as contain $(0, b)$) contains a unique pair (h, k) where h.c.f. $(h, k) = 1$, often used to denote the class; a class containing (nb, b) is generally denoted by the integer n. Thus we have

$$\tfrac{7}{2} + \tfrac{5}{8} = \tfrac{66}{16} = \tfrac{33}{8}; \quad \tfrac{7}{2} \times \tfrac{5}{8} = \tfrac{35}{16}; \quad \tfrac{33}{-11} = -3.$$

Exercises

31. Show that the set of integers is closed with respect to subtraction.
32. Prove that for integers "minus times minus equals plus".
33. Verify the statements at the end of Example 9.
34. Let p be some fixed prime, and let A_p be the set of those rationals $\frac{a}{b}$ where $b \not\equiv 0 \pmod{p}$. Show that A_p is a subalgebra of the rationals. Let a relation C_p be defined by $\frac{a}{b}\, C_p\, \frac{c}{d}$ if and only if $ad \equiv bc \pmod{p}$; show that C_p is a congruence relation over A_p.

CHAPTER 2

DEFINITION OF A LATTICE

6. Partial Order

In this chapter we define first the relation of partial order and then partially ordered sets, including chains; next we give two definitions of a lattice and prove them equivalent; we conclude with a number of examples of lattices.

Definition 10. Let S be a set of elements $a, b, c, \ldots$ where a relation of equality $x = y$ is already defined; then a relation O of partial order over S is any dyadic relation over S which is:

(i) reflexive: for every a in S, aOa;
(ii) anti-symmetric: if aOb and bOa, then $a = b$;
(iii) transitive: if aOb and bOc, then aOc.

The symbol O in aOb will generally be replaced by $\leqq$; if $a \leqq b$, we say that a is less than or equal to b, a is contained in b, a is included in b, etc. If $a \leqq b$ and $a \neq b$, we may write $a < b$. $b \geqq a$ means $a \leqq b$, $b > a$ means $a < b$. If $a \leqq b$ or $b \leqq a$, we say that a, b are comparable.

Definition 11. A set S over which a relation O of partial order is defined is called a partially ordered set.

Notice that elements of a partially ordered set need not be comparable with one another, though each must be with itself.

Example 11. S is a collection of sets $A, B, \ldots$ and $A \leqq B$ means that A is a subset of B; $A < B$ means that A is a proper subset of B.

Example 12. S is a set of natural numbers $a, b, \ldots,$ and $a \leqq b$ means either that $a = b$ or that there exists c such that $a + c = b$.

Example 13. S is a set of natural numbers and $a \leqq b$ means that there exists c such that $a \times c = b$; that is, a divides b, $a|b$.

Example 14. S is a set of natural numbers and $a \leqq b$ means that $b|a$; that is, a is a multiple of b.

Example 15. S is a set of powers p^n of a prime p, and $p^m \leqq p^n$ means that $m \leqq n$ in the sense of Example 12.

Example 16. S is a set of equivalence relations $E_L, E_M, \ldots$ (over some basic set T), and $E_L \leqq E_M$ means that E_L is contained in E_M; that is, for u, v in T uE_Lv implies uE_Mv as in § 4.

Example 17. S is a set of partitions $L, M, \ldots$ (of some basic set T), and $L \leqq M$ means that L is a refinement of M, as in § 4.

Example 18. S is a set of integers $a, b, \ldots,$ and $a \leqq b$ means that $a - b$ is a negative integer or zero; in particular, $a < 0$ means that a is a negative integer.

Example 19. S is a set of congruence relations C_j, C_k, ..., over the integers, as defined in Example 9, and $C_j \leqq C_k$ means that $k|j$, that is, j is a multiple of k.

Example 20. S is a set of rational numbers $\frac{a}{b}$, $\frac{c}{d}$, ..., and $\frac{a}{b} \leqq \frac{c}{d}$ means that $[(a \times d) - (b \times c)] \times b \times d$ is a negative integer or zero.

Example 21. S is a set of ordered pairs (a, b), (c, d), ... where a, b, c, d, ... are integers positive or zero, and $(a, b) \leqq (c, d)$ means that $a \leqq c$, $b \leqq d$ in the sense of Example 18.

Definition 12. Let S be a partially ordered set of elements $a, b, \ldots$; if $a < b$ and if there is no element x in S such that $a < x < b$ we say that b covers a.

A partially ordered set is conventionally represented by a diagram as follows. Elements are represented by small circles; if b covers a, the circle representing a is joined to that representing b by a *rising* line. The small circles can, of course, be thought of as small spheres in space.

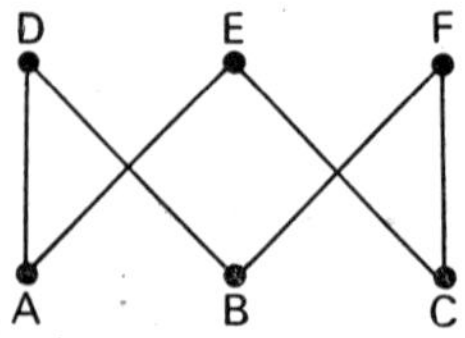

FIG. 1.

Example 22. Let S be the set of proper non-empty subsets of $\{a, b, c\}$: $A = \{a\}$, $B = \{b\}$, $C = \{c\}$, $D = \{a, b\}$, $E = \{a, c\}$, $F = \{b, c\}$; let set-inclusion be the ordering relation. The diagram is given in Fig. 1.

Example 23. Let S comprise the following partitions of $\{a, b, c\}$: $L(ab/c)$, $M(ac/b)$, $N(bc/a)$, $U(abc)$, with the more refined partition contained in the less refined. The diagram is given in Fig. 2.

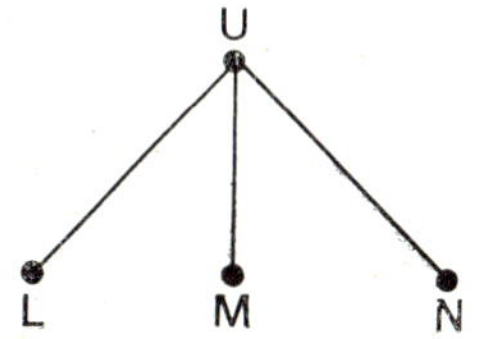

FIG. 2.

Example 24. Let S be the set of non-trivial factors of 12; if $a \leqq b$ means $a|b$, the diagram is as in Fig. 3.

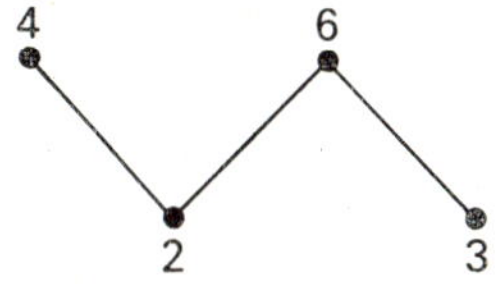

FIG. 3.

Example 25. Let S be the set of even numbers up to 12, with divisibility again the ordering relation. The diagram is given in Fig. 4.

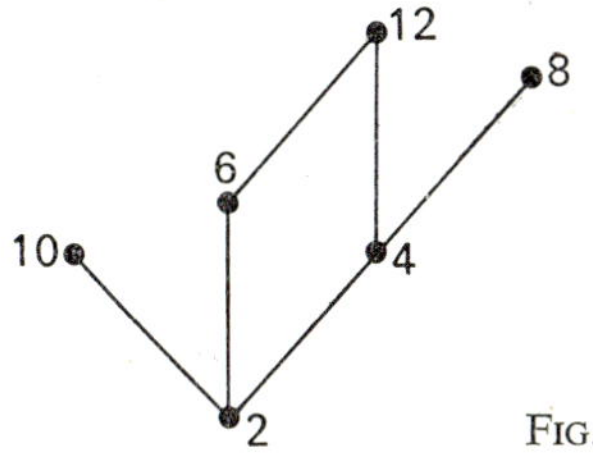

FIG. 4.

Definition 13. Let S, T be two partially ordered sets, and let $S \sim T$, that is, let there be a one-to-one correspondence between the elements of S and the elements of T. In this correspondence let s_1, s_2 correspond to t_1, t_2, respectively; we write $s_1 \sim t_1$, $s_2 \sim t_2$. Then if $s_1 \leqq s_2$ in S implies $t_1 \leqq t_2$ in T and $t_1 \leqq t_2$ implies $s_1 \leqq s_2$, the correspondence is called an isomorphism, S and T are said to be isomorphic, or one set is said to be isomorphic with the other; we may write $S \overset{0}{\sim} T$. Thus if T is the set of numbers 2, 3, 5, 6, 10, 15 where $t_1 \leqq t_2$ means that $t_1 | t_2$, and S is the set of Example 22, we may set up the correspondence $A \sim 2$, $B \sim 3$, $C \sim 5$, $D \sim 6$, $E \sim 10$, $F \sim 15$, and $S \overset{0}{\sim} T$. On the other hand, if T is the set of numbers 2, 3, 5, 6 again with divisibility as order relation, and S is the set of Example 23, the correspondence $L \sim 2$, $M \sim 3$, $N \sim 5$, $U \sim 6$ is not an isomorphism, for $N \leqq U$ but 5 does not divide 6. It is clear that isomorphic partially ordered sets must have the same diagram.

An isomorphism between partially ordered sets is an equivalence relation. $S \overset{0}{\sim} S$; if $S \overset{0}{\sim} T$, then $T \overset{0}{\sim} S$. If $R \overset{0}{\sim} S$ and $S \overset{0}{\sim} T$, let $r_1 \sim s_1$, $r_2 \sim s_2$, $s_1 \sim t_1$, $s_2 \sim t_2$; since each correspondence is strictly one-to-one, we may make $r_1 \sim t_1$, $r_2 \sim t_2$; but if $r_1 \leqq r_2$, $s_1 \leqq s_2$ and if $s_1 \leqq s_2$, $t_1 \leqq t_2$; hence if $r_1 \leqq r_2$, $t_1 \leqq t_2$; the converse is proved in similar fashion; therefore $R \overset{0}{\sim} T$ and transitivity is proved.

Definition 14. Let F be a family (or collection) of equivalent sets, all partially ordered; then an isomorphism as defined above will cause the sets in F to fall into equivalence classes of isomorphic sets; each of these classes is called an abstract partially ordered set.

Example 26. We will now determine the abstract partially ordered sets of up to three elements. (This is a less trivial exercise than might appear at first sight.) Of one-element sets there is, of course, a single abstract type (Fig. 5a). There are two abstract sets of two elements: Fig. 5b shows that in which the two elements are not comparable, Fig. 5c that in which they are. A set of three elements may be partially ordered in nineteen ways; these nineteen equivalent partially ordered sets fall into five classes as follows: we have one of the type of Fig. 5d, six of the type of Fig. 5e, three of the type of Fig. 5f, three of the type of Fig. 5g, six of the type of Fig. 5h.

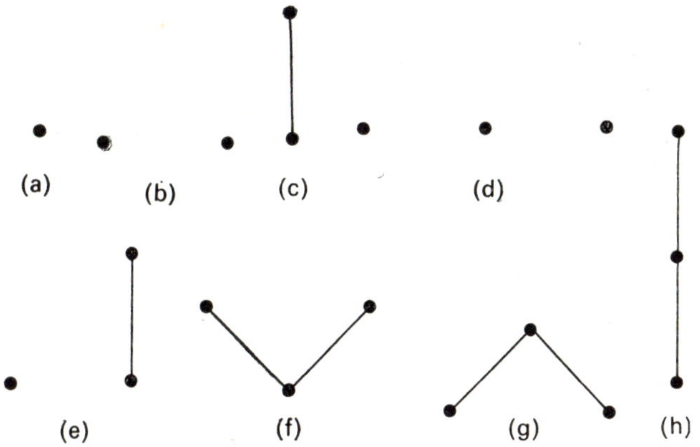

FIG. 5.

Definition 15. A dyadic relation was defined as a set of ordered pairs (Def. 2); if we interchange antecedents with consequents throughout, we get a new relation, called the converse relation; that is, given a dyadic relation R, we define the converse relation R' by $xR'y$ if and only if yRx.

THEOREM 4. If a set S is partially ordered by a relation O, then S is partially ordered by the converse relation O'.

Proof. Since aOa, we have $aO'a$ for every a in S. If $aO'b$ and $bO'a$, then by definition of O' we have bOa and aOb; but O is a relation of partial order, whence $b = a$; therefore $aO'b$ and $bO'a$ imply $a = b$. Lastly, if $aO'b$ and $bO'c$, then by definition of O' we have bOa and cOb; but O is transitive, whence cOa; therefore by Definition 15 $aO'c$, and O' is transitive.

Definition 16. The set S partially ordered by O' is called the dual of S partially ordered by O. For instance, in Example 25 we had the numbers 2, 4, 6, 8, 10, 12 with $a \leqq b$ meaning $a|b$, a divides b; the dual of this set consists of the same numbers with $a \leqq b$ meaning $b|a$, a is a multiple of b. The diagram of the dual set is obtained by turning the diagram of the original set upside down. If we denote the dual of S by S', and S' is isomorphic with a set T, we may say S, T are dually isomorphic; for example, if S is the set of partitions of Example 23, and T is the set of numbers 1, 2, 3, 5 with $a \leqq b$ meaning $a|b$, S and T are dually isomorphic. If S' is isomorphic with S itself, we say S is self-dual; thus Examples 22 and 24 are both self-dual partially ordered sets.

From a partially ordered set we now single out elements having special properties.

Definition 17. Let T be a subset of a partially ordered set S.

If a is an element of T such that $a \leqq t$ for all t in T, a is called a least element of T.

A least element, if it exists, is unique; for if a_1, a_2 are least elements, $a_1 \leqq a_2$ and $a_2 \leqq a_1$, whence by Def. 10 (ii) $a_1 = a_2$.

If a is an element of T such that $a \geqq t$ for all t in T, a is called a greatest element of T.

A greatest element, if it exists, is unique; for if a_1, a_2 are greatest elements, $a_1 \geqq a_2$ and $a_2 \geqq a_1$, whence by Def. 10 (ii) and

If $T = S$, such a least element is often called the zero element, with notation o or O, or 0.

the definition of $\geqq$, $a_1 = a_2$. If $T = S$, such a greatest element is often called the unity element, with notation u or U, or I.

If a is in T and there is no element t of T such that $t < a$, a is called a minimal element of T. Minimal elements need not be unique.

If a is in T and there is no element t of T such that $t > a$, a is called a maximal element of T. Maximal elements need not be unique.

If b is an element of S such that $b \leqq t$ for every t in T, b is called a lower bound of the subset T. Note that b need not belong to T.

If b is an element of S such that $b \geqq t$ for every t in T, b is called an upper bound of the subset T. Note that b need not belong to T.

If g is a lower bound of T such that $b \leqq g$ for every lower bound b of T, g is called a greatest lower bound of T.

If g is an upper bound of T such that $b \geqq g$ for every upper bound b of T, g is called a least upper bound of T.

If such an element g exists, it is unique; for g being a lower bound, the set of lower bounds is not empty, and g is the greatest element of this set.

If such an element g exists, it is unique; for g being an upper bound, the set of upper bounds is not empty, and g is the least element of this set.

Examples of these special elements will be found in Figs. 1–5; for instance, in Fig. 4 the number 2 is the least or zero element of the whole set, the numbers 8, 10 and 12 are maximal elements of the whole set, whilst the number 12 is the least (since it is the only) upper bound of the subset consisting of the numbers 2, 4 and 6.

Exercises

35. Show that a set of four elements can be partially ordered in 219 ways; show that isomorphism classifies these 219 equivalent sets into 16 abstract partially ordered sets.
36. A dyadic relation Q which is reflexive and transitive is called a relation of quasi-order. Let S be a set quasi-ordered by such a relation Q; define a new relation R between the elements of S by the following:

$$aRb \quad \text{if and only if} \quad aQb \quad \text{and} \quad bQa;$$

show that R is an equivalence relation. If $T = \{X, Y, \ldots\}$ is the set of equivalence classes into which R partitions S, and if we lay down that

$$X \leqq Y \text{ if and only if } xQy \text{ for } x \text{ in } X \text{ and } y \text{ in } Y,$$

show that with this relation T is a partially ordered set.

7. Chains

It was not required of a partially ordered set that any two elements should be comparable; partially ordered sets where this is the case are singled out by

Definition 18. If for every pair of elements a, b of a partially ordered set K we have either $a \leqq b$ or $b \leqq a$ or both, the set K is said to be simply or totally ordered, and is called a chain. By Def. 10 (ii) $a \leqq b$ and $b \leqq a$ imply $a = b$; hence we may define a chain as a partially ordered set in which for every pair of distinct elements a, b we have either $a < b$ or $b < a$. We note that any subset of a chain is itself a chain.

A finite chain of n elements has a least and a greatest member, and is isomorphic with the sequence of natural numbers $(1, 2, 3, \ldots, n)$. For if the chain consists of the n distinct elements $x_1, \ldots, x_n$ (taken in some random sequence) let $y_0 = x_1$, $y_1 = \min(y_0, x_1)$, $\ldots, y_k = \min(y_{k-1}, x_k), \ldots, y_n = \min(y_{n-1}, x_n)$, where min refers, of course, to the order relation of the given chain. Then since

$$y_n \leqq y_{n-1} \leqq \cdots \leqq y_k \leqq x_k$$

for $k = 1, \ldots, n$, it follows that y_n is least element of the chain. Now let y_n be renamed z_1 and removed from the chain; obtain by the process just outlined the least element z_2 of the chain of $n - 1$ elements consisting of the elements of the original chain less z_1; next find z_3, the least element of the chain of $n - 2$ elements consisting of the elements of the original chain less z_1 and z_2; continuing in this way, we arrive at z_n which is the least and indeed only element of the chain consisting of the elements of the original chain less $z_1, z_2, z_3, \ldots, z_{n-1}$. Thus we have ordered and indexed the elements of the chain as follows:

$$z_1 < z_2 < z_3 < \cdots < z_n,$$

and the required isomorphism is proved. By construction z_n is the greatest element.

Example 27. Consider the numbers

$$4, \quad 32, \quad 8, \quad 64, \quad 16, \quad 128, \quad 2$$

ordered by the relation $a \leqq b$ if a is a multiple of b. Since the numbers are distinct powers of 2, of every pair one is a multiple of the other, and the numbers constitute a chain of seven elements. $y_0 = 4$, $y_1 = \min(4, 4) = 4$, $y_2 = \min(4, 32) = 32$, $y_3 = \min(32, 8) = 32$, $y_4 = \min(32, 64) = 64$, $y_5 = \min(64, 16) = 64$, $y_6 = \min(64, 128) = 128$, $y_7 = \min(128, 2) = 128 = z_1$. Omitting 128 from the set we find $z_2 = 64$; then omitting 128 and 64 we find $z_3 = 32$; continuing in this way we arrange the elements of the chain in *ascending* order (ascending, that is, with respect to the defined order relation):

$$128, \quad 64, \quad 32, \quad 16, \quad 8, \quad 4, \quad 2$$

isomorphic with

$$1, \quad 2, \quad 3, \quad 4, \quad 5, \quad 6, \quad 7;$$

128 is *least* or zero element, 2 is *greatest* or unity element.

We now list some examples of abstract chains.

Example 28. As we have just seen, any finite chain is isomorphic with a finite sequence of natural numbers (1, ..., n). See Fig. 6a.

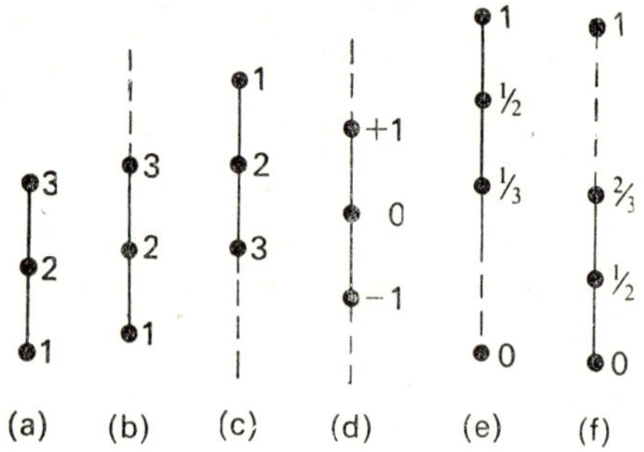

FIG. 6.

Example 29. An infinite chain isomorphic with the sequence of natural numbers, with a least member (Fig. 6b) or dually with a greatest member (Fig. 6c).

Example 30. An infinite chain isomorphic with the sequence of integers, with neither least nor greatest member (Fig. 6d). For the ordering of the integers see Example 18.

Example 31. An infinite chain isomorphic with the rational numbers between 0 and 1. The ordering of the rationals is given in Example 20. Since there is an infinite (though countable) number of rationals between any two distinct rationals, a diagram here is of little value. Note that we have four distinct abstract chains according as we include or exclude one or both of the extreme elements.

Example 32. An infinite chain as in Fig. 6e isomorphic with the rationals of the form

$$\frac{1}{n}$$

lying between 0 and 1.

Example 33. An infinite chain isomorphic with the rationals of the form

$$\frac{n}{n+1}$$

lying between 0 and 1. See Fig. 6f.

THEOREM 5. Let A, B be two partially ordered sets and let P be the set of all ordered pairs (a, b) where a belongs to A, b to B. Then P is a partially ordered set if we lay down that

$$(a_1, b_1) \leqq (a_2, b_2)$$

if and only if $a_1 \leqq a_2$ in A and $b_1 \leqq b_2$ in B

Proof. Clearly $(a, b) \leqq (a, b)$. Again, if $(a_1, b_1) \leqq (a_2, b_2)$ and $(a_2, b_2) \leqq (a_1, b_1)$, then we have $a_1 \leqq a_2$ and $a_2 \leqq a_1$, $b_1 \leqq b_2$ and $b_2 \leqq b_1$; whence by Def. 10 (ii) $a_1 = a_2$, $b_1 = b_2$. Lastly, if $(a_1, b_1) \leqq (a_2, b_2)$ and $(a_2, b_2) \leqq (a_3, b_3)$, then transitivity in A implies that $a_1 \leqq a_3$, and transitivity in B that $b_1 \leqq b_3$; whence $(a_1, b_1) \leqq (a_3, b_3)$. The relation defined between the ordered pairs being thus reflexive, anti-symmetric and transitive is a relation of partial order.

Definition 19. The partially ordered set P of Th. 5 is called the cardinal product of the partially ordered sets A, B; we may write $P = A \times B$. Note that the sets A, B need not be equivalent or isomorphic, nor need they be finite, but they may be the same set. The definition can be extended in an obvious way to three or any other finite number of sets.

Example 34. The cardinal product of the three finite chains of natural numbers $\{1, 2, 3, 4\}$, $\{1, 2\}$, $\{1, 2\}$. This set consists of sixteen elements:

$$\begin{array}{llll} (4, 1, 1), & (4, 1, 2), & (4, 2, 1), & (4, 2, 2), \\ (3, 1, 1), & (3, 1, 2), & (3, 2, 1), & (3, 2, 2), \\ (2, 1, 1), & (2, 1, 2), & (2, 2, 1), & (2, 2, 2), \\ (1, 1, 1), & (1, 1, 2), & (1, 2, 1), & (1, 2, 2); \end{array}$$

a partially ordered set with least or zero element (1, 1, 1) and greatest or unity element (4, 2, 2). For a diagram of this set see Chapter 2, § 9, Fig. 12c.

Exercises

37. Prove the statements made about Example 31.
38. Show that finite chains are self-dual but infinite chains not necessarily so. (Cf. Fig. 6.)
39. Prove that the chains of Examples 32 and 33 are dually isomorphic.
40. Prove that if two chains each contain two or more elements, their cardinal product cannot be a chain.
41. Prove that if two partially ordered sets are self-dual, then so is their cardinal product.
42. Let Q be the set of all ordered pairs (a, b) of rationals. (i) Consider Q to be the cardinal product $R \times R$ where R is the infinite chain of the rationals in

their usual order (that of Example 20). Show that Q ordered as in Theorem 5 is not a chain. (ii) Convert Q into an algebra by introducing two binary operations:

$$(a, b) + (c, d) = (a + c, b + d);$$

$$(a, b) \times (c, d) = (ac + 2bd, ad + bc),$$

multiplication signs between rationals being here suppressed. The ordered pairs thus related we call surds. The surd $(0, 0)$ is called zero; all other surds we classify as positive or negative as follows: if both a and b are positive, or if one is zero, the other positive, (a, b) is deemed positive; similarly, if both negative, or one zero and the other negative, (a, b) is deemed negative; if $a > 0 > b$, we ascribe to (a, b) the sign of $a^2 - 2b^2$, if $a < 0 < b$, we ascribe the sign of $2b^2 - a^2$. Thus $(2, -2)$ is negative, $(-2, 3)$ is positive. We say $(a, b) = (c, d)$ if and only if $a = c$, $b = d$; and we lay down that $(a, b) \leqq (c, d)$ if and only if $(a - c, b - d)$ is negative or zero. Prove that with this relation Q is a chain, not isomorphic with R. (*Hint:* (a, b) is usually written $a + b\sqrt{2}$.)

8. Lattices

A lattice may be looked at in two distinct ways—from the point of view of either algebra or set theory. This is the reason why the applications of lattice theory are so remarkably widespread in other branches of mathematics and in the cognate sciences. We take first the algebraic standpoint.

Definition 20. A lattice L is an algebra with two binary operations (symbolized by multiplication and addition) satisfying for all a, b, c in L the following postulates:

Postulate IA

To every ordered pair (a, b) of elements a, b is assigned a unique element ab of L.

Postulate IB

To every ordered pair (a, b) of elements a, b is assigned a unique element $a + b$ of L.

Postulate IIA:

$$ab = ba;$$

Postulate IIB:

$$a + b = b + a;$$

Postulate IIIA:

$$a\,(bc) = (ab)\,c;$$

Postulate IIIB:

$$a + (b + c) = (a + b) + c;$$

Postulate IVA:

$$a\,(a + b) = a;$$

Postulate IVB:

$$a + ab = a.$$

Postulates IA, B are set down explicitly for completeness, although they are really contained in the words "algebra with two binary operations" (see Defs. 3, 5); Postulates IIA, B require that both operations be commutative, Postulates IIIA, B that they be associative (see Def. 4); the strikingly unusual Postulates IVA, B require the property of "absorption" and evidently rule out ordinary multiplication and addition. The reader unfamiliar with definitions such as this, with a list of postulates or axioms (words from Latin and Greek respectively, meaning "demands", "things asked for"), will meet them everywhere in modern algebra, geometry and topology and must not imagine that their authors conjure them up from nothing; algebraic systems are discovered in use, in uncritical use that is, or they are tentatively constructed for some particular purpose; it is afterwards that close scrutiny of systems of proved interest or value reveals their essential and their non-essential properties. Lattices first appeared in Boole's *The Mathematical Analysis of Logic* in 1847; the postulates of Def. 20 were separated out by Schröder and Dedekind in the 1890's.

We will now prove a number of theorems about lattices, giving the proofs in detail to exemplify deduction from postulates.

THEOREM 6. $aa = a$.

Proof. $aa = a\,(a + ab)$ by IVB

$= a$ by IVA.

THEOREM 7. $a + a = a$.

Proof. $a + a = a + aa$ by Theorem 6

$= a$ by IVB.

These theorems establish that multiplication and addition are "idempotent"; we do not need exponents or numerical coefficients in lattice theory.

THEOREM 8. If $ab = a$, then $a + b = b$.

Proof. $a + b = ab + b$ by hypothesis

$= b + ab$ by IIB

$= b + ba$ by IIA

$= b$ by IVB.

THEOREM 9. If $a + b = b$, then $ab = a$.

Proof. $ab = a(a + b)$ by hypothesis

$= a$ by IVA.

Definition 21. We define a relation R between two elements of a lattice by

(i) aRb if and only if $ab = a$.

In view of Ths. 8 and 9 this is equivalent to

(ii) aRb if and only if $a + b = b$.

THEOREM 10. *aRa.*

Proof. $aa = a$ by Th. 6; hence aRa by Def. 21(i).

THEOREM 11. *If aRb and bRa, then $a = b$.*

Proof. $a = ab$ by the first hypothesis and Def. 21(i)
$= ba$ by IIA
$= b$ by the second hypothesis and Def. 21(i).

THEOREM 12. *If aRb and bRc, then aRc.*

Proof. $ac = (ab)\,c$ by the first hypothesis and Def. 21(i)
$= a\,(bc)$ by IIIA
$= ab$ by the second hypothesis and Def. 21(i)
$= a$ by the first hypothesis and the same definition;

hence aRc by the same definition.

The relation R is thus dyadic (by definition), reflexive (Th. 10), anti-symmetric (Th. 11) and transitive (Th. 12), hence a relation of partial order; we may write $a \leqq b$ for aRb. No further proof is required for

THEOREM 13. A lattice is a partially ordered set, with $a \leqq b$ meaning $ab = a$ and $a + b = b$.

Example 35. Let the elements of L be all the sixteen factors of the natural number 216, namely

1, 2, 3, 4, 6, 8, 9, 12, 18, 24, 27, 36, 54, 72, 108, 216.

This set contains the unique h.c.f. and unique l.c.m. of any two of its members; hence if we define ab as h.c.f. (a, b) and $a + b$ as l.c.m. (a, b), Postulates IA, IB of Def. 20 are satisfied. Commutativity (Postulates IIA, IIB) is obvious. The proof of associativity (Postulates IIIA, IIIB) was asked for in Exercise 13, § 2. For the absorption postulates (IVA, IVB) see formula (9) (proved in § 2)

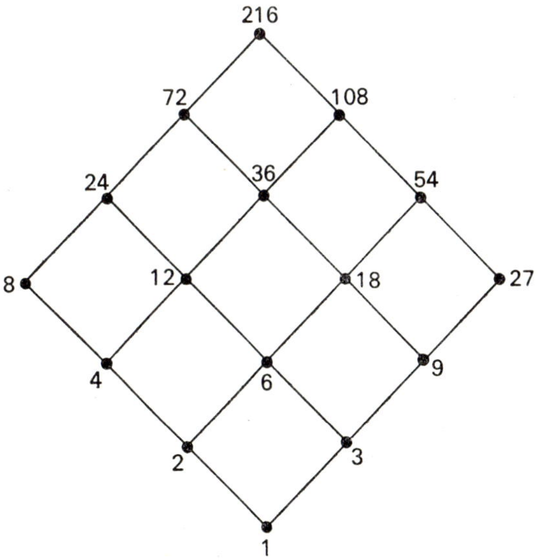

FIG. 7.

and formula (10) (proof indicated in § 2). $a \leqq b$ means h.c.f. $(a, b) = a$, that is $a|b$. The diagram of the lattice as a partially ordered set is given in Fig. 7 and shows the appropriateness (in this case at any rate) of the picturesque name "lattice".

THEOREM 14. $ab \leqq a$.

Proof.

$$ab + a = a + ab \quad \text{by IIB}$$
$$= a \quad \text{by IVB;}$$

hence $ab \leqq a$ by Def. 21 (ii).

THEOREM 15. $a \leqq a + b$.

Proof. $a(a + b) = a$ by IVA; hence $a \leqq a + b$ by Def. 21 (i).

THEOREM 16. $ab \leqq b$.

Proof. $ba \leqq b$ by Theorem 14;

but $ba = ab$ by IIA;

hence $ab \leqq b$.

It follows from the above that ab is a lower bound of the pair a, b.

THEOREM 17. $b \leqq a + b$.

Proof.

$$b \leqq b + a \quad \text{by Theorem 15}$$
$$= a + b \quad \text{by IIB.}$$

It follows from the above that $a + b$ is an upper bound of the pair a, b.

THEOREM 18. If $c \leqq a$ and $c \leqq b$, then $c \leqq ab$.

Proof.

$$c = ca$$

by first hyp. and Def. 21 (i)

THEOREM 19. If $a \leqq d$ and $b \leqq d$, then $a + b \leqq d$.

Proof.

$$(a + b) + d = a + (b + d)$$

by IIIB

$= (cb)\,a$

by second hyp. and same def.

$= c\,(ba)$ by IIIA

$= c\,(ab)$ by IIA;

hence

$c \leqq ab$ by same def.

Hence ab is greatest lower bound of the pair a, b.

$= a + d$

by second hyp. and Def. 21 (ii)

$= d$

by first hyp. and same def.; hence

$a + b \leqq d$ by same def.

Hence $a + b$ is least upper bound of the pair a, b.

THEOREM 20. A lattice is a partially ordered set, with $a \leqq b$ meaning $ab = a$ and $a + b = b$, in which every pair of elements possesses a greatest lower bound and a least upper bound within the set.

Proof. Theorem 13 covers the first part. As regards the second part, by Defs. 20 IA, IB every pair of elements a, b possesses a unique product ab and a unique sum $a + b$ within the lattice, and by Ths. 14–19 these are the required bounds.

Defining a lattice in algebraic terms (Def. 20), we have thus proved (Th. 20) that every lattice is a partially ordered set with special properties. We now make a fresh start, defining a lattice in terms of set theory as just such a partially ordered set (Def. 22); we proceed to show (Th. 30) that the newly defined lattice has the algebraic properties required by the postulates in Def. 20.

Definition 22. A lattice is a partially ordered set in which every pair of elements a, b has a greatest lower bound (represented by $a \cap b$) and a least upper bound (represented by $a \cup b$) within the set.

THEOREM 21. A lattice is an algebra with two binary operations.

Proof. Let the operations be formation of $a \cap b$ and of $a \cup b$. By Def. 22 for any a, b there exists $a \cap b$ within the lattice; also the set of lower bounds of the pair a, b is not empty for $a \cap b$ belongs to it; hence $a \cap b$ being a greatest lower bound is unique (cf. Def. 17). Similarly it is shown that $a \cup b$ exists within the lattice and is unique.

THEOREM 22. $a \cap b = b \cap a$.

THEOREM 23. $a \cup b = b \cup a$.

Proof (for both). When considering bounds of a finite set of two elements a, b, it is clearly immaterial whether we deal first with a and then with b, or vice versa.

THEOREM 24. $a \cap (b \cap c) = (a \cap b) \cap c$.

Proof. From the definition of lower bound

$$(a \cap b) \cap c \leqq a \cap b \leqq b$$

and

$$(a \cap b) \cap c \leqq c;$$

hence from the definition of greatest lower bound

$$(a \cap b) \cap c \leqq b \cap c.$$

Also

$$(a \cap b) \cap c \leqq a \cap b \leqq a.$$

THEOREM 25. $a \cup (b \cup c) = (a \cup b) \cup c$.

Proof. From the definition of upper bound

$$b \leqq a \cup b \leqq (a \cup b) \cup c$$

and

$$c \leqq (a \cup b) \cup c;$$

hence from the definition of least upper bound

$$b \cup c \leqq (a \cup b) \cup c.$$

Also

$$a \leqq a \cup b \leqq (a \cup b) \cup c.$$

Therefore

$$(a \cap b) \cap c \leqq a \cap (b \cap c).$$

Again,

$$a \cap (b \cap c) \leqq a$$

and

$$a \cap (b \cap c) \leqq b \cap c \leqq b;$$

hence

$$a \cap (b \cap c) = a \cap b.$$

Also

$$a \cap (b \cap c) \leqq b \cap c \leqq c.$$

Therefore

$$a \cap (b \cap c) \leqq (a \cap b) \cap c.$$

But the relation $\leqq$ is anti-symmetric (see Def. 10 (ii)); hence

$$a \cap (b \cap c) = (a \cap b) \cap c.$$

Therefore

$$a \cup (b \cup c) \leqq (a \cup b) \cup c.$$

Again,

$$a \leqq a \cup (b \cup c)$$

and

$$b \leqq b \cup c \leqq a \cup (b \cup c);$$

hence

$$a \cup b \leqq a \cup (b \cup c).$$

Also

$$c \leqq b \cup c \leqq a \cup (b \cup c).$$

Therefore

$$(a \cup b) \cup c \leqq a \cup (b \cup c).$$

But the relation $\leqq$ is anti-symmetric (see Def. 10 (ii)); hence

$$a \cup (b \cup c) = (a \cup b) \cup c.$$

THEOREM 26. If $a \leqq b$, then $a \cap b = a$.

THEOREM 27. If $a \leqq b$, then $a \cup b = b$.

Proof. $a \leqq a$ by reflexivity;
$a \leqq b$ by hypothesis;
hence a is a lower bound of the pair a, b, and clearly the greatest such.

Proof. $a \leqq b$ by hypothesis;
$b \leqq b$ by reflexivity;
hence b is an upper bound of the pair a, b and clearly the least such.

THEOREM 28. $a \cap (a \cup b) = a$.

THEOREM 29. $a \cup (a \cap b) = a$.

Proof. $a \leqq a \cup b$ by definition of upper bound; hence $a \cap (a \cup b) = a$ by Th. 26.

Proof. $a \cap b \leqq a$ by definition of lower bound; hence $(a \cap b) \cup a = a$ by Th. 27; but $(a \cap b) \cup a = a \cup (a \cap b)$ by Th. 23; therefore $a \cup (a \cap b) = a$.

THEOREM 30. Every lattice is an algebra with two binary operations, which are commutative, associative and mutually absorptive.

Proof. The first part is proved in Th. 21; the operations are proved commutative in Ths. 22 and 23, and associative in Ths. 24 and 25; the absorption formulae are proved to hold in Ths. 28 and 29.

We have thus shown that the two definitions of a lattice are equivalent. The product ab or $a \cap b$ is often called intersection (as of sets, in set theory) or meet (as of lines, meeting in points, in geometry); the sum $a + b$ or $a \cup b$ is then correspondingly called union (as of sets) or join (as of points, joined by lines). We shall commonly use the algebraic notation, which is much the easier to read and work with, although it has the defect of sometimes obscuring the duality brought out by the use of $\cap$ and $\cup$; compare

$$\begin{matrix} a(b + c) & & a \cap (b \cup c) \\ & \text{with} & \\ a + bc & & a \cup (b \cap c). \end{matrix}$$

As regards names, we shall generally prefer meet for ab and join for $a + b$.

Exercises

In Exercises 43–46 a, b, c, etc., refer to elements of a lattice defined as in Def. 20.

43. Show that if $a \leqq b \leqq c$ and $a = c$, then $a = b = c$, and hence that if $xy = x + y$, then $x = y$.
44. Without reference to the last exercise prove that if $x \neq y$, then $xy < x + y$.
45. Show that if $a \leqq b \leqq c$, then $a + b = bc$ and that $ab + bc = b = (a + b)(a + c)$.
46. Show that if $a \leqq b$, then for any c $ac \leqq bc$ and $a + c \leqq b + c$.
47. By considering the prime factorizations of the numbers in Example 35 show that the lattice diagram given there is also that of a cardinal product of two chains each of four elements.
48. Prove that none of the partially ordered sets of Figs. 1–4 is a lattice.

9. Examples of Lattices

(1) *Small finite lattices*

THEOREM 31. A finite lattice has a zero or least element and a unity or greatest element.

Proof. Let the elements of the lattice in any random arrangement be $x_1, \ldots, x_n$. Define

$$p_0 = x_1, \quad p_1 = p_0 x_1, \quad p_2 = p_1 x_2, \ldots, \quad p_n = p_{n-1} x_n$$

and

$$s_0 = x_1, \quad s_1 = s_0 + x_1, \quad s_2 = s_1 + x_2, \ldots, \quad s_n = s_{n-1} + x_n.$$

Then by definition of meet

$$p_n \leqq p_{n-1} \leqq \cdots \leqq p_1 = p_0,$$

and by that of join

$$s_n \geqq s_{n-1} \geqq \cdots \geqq s_1 = s_0;$$

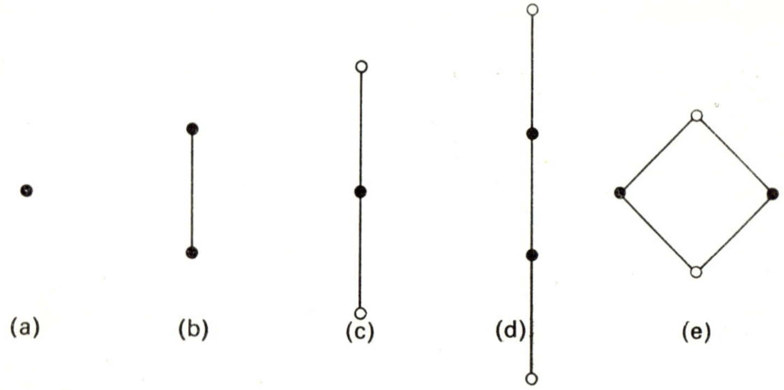

FIG. 8.

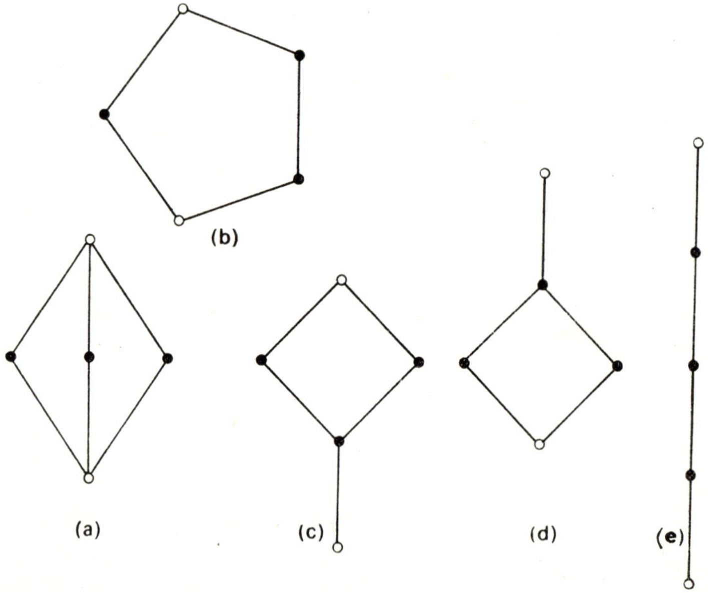

FIG. 9.

hence for any element x_k ($k = 1, \ldots, n$)

$$p_n \leqq p_k = p_{k-1}x_k \leqq x_k \leqq s_{k-1} + x_k = s_k \leqq s_n;$$

therefore p_n is zero element and s_n unity element.

This theorem indicates how we may form a lattice of n elements from a partially ordered set of $n - 2$ elements by adding a zero element o and a unity element u; in particular we may use Example 26, § 6, to form all abstract lattices of three to five elements.

Example 36. Abstract lattices of up to five elements are illustrated in Figs. 8, 9; several of these are important in subsequent theory. Of one, two and three elements there is just one abstract lattice; of four elements there are two such lattices; of five elements there are five.

We now give some concrete examples of lattices, using the material accumulated for this purpose in Chapter 1.

(2) *Boolean lattices*

Let S be a set of n elements. Then the subsets of S, including the empty set and S itself, number 2^n; for this result see Exercise 22, § 4. These subsets X, Y, ... with set intersection XY for meet and set union $X + Y$ for join constitute a lattice. The proof of commutativity is trivial; proof of associativity was asked for in Exercise 7, § 1; absorption was dealt with in formulae (1) and (2), § 1. The relation of partial order is set inclusion; XY is the largest set contained in X and in Y, whilst $X + Y$ is the smallest set containing both X and Y. The empty set is zero element, S itself unity element. A lattice of subsets of this kind is an example of a Boolean lattice or Boolean algebra; these will be defined and studied in a later chapter.

Example 37. In Figs. 10a–g full diagrams are given for $n = 0, 1, \ldots, 6$. Fig. 10e, for instance, shows the lattice of the subsets of $\{a, b, c, d\}$:

$$\{a, b, c, d\}$$

$$\{a, b, c\} \quad \{a, b, d\} \quad \{a, c, d\} \quad \{b, c, d\}$$

$$\{a, b\} \quad \{a, c\} \quad \{a, d\} \quad \{b, c\} \quad \{b, d\} \quad \{c, d\}$$

$$\{a\} \quad \{b\} \quad \{c\} \quad \{d\}$$

$$O$$

It will be observed that in each diagram the number of elements lying at the same height above the lowest element is always $\binom{n}{r}$; hence the triangular table of values of $\binom{n}{r}$ associated with the name of Pascal gives for each diagram the distribution of the elements at the various levels.

10											1
9										1	10
8									1	9	45
7								1	8	36	120
6							1	7	28	84	210
5						1	6	21	56	126	252
4					1	5	15	35	70	126	210
3				1	4	10	20	35	56	84	120
2			1	3	6	10	15	21	28	36	45
1		1	2	3	4	5	6	7	8	9	10
0	1	1	1	1	1	1	1	1	1	1	1
r	1	2	4	8	16	32	64	128	256	512	1024
2^n	2^0	2^1	2^2	2^3	2^4	2^5	2^6	2^7	2^8	2^9	2^{10}

The exponents in the bottom row give the values of n; the numbers in the left-hand column give the values of r; in the next chapter we shall see they are the "heights" of the corresponding elements.

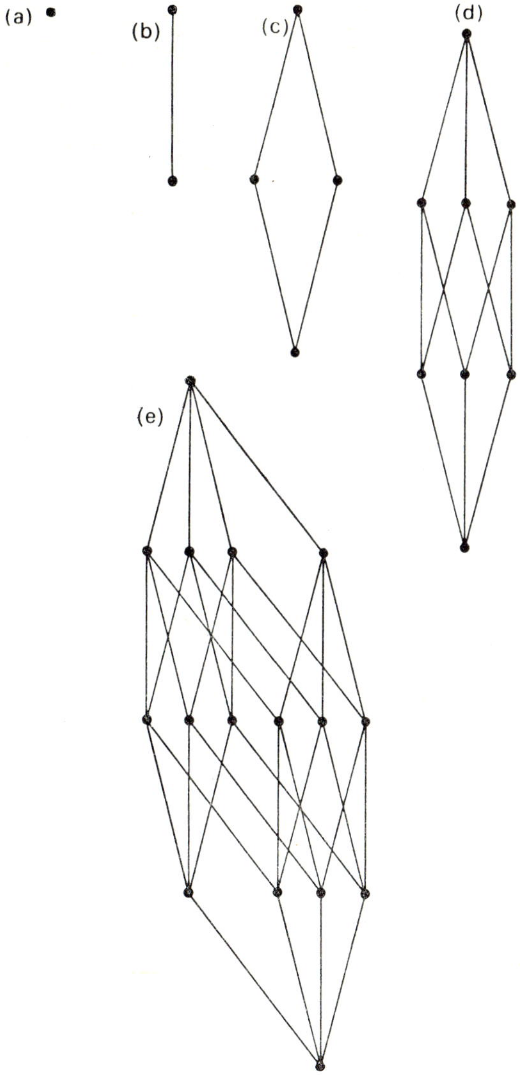

FIG. 10. (a)–(e)

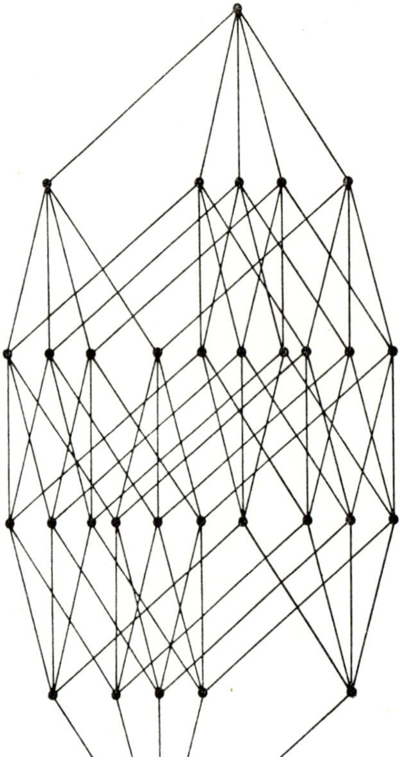

FIG. 10. (f)

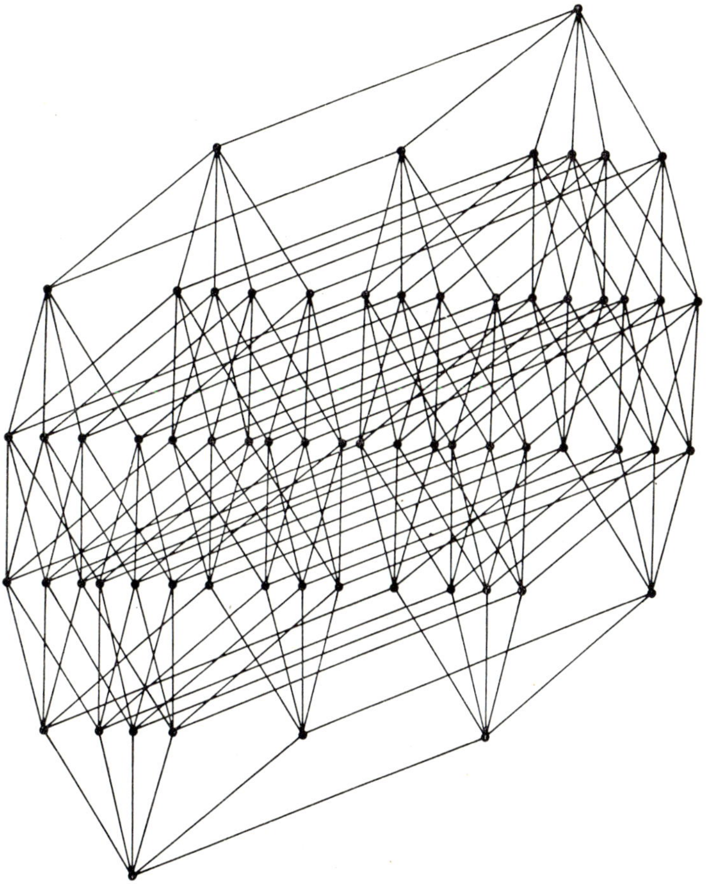

FIG. 10. (g)

(3) *Factorization lattices*

The famous German mathematician Richard Dedekind (1831–1916) published the first of his two pioneering papers on lattice theory in 1897; he began with a study of highest common factors of sets of natural numbers. These numbers with their divisibility properties provide many examples of lattices.

Example 38. Let S be a finite set of natural numbers containing a number e which divides all the others and a number u which is divisible by all the others. If a, b are any two members of S, let X denote the set of all x in S which divide both a and b; X is not empty, for e belongs to X, and X is finite since S is finite; hence X must contain a greatest member c (greatest in the technical sense in that every member of X divides c, and greatest in the ordinary sense); we define c as the meet of a and b. Let Y be the set of all y in S which are divisible by a and by b; Y is not empty, for u belongs to Y; Y is finite; hence Y must have a least member d (least in both senses); we define d as join of a and b. Briefly, c and d are respectively h.c.f. and l.c.m. of a, b *relative to* S. By Def. 22 S is a lattice. Figure 11 shows several examples. Obviously any finite lattice could be exemplified in this way by attaching suitable numbers to the elements, working upwards from the lowest.

Let now S be the set of *all* the factors of some natural number $a = p_1^{m_1} \times p_2^{m_2} \times \cdots \times p_n^{m_n}$, where the p_i are distinct primes. Since every factor is of the form $p_1^{\alpha} \times p_2^{\beta} \times \cdots \times p_n^{\nu}$ where $\alpha = 0, 1, \ldots, m_1$, $\beta = 0, 1, \ldots, m_2, \ldots, \nu = 0, 1, \ldots, m_n$, we see that the number of factors is given by the product of the exponents, each having been increased by 1; for instance, $5880 = 2^3 \times 3 \times 5 \times 7^2$ has $4 \times 2 \times 2 \times 3 = 48$ factors. The set S clearly satisfies the conditions laid down in the preceding paragraph and thus is a lattice; if on the other hand we define meet as h.c.f. and join as l.c.m., the algebraic require-

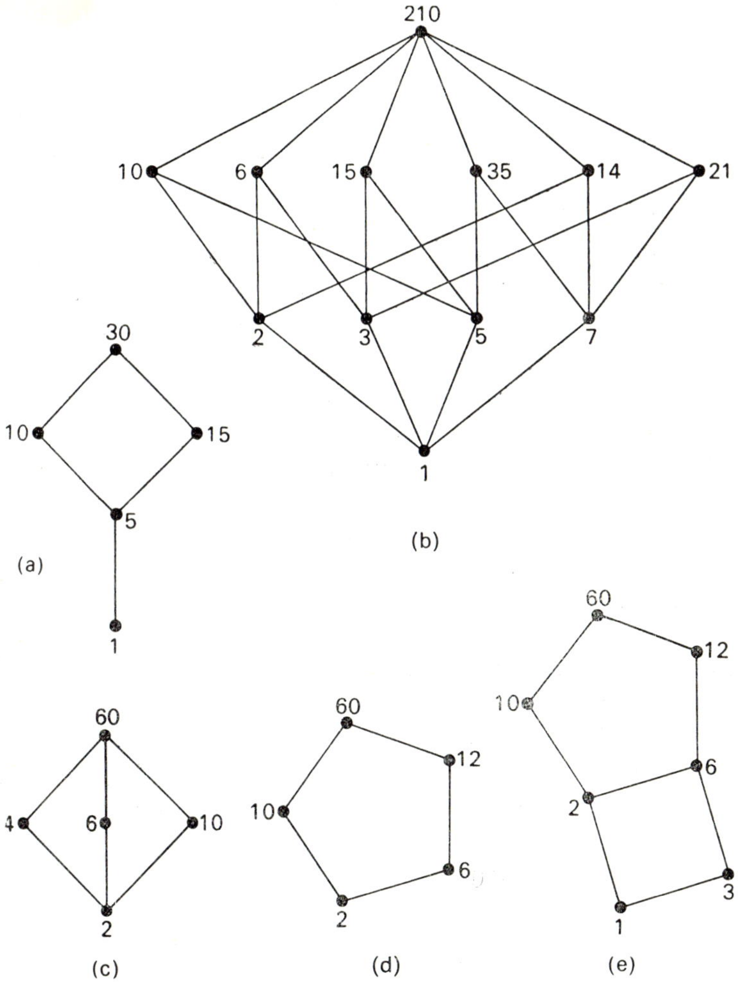
210
10
6
15
35
14
21
2
3
5
7
1
(b)
30
10
15
5
(a)
1
60
4
6
10
2
(c)
60
12
10
6
2
(d)
60
12
10
6
2
3
1
(e)

FIG. 11.

ments of Def. 20 can be met directly from § 2, as was shown in Example 35, § 8. Two kinds of lattice arise in this way, the difference depending upon the prime factorization of a.

Firstly, let a be of the form $p_1 \times p_2 \times \cdots \times p_n$; a number of this form contains no square factor apart from 1 and is sometimes described by the German word "quadratfrei". There are 2^n factors of such a number, these being 1, $\binom{n}{1}$ factors of type p_i, $\binom{n}{2}$ factors of type $p_i \times p_j$, and so on; clearly we have here a Boolean lattice isomorphic with the lattice of subsets of a finite set of n objects. Exercise 20, § 3, dealt with a lattice of this type; $210 = 2 \times 3 \times 5 \times 7$ has 2^4 factors which ordered by divisibility give a lattice isomorphic with the lattice of the 2^4 subsets of a set of four objects ordered by set inclusion, illustrated in Fig. 10e.

Secondly, let $a = p_1^{m_1} \times p_2^{m_2} \times \cdots \times p_n^{m_n}$ where one or more of the exponents exceeds 1; then the factors constitute a lattice which we shall later prove to be not Boolean, even when the number of factors is a power of 2. Figure 12 displays lattices for cases where $n = 1, \ldots, 4$. In Fig. 12a $n = 1$, $a = p_1^{m_1}$. The factors form a chain; for instance, 1, 2, 4, 8 are the four factors of $8 = 2^3$. In Fig. 12b $n = 2$, $a = p_1^{m_1} \times p_2^{m_2}$; for instance, $a = 24 = 2^3 \times 3$, with $4 \times 2 = 8$ factors. The lattice diagram may alway be drawn as a parallelogram divided into $m_1 \times m_2$ smaller congruent parallelograms, cf. Fig. 7 (Example 35, § 8, where $m_1 = m_2 = 3$). Figure 12c illustrates the case $n = 3$, $a = p_1^{m_1} \times p_2^{m_2} \times p_3^{m_3}$; for instance, $a = 120 = 2^3 \times 3 \times 5$ has sixteen factors, which could be arranged as follows:

$$
\begin{array}{llllllll}
120 & & & & & & & \\
24 \;\; 40 \;\; 60 & & & & & & & \\
& 8 \;\; 12 \;\; 20 \;\; 30 & & & & & & \\
& & 4 \;\; 6 \;\; 10 \;\; 15 & & & & & \\
& & & 2 \;\; 3 \;\; 5 & & & & \\
& & & \quad 1. & & & &
\end{array}
$$

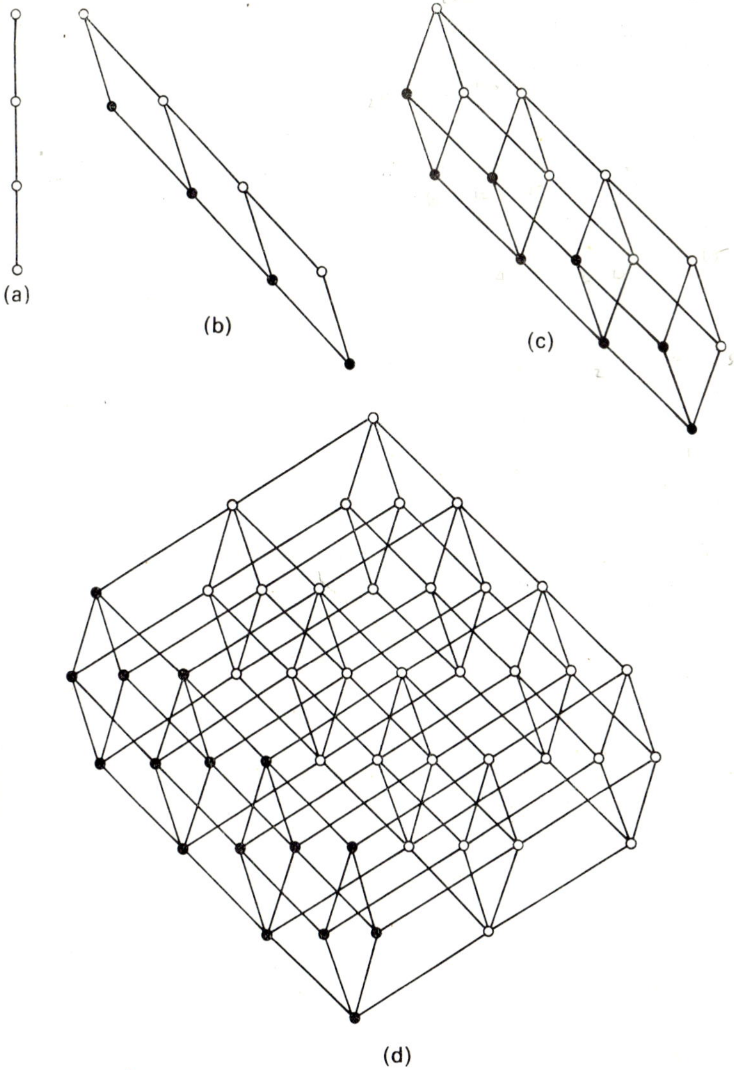

FIG. 12.

In Fig. 12d $n = 4$, $a = p_1^{m_1} \times p_2^{m_2} \times p_3^{m_3} \times p_4^{m_4}$; for instance, $a = 2^3 \times 3 \times 5 \times 7^2 = 5880$ with 48 factors. Factors could be arranged as follows in the lower half of the diagram:

8 12 20 30 28 42 70 105 98 147 245

4 6 10 15 14 21 35 49

2 3 5 7

1.

If we replace each number $2^\alpha \times 3^\beta \times 5^\gamma \times 7^\delta$ by the symbol $\alpha\beta\gamma\delta$, we see that the level at which a number is found is given by the sum of the exponents:

3	3000 2100 2010 1110 2001 1101 1011 0111 1002 0102 0012
2	2000 1100 1010 0110 1001 0101 0011 0002
1	1000 0100 0010 0001
0	0000

A method of drawing "by induction" the diagram of any of these complete factorization lattices is the following: first note that the lattice is a chain if $a = p_1^{m_1}$; to draw the lattice of the factors of $p_1^{m_1} \times \cdots \times p_k^{m_k}$ draw that of the factors of $p_1^{m_1} \times \cdots \times p_{k-1}^{m_{k-1}}$ and repeat a further m_k times along a rising line; then join corresponding vertices. For example, Fig. 12d ($2^3 \times 3 \times 5 \times 7^2$) consists of Fig. 12c ($2^3 \times 3 \times 5$) drawn once and repeated twice more, with corresponding vertices joined by sixteen rising parallel lines. This rule, of course, gives a method for drawing the diagram of any finite Boolean lattice; see Figs. 10a–g.

Finally, we observe that the totality of the natural numbers ordered by divisibility gives an infinite lattice with least element 1 but with no greatest element.

(4) ***Equivalence or partition lattices***

The foremost modern authority on lattices is the eminent American scholar Garrett Birkhoff; his treatise on lattice theory (1st edition 1940; 2nd edition 1948) was the first full account of the subject, and on it all subsequent authors, including the present writer, depend.

In 1935 Birkhoff introduced the interesting lattices of which the elements are equivalence relations or the corresponding partitions, concepts which we studied in § 4.

Example 39. Let S be a finite set of n objects; then the number of possible equivalence relations over S or partitions of S is known, and these relations or partitions form a lattice if we define meet and join of two elements as in § 4. Commutativity is obvious; properties of associativity and absorption were proved in formulae (17)–(20) and (17′)–(20′) of § 4. The relation of partial order is containment as defined in § 4; greatest lower bound and least upper bound are neatly described in terms of partitions as follows: LM is the least refined partition contained in L and M, whilst $L + M$ is the most refined partition containing L and M.

Figure 13 gives diagrams of lattices of partitions of a set of n objects for $n = 1, \ldots, 5$. Figure 13a shows the unique partition of a set of one object; Fig. 13b the two partitions of a set $\{a, b\}$, namely (a/b) and (ab). In Fig. 13c we have the five partitions of a set $\{a, b, c\}$; these, apart from the zero partition $(a/b/c)$, were given in Example 23, § 6. Figure 13d shows the fifteen partitions of a set $\{a, b, c, d\}$, which were listed in Example 7, § 4; the three non-singular elements are distinguished from the rest. The frontispiece shows the fifty-two partitions of a set $\{a, b, c, d, e\}$, Fig. 13e the twenty-seven singular partitions; each of these last-mentioned diagrams is laid out as on the wall of a right cylinder (with conical caps). If a partition of a set

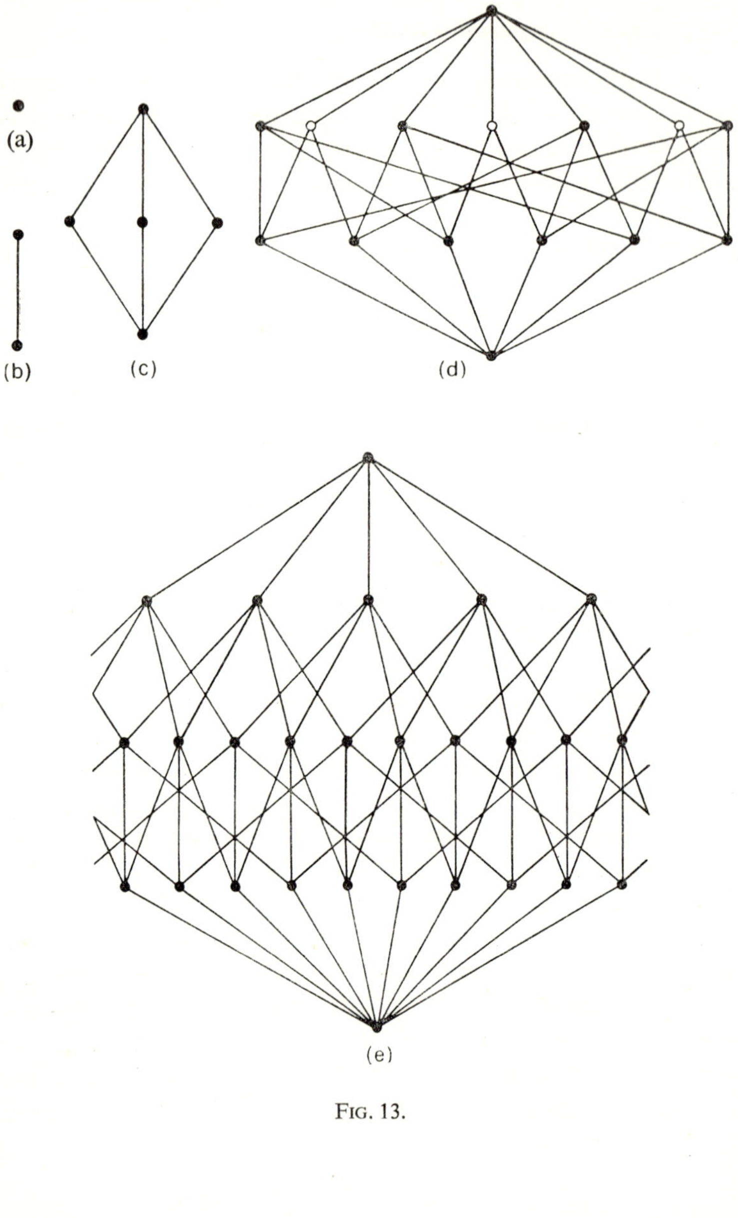

Fig. 13.

of n objects consists of k blocks, the number $n - k$ is called the rank of the partition. The fifty-two partitions of the frontispiece are tabulated (Table 1) with their order relations.

TABLE 1

Rank	Type	Number	Each contained in	Each containing	Description
4	*U* *abcde*	1		all others	unity
3	*W* *abc/de*	10	*U* only	3 of *R* 1 of *Q* 4 of *P*	non-singular
	V *abcd/e*	5	*U* only	3 of *R* 4 of *Q* 6 of *P*	singular
2	*R* *ab/cd/e*	15	2 of *W* 1 of *V*	2 of *P*	non-singular
	Q *abc/d/e*	10	1 of *W* 2 of *V*	3 of *P*	singular
1	*P* *ab/c/d/e*	10	4 of *W* 3 of *V* 3 of *R* 3 of *Q*	*O* only	singular
0	*O* *a/b/c/d/e*	1	all others		zero

In Table 2 statistics are given for the lattices of partitions of sets of from one to ten objects. The total number of partitions is shown, the number of elements which are singular (s) or non-singular (ns), and the distribution of the elements according to rank at the various levels in each lattice. Note that if the number of objects is n and the rank of the partition is r, the number of blocks in the partition is $n - r$.

TABLE 2

Rank	s	s	s	s	ns	s	ns	s	ns	s	ns	s	ns	s	ns	s	ns
9																1	
8														1		10	501
7												1		9	246	45	9285
6										1		8	119	36	2989	120	33,985
5								1		7	56	28	938	84	7686	210	42,315
4						1		6	25	21	280	56	1645	126	6825	252	22,575
3				1		5	10	15	75	35	315	70	980	126	2520	210	5670
2			1	4	3	10	15	20	45	35	105	56	210	84	378	120	630
1		1	3	6		10		15		21		28		36		45	
0	1	1	1	1		1		1		1		1		1		1	
	1	2	5	12	3	27	25	58	145	121	756	248	3892	503	20,644	1014	114,961
Totals	1	2	5	15		52		203		877		4140		21,147		115,975	
n	1	2	3	4		5		6		7		8		9		10	

An example of an infinite lattice of equivalence relations is furnished by the congruence relations C_j over the integers, for which see Example 9, § 5; this lattice is plainly dually isomorphic with the lattice of the totality of the natural numbers ordered by divisibility.

(5) *Chains*

Every chain is a lattice; we need only take min (a, b) as the meet of elements a, b and max (a, b) as their join. Commutativity is trivial; for associativity see Exercise 9, § 2; for absorption see formulae (5) and (6) of § 2. The proofs given in § 2 refer to natural numbers, but apply unchanged to the elements of any chain.

Example 40. All the chains mentioned in Examples 28–33, § 7, are lattices. We add a further interesting example. Figure 14 illus-

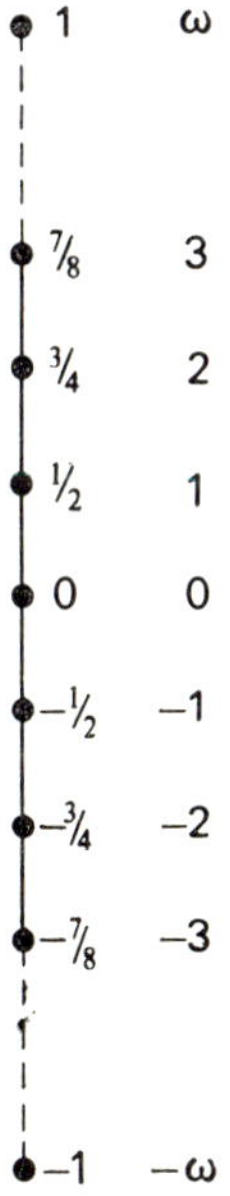

FIG. 14.

trates an infinite chain of rational numbers

$$-1, \ldots, \quad \frac{1 - 2^n}{2^n}, \ldots, \quad 0, \ldots, \quad \frac{2^n - 1}{2^n}, \ldots, 1$$

for $n = 1, 2, 3, \ldots$, arranged in their customary order. From consideration of the exponents it is clear that if we exclude the least and greatest elements these numbers form a chain isomorphic with that of the integers in their usual ordering. We therefore rename the elements as shown.

(6) *Cardinal products*

Let A, B be two lattices. Since lattices are partially ordered sets, the cardinal product $A \times B$ of Def. 19, § 7, exists. Let (a_1, b_1), (a_2, b_2) be two elements of this partially ordered set $A \times B$, with a_1, a_2 any two elements from A, b_1, b_2 any two from B. Then from the existence and unicity of a_1a_2, $a_1 + a_2$, b_1b_2 and $b_1 + b_2$, there exist unique elements (a_1a_2, b_1b_2) and $(a_1 + a_2, b_1 + b_2)$ in $A \times B$, and it is clear from the definition of order in a cardinal product (Th. 5, § 7) that these elements are respectively greatest lower bound and least upper bound of (a_1, b_1), (a_2, b_2). Hence $A \times B$ is a lattice (Def. 22). We have proved

THEOREM 32. The cardinal product of two lattices is itself a lattice. The theorem is true for any finite number of lattices.

Definition 23. Let A, B be two algebras with finitary operations matching in number and kind. Then the ordered pairs (a, b), with a from A and b from B, constitute an algebra with the same number and kind of operations defined in the manner of the following example (for a binary operation $\times$)

$$(a_1, b_1) \times (a_2, b_2) = (a_1 \times a_2, b_1 \times b_2).$$

Such an algebra is termed the direct product of the algebras *A*, *B*. Since the bounds mentioned in the proof of Th. 32 are also algebraic meet and join, the cardinal product of two lattices considered as partially ordered sets with bounded pairs coincides with the direct product of the lattices considered as algebras with binary operations.

Example 41. Figure 15 shows the formation of the product of the lattices of Figs. 13c and 13b.

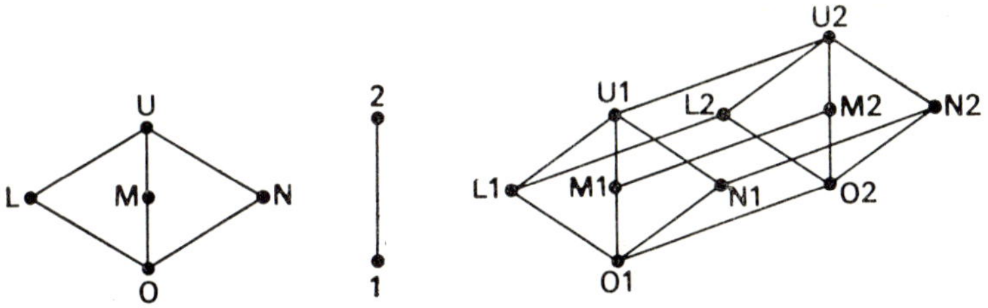

FIG. 15.

Example 42. Products in which all the component lattices are chains are exemplified by the complete factorization lattices of Example 38 and consequently by the Boolean lattices of Example 37. Let the natural number $a = p_1^{m_1} \times p_2^{m_2} \times \cdots \times p_n^{m_n}$ where the p_i are distinct primes, and let each factor of a be written as $p_1^{\alpha} \times p_2^{\beta} \times \cdots \times p_n^{\nu}$ where exponents may be zero; then the various sequences

$(\alpha, \beta, \dots, \nu)$ are the elements of the cardinal product of n chains

$$0 < 1 \leqq \cdots \leqq m_1,$$

$$0 < 1 \leqq \cdots \leqq m_2,$$

$$\cdots \qquad \cdots$$

$$0 < 1 \leqq \cdots \leqq m_n.$$

Figure 16 illustrates the case $a = 54 = 2 \times 3^3$; the eight factors of this number ordered by divisibility give a lattice isomorphic with the product of two chains, one of two elements, the other of four. If we denote the finite abstract chain of n elements by K_n, we may describe the product of Fig. 16 by the symbol $K_2 \times K_4$.

Since any finite Boolean lattice of 2^n elements can be represented by the factors, ordered by divisibility, of a "square-free" number with n prime factors, we now have the notable result that any such Boolean lattice can be represented as the product of n chains each of two elements, or K_2^n.

Example 43. We end this section with examples of lattices which are products of infinite chains. Let N denote the chain of the natural numbers in their usual order, N' the dual of N, J the chain of integers in their usual order, J_ω the augmented chain of Fig. 14 (Example 40). Figure 17a illustrates the product $N \times N$; this was introduced in Example 3, § 3, as a lattice of ordered pairs, with meet and join termed respectively inf and sup (Latin *infimum* = lowermost, *supremum* = uppermost); formulae (13) and (14) are, of course, the absorption rules. Figure 17b shows the product $N \times N'$ which we shall take as displaying the ordered pairs of natural numbers of Example 8, § 5; it will be recalled that we made these into an algebra A by introducing binary operations of addition and multiplication before proceeding to construct from them the in-

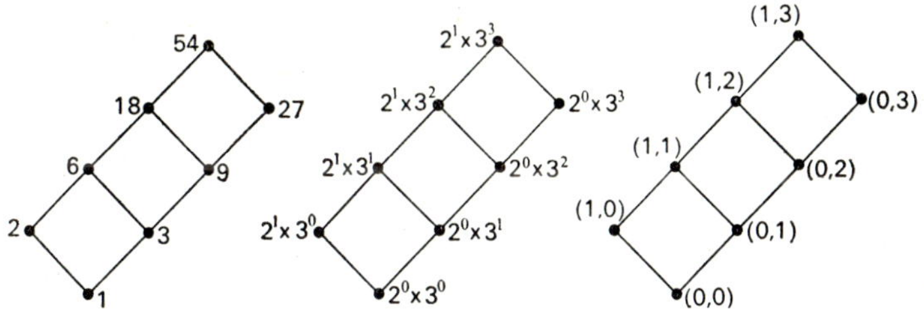
54
18
27
6
9
2
3
1
$2^1 \times 3^3$
$2^1 \times 3^2$
$2^0 \times 3^3$
$2^1 \times 3^1$
$2^0 \times 3^2$
$2^1 \times 3^0$
$2^0 \times 3^1$
$2^0 \times 3^0$
(1,3)
(1,2)
(0,3)
(1,1)
(0,2)
(1,0)
(0,1)
(0,0)

FIG. 16.

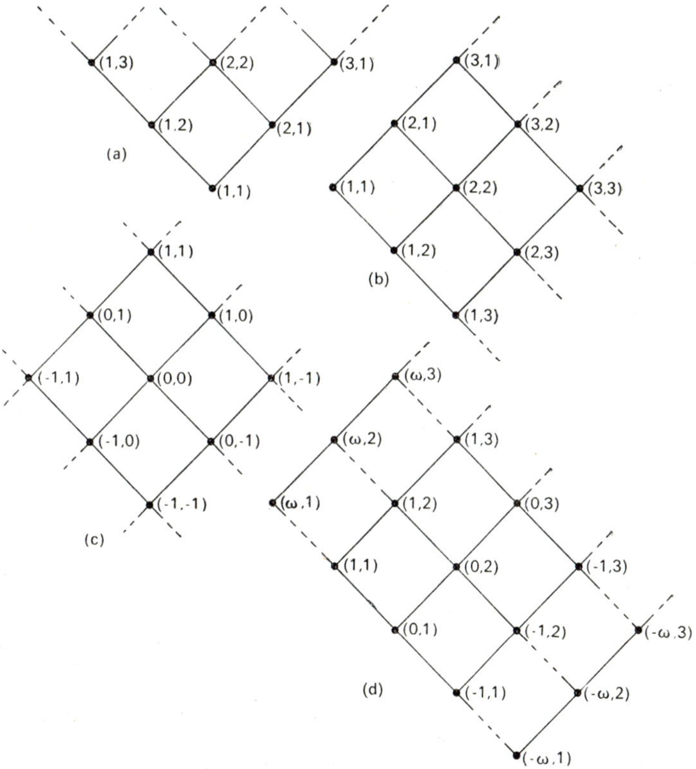
(1,3)
(2,2)
(3,1)
(1,2)
(2,1)
(a)
(1,1)
(3,1)
(2,1)
(3,2)
(1,1)
(2,2)
(3,3)
(1,2)
(2,3)
(b)
(1,3)
(1,1)
(0,1)
(1,0)
(-1,1)
(0,0)
(1,-1)
(-1,0)
(0,-1)
(-1,-1)
(c)
(ω,3)
(ω,2)
(1,3)
(ω,1)
(1,2)
(0,3)
(1,1)
(0,2)
(-1,3)
(0,1)
(-1,2)
(-ω,3)
(d)
(-1,1)
(-ω,2)
(-ω,1)

FIG. 17.

tegers; these operations of addition and multiplication are not to be confused with the lattice operations in $N \times N'$, which contrast as follows:

Algebra A	Lattice $N \times N'$
$(a, b) + (c, d)$ $= (a + c, b + d)$	$(a, b) \cup (c, d)$ $= [\max (a, c), \min (b, d)]$
$(a, b) \times (c, d)$ $= (ac + bd, ad + bc)$	$(a, b) \cap (c, d)$ $= [\min (a, c), \max (b, d)]$.

The connexion between the lattice and the integers will be considered in a subsequent chapter.

Figure 17c shows $J \times J$, and Fig. 17d illustrates $J_\omega \times N$.

Exercises

49. Show that there are fifteen abstract lattices of six elements. Use Exercise 35.
50. (In this exercise the notation refers to ordinary elementary algebra.) Show that the factors of $a = p_1^{m_1} \times \ldots \times p_n^{m_n}$ are given by the separate terms of the product

$$(1 + p_1 + p_1^2 + \cdots + p_1^{m_1}) \times (1 + p_2 + p_2^2 + \cdots + p_2^{m_2})$$
$$\times \cdots \times (1 + p_n + p_n^2 + \cdots + p_n^{m_n});$$

also that the number of elements at each level in the lattice of factors can be ascertained from consideration of the coefficients of the powers of x in

$$(1 + x + x^2 + \cdots + x^{m_1}) \times (1 + x + x^2 + \cdots + x^{m_2})$$
$$\times \cdots \times (1 + x + x^2 + \cdots + x^{m_n}).$$

Prove further that such a factorization lattice is self-dual.
51. Draw a diagram for the lattice of the factors of the number 27,000, ordered by divisibility; show that this lattice is isomorphic with the cardinal product of three chains of equal length.
52. Tabulate the 203 elements of the lattice of partitions of a set of six objects, giving rank, type, number, ordering and description, as is done in the text for the fifty-two partitions of a set of five objects.
53. Show that in the lattice of all partitions of a set of n objects the total number of singular partitions is $2^n - n$.
54. If X, Y are lattices, let $X = Y$ mean that X, Y are isomorphic (Def. 13, § 6). Prove that cardinal multiplication of lattices is associative and commutative.

CHAPTER 3

LATTICES IN GENERAL

10. Duality

In this chapter we investigate further properties of meet and join; then after dimensional considerations we deal in turn with certain relations between individual elements of a lattice, between subsets of a lattice and finally between lattices themselves.

If we examine the postulates for a lattice listed in Def. 20 we see that replacement of meet by join in IA, IIA, IIIA, IVA gives IB, IIB, IIIB, IVB; conversely replacement of join by meet in the second set gives the first. This exact parallelism has the following consequence:

Let T be a valid theorem of lattice theory the enunciation of which contains besides logical connectives only meets, joins and the equality sign, and which is proved from some or all of the postulates by a deduction containing only connectives, meets, joins and the equality sign; then the assertion T' which results from writing join for meet and meet for join everywhere in T is itself a valid theorem. T' does not require separate proof and is called the dual of T.

Thus in § 8 above $aa = a$ was proved as Th. 6 and is a theorem satisfying the conditions just stated. Therefore $a + a = a$ (Th. 7) is true and requires no proof. In § 8 we used Th. 6 to prove Th. 7, and for Th. 8 and 9 dissimilar proofs were given; we may now reset the proofs to illustrate the dualism:

Th. 6. $aa = a(a + ab) = a$ by IVB and IVA.

Th. 7. $a + a = a + a(a + b) = a$ by IVA and IVB.

Th. 8. If $ab = a, a + b = ab + b = b$ by hyp., IIB, IIA and IVB.

Th. 9. If $a + b = a$, $ab = (a + b)\,b = b$ by hyp., IIA, IIB and IVA.

Definition 21 defined partial order in a lattice as follows:

(i) $a \leqq b$ if and only if $ab = a$;
(ii) $a \leqq b$ if and only if $a + b = b$.

If in the statements $ab = a$ and $a + b = b$ we replace meet by join and join by meet, we obtain $a + b = a$ and $ab = b$; consequently by Def. 21 $a \geqq b$. Therefore the interchange of meets and joins in a formula reverses all inequality signs. We now have the useful duality rule:

If in any theorem deduced from some or all of the eight postulates IA–IVB we interchange meet and join everywhere and reverse all inequalities, we obtain a valid theorem.

Thus the burden of proof in the rest of this book is reduced by one-half. For instance, when we prove later in this chapter that for a, b, c in any lattice

$$a\,(b + c) \geqq ab + ac,$$

we know at once that

$$a + bc \leqq (a + b)\,(a + c).$$

The $\cap$, $\cup$ notation shows duality with complete clarity:

$$a \cap (b \cup c) \geqq (a \cap b) \cup (a \cap c)$$

$$a \cup (b \cap c) \leqq (a \cup b) \cap (a \cup c)$$

and should be resorted to on occasion. Note that definitions, like theorems, frequently occur in dual pairs; thus in Def. 17 each of the two columns is the dual rendering of the other.

11. Meets and Joins

THEOREM 33. If in a lattice $a \leqq b$ and $c \leqq d$, then $ac \leqq bd$.

Proof. From the hypotheses $ab = a$, $cd = c$ (Def. 21 (i)). Now

$$\begin{aligned}(ac)(bd) &= [(ac)\,b]\,d && \text{by IIIA}\\ &= [a\,(cb)]\,d && \text{by IIIA}\\ &= [a\,(bc)]\,d && \text{by IIA}\\ &= [(ab)\,c]\,d && \text{by IIIA}\\ &= (ab)(cd) && \text{by IIIA}\\ &= ac && \text{from hyp.;}\end{aligned}$$

therefore $ac \leqq bd$ by Def. 21 (i).

By duality we have

THEOREM 34. If in a lattice $a \geqq b$ and $c \geqq d$, then $a + c \geqq b + d$.

In order to abbreviate proofs such as that just given, we proceed to exploit the properties of associativity and commutativity required for meets and joins by Postulates IIA–IIIB. First we establish for meets in lattices a definition and theorems applicable to any associative binary operation in any algebra.

Definition 24. Let $a_1, \ldots, a_n$ be any sequence of n elements of a lattice; the elements need not be all different. The meet a_1a_2 of two elements was defined in Def. 20. We now define by recurrence the meet of n elements, for $n \geqq 3$, as follows:

$$a_1a_2a_3 = (a_1a_2)\,a_3, \quad a_1a_2a_3a_4 = (a_1a_2a_3)\,a_4, \ldots,$$
$$a_1 \cdots a_n = (a_1 \cdots a_{n-1})\,a_n.$$

Dually $a_1 + \cdots + a_n$ is defined as $(a_1 + \cdots + a_{n-1}) + a_n$. The existence of all elements is secured by Postulates IA, IB.

THEOREM 35. For $n \geqq 3$, $a_1 \cdots a_n = a_1(a_2 \cdots a_n)$.

Proof. We remark that the assertion is true for $n = 3$

since
$$a_1a_2a_3 = (a_1a_2)\,a_3 \quad \text{by Def. 24}$$
$$= a_1(a_2a_3) \quad \text{by IIIA.}$$

Let N be the set of those subscript natural numbers n for which the assertion is true; N is not empty for 3 belongs to it. We now prove that if k belongs to N, so does the next subscript $k + 1$.

Let
$$a_1 \cdots a_k = a_1(a_2 \cdots a_k).$$
Then
$$a_1 \cdots a_{k+1} = (a_1 \cdots a_k)\,a_{k+1} \quad \text{by Def. 24}$$
$$= [a_1(a_2 \cdots a_k)]\,a_{k+1} \quad \text{by hyp.}$$
$$= a_1[(a_2 \cdots a_k)\,a_{k+1}] \quad \text{by IIIA}$$
$$= a_1(a_2 \cdots a_{k+1}) \quad \text{by Def. 24.}$$

It follows that all the natural numbers from 3 onwards belong to N.

THEOREM 36. Let P be any partition of the set $a_1, \ldots, a_n$ which does not disturb the order of the elements; thus

$$P\colon\ a_1, \ldots, a_p/\ldots/a_{r+1}, \ldots, a_s/a_{s+1}, \ldots, a_t/a_{t+1}, \ldots, a_n$$

where $1, p, r, s, t, n$ are subscript natural numbers in ascending order. Then the meet

$$a = (a_1 \cdots a_p) \cdots (a_{s+1} \cdots a_t)\,(a_{t+1} \cdots a_n) = a_1 \cdots a_n.$$

Proof. Definition 24 secures the existence of all meets mentioned. The zero and unity partitions give the meets $(a_1) \cdots (a_n)$ and $(a_1 \cdots a_n)$ respectively, where the parentheses are superfluous and the assertion trivial; let P be other than zero or unity. If the last block contains more than one element, we see that

$$\begin{aligned}
&(a_{s+1} \cdots a_t)(a_{t+1} \cdots a_n) \\
&= (a_{s+1} \cdots a_t)[a_{t+1}(a_{t+2} \cdots a_n)] && \text{by Th. 35} \\
&= [(a_{s+1} \cdots a_t)\, a_{t+1}](a_{t+2} \cdots a_n) && \text{by IIIA} \\
&= (a_{s+1} \cdots a_{t+1})(a_{t+2} \cdots a_n) && \text{by Def. 24,}
\end{aligned}$$

and this by a repetition of the same process as often as is necessary can be reduced to the form

$$(a_{s+1} \cdots a_{n-1})\, a_n.$$

If P has more than two blocks, reduce the meet

$$(a_{r+1} \cdots a_s)(a_{s+1} \cdots a_{n-1})\, a_n$$

by the same process to

$$(a_{r+1} \cdots a_{n-1})\, a_n.$$

In this way we may work steadily across to the left, merging parenthesis with parenthesis, till after a finite number of transfers we have

$$a = (a_1 \cdots a_{n-1})\, a_n = a_1 \cdots a_n \quad \text{by Def. 24.}$$

This theorem enables us to combine adjacent elements in a multiple meet in any way we please, provided we do not disturb their order; for instance, $abcd = a\,(bcd) = (ab)\,(cd) = a\,(bc)\,d = (abc)\,d$.

Next we invoke commutativity; the results are again valid for any binary operation which is at once commutative and associative.

THEOREM 37. Let $a = a_1 \cdots a_p \cdots a_q \cdots a_n$. Then

(i) $a = a_1 \cdots a_{p-1}a_qa_pa_{p+1} \cdots a_{q-1}a_{q+1} \cdots a_n$

and

(ii) $a = a_1 \cdots a_{p-1}a_{p+1} \cdots a_{q-1}a_qa_pq_{q+1} \cdots a_n$.

In words, an element appearing in the pth place in the meet may be made to appear in the qth place, for any p, q, $1 \leqq p \leqq n$, $1 \leqq q \leqq n$.

Proof. We prove only the legitimacy of the leftward shift (i). Using Th. 36 we insert parentheses in the given expression for a:

$$a = (a_1 \cdots a_{q-2})(a_{q-1}a_q)(a_{q+1} \cdots a_n).$$

By IIA $a_{q-1}a_q = a_q a_{q-1}$, so that

$$a = (a_1 \cdots a_{q-2})(a_q a_{q-1})(a_{q+1} \cdots a_n)$$
$$= a_1 \cdots a_{q-2}a_q a_{q-1}a_{q+1} \cdots a_n \quad \text{again by Th. 36.}$$

If $p < q - 1$, regroup a second time:

$$a = (a_1 \cdots a_{q-3})(a_{q-2}a_q)(a_{q-1}a_{q+1} \cdots a_n),$$

commute $a_{q-2}a_q$ and remove parentheses. It is clear that we may repeat this process as often as is necessary till a_q arrives at the desired position on the left of a_p. The rightward shift (ii) is carried out in similar fashion.

THEOREM 38. Let P be any partition whatsoever of the set $a_1, \ldots, a_n$ into, say, k blocks; let the meets $b_1, \ldots, b_k$ of the elements of each block be formed, the elements in each being taken in any order; then if a is the meet of the b_i ($i = 1, \ldots, k$) we have

$$a = b_1 \cdots b_k = a_1 \cdots a_n.$$

Proof. Writing each b_i in full and using Th. 36 we see that

$$a = b_1 \cdots b_k = a_{r_1} \cdots a_{r_n}$$

where

$$r_1, \ldots, r_n$$

is some permutation of

$$1, \ldots, n.$$

Using Th. 37 as necessary, we obtain the desired result by working each element a_{r_j} into the r_jth position ($j = 1, \ldots, n$).

A small-scale example of the procedure in this theorem will be found in the proof of Th. 33 where the set a, b, c, d was partitioned as ac/bd and the meet $(ac)(bd)$ was transformed into $(ab)(cd) = abcd$.

To summarize: Def. 24 and Ths. 36–38 show that the unique element

$$a_1 \cdots a_n$$

is disturbed in its identity neither by any grouping or regrouping of component elements nor by any alteration of their order. We have used only the properties of associativity and commutativity; hence the result is true for any binary operation enjoying these properties in any algebra closed with respect to the operation, and in particular for joins in lattices.

We now enlarge on Ths. 33 and 34.

THEOREM 39. If $a_i \leqq b_i$ for $i = 1, \ldots, n$, then $a_1 \cdots a_n \leqq b_1 \cdots b_n$.

Proof. $(a_1 \cdots a_n)(b_1 \cdots b_n) = (a_1b_1)(a_2b_2) \cdots (a_nb_n)$ by Th. 38.

$= a_1 \cdots a_n$ by hyp. and Def. 21 (i).

Therefore

$$a_1 \cdots a_n \leqq b_1 \cdots b_n \quad \text{by the same definition.}$$

Dually we have:

THEOREM 40. If $a_i \geqq b_i$ for $i = 1, \ldots, n$, then $a_1 + \cdots + a_n \geqq b_1 + \cdots + b_n$.

The dual Ths. 33 and 34 and their generalizations Ths. 39 and

40 are used over and over again in lattice theory. We give some instances in the following important theorems, valid in all lattices.

THEOREM 41. *(Distributive inequality.)* For a, b, c in any lattice

$$a\,(b + c) \geqq ab + ac.$$

Proof. $a \geqq ab$ (Th. 14); $b + c \geqq b \geqq ab$ (Ths. 15, 16); hence

$$a\,(b + c) \geqq (ab)\,(ab) = ab \qquad \text{(Ths. 33, 6).}$$

$$a \geqq ac \text{ (Th. 14)}; \quad b + c \geqq c \geqq ac \qquad \text{(Ths. 17, 16)};$$

hence

$$a\,(b + c) \geqq (ac)\,(ac) = ac \qquad \text{(Ths. 33, 6).}$$

Therefore

$$a\,(b + c) + a\,(b + c) \geqq ab + ac \qquad \text{(Th. 34)},$$

that is

$$a\,(b + c) \geqq ab + ac \qquad \text{(Th. 7).}$$

The dual theorem is

THEOREM 42. *(Dual distributive inequality.)* For a, b, c in any lattice

$$a + bc \leqq (a + b)\,(a + c).$$

THEOREM 43. For a, b, c in any lattice

$$(a + b)\,(b + c)\,(c + a) \geqq ab + bc + ca.$$

Proof. $a + b \geqq a$ (Th. 15) and $b + c \geqq b$ (Th. 15) yield by Th. 33

$$(a + b)(b + c) \geqq ab.$$

Similarly

$$(b + c)(c + a) \geqq ba \quad \text{(Ths. 15, 17, 33).}$$

Hence

$$(a + b)(b + c)(b + c)(c + a) \geqq (ab)(ba) \quad \text{(Th. 33)}$$

or

$$(a + b)(b + c)(c + a) \geqq ab \quad \text{(Ths. 38, 6).}$$

Similarly

$$(a + b)(b + c)(c + a) \geqq bc$$

and

$$(a + b)(b + c)(c + a) \geqq ca.$$

Therefore

$$(a + b)(b + c)(c + a) \geqq ab + bc + ca \quad \text{by Th. 40 and Th. 7.}$$

The dual is the same statement read from right to left; we say that Th. 43 is self-dual.

THEOREM 44. *(Modular inequality.)* For a, b, c in any lattice where $a \geqq b$ and c is arbitrary,

$$a(b + c) \geqq b + ac.$$

Proof. Since $a \geqq b$, $ab = b$; then by Th. 41, the dual of Th. 44 reads:

For a, b, c in any lattice where $a \leqq b$ and c is arbitrary,

$$a + bc \leqq b(a + c),$$

which is exactly the same assertion though with a different choice of letters; Th. 44 is self-dual.

Definition 24 provided a definition of meet and join of the elements of any finite subset A of a lattice L. Now let A be any subset, finite or infinite. If there is an element x in L such that $x \leqq a$ for every a in A, x is a lower bound to A (Def. 17, § 6). Let X be the set of lower bounds in L to A. If X is not empty and has a greatest member b such that $x \leqq b$ for all x in X, b is greatest lower bound to A; we write

$$b = \inf A \quad \text{or} \quad b = \bigcap_{a \in A} a,$$

where $a \in A$ means that a belongs to A. If A is finite and consists of the elements $a_1, \ldots, a_n$, b always exists and coincides with the meet $a_1 \cdots a_n$; if A is infinite, such an element b may or may not exist in L. The least upper bound to A was defined in dual terms in Def. 17 and is written

$$\sup A \quad \text{or} \quad \bigcup_{a \in A} a.$$

If A consists of $a_1, \ldots, a_n$, $\sup A$ always exists and coincides with the join $a_1 + \cdots + a_n$. If a lattice L has the property that $\inf A$ and $\sup A$ exist for every non-empty subset A of L, we say that L is complete. All finite lattices are complete, but many infinite lattices are not; the most notorious example of a lattice which is not complete is the chain of the rationals; a major problem in the history of mathematics has been to embed the chain of the rationals in a larger, complete chain, that of the real numbers; thus the construction of the real number system can be regarded as a special case of a problem of lattice theory. Since we prefer, for the most part, to concern ourselves with algebraic finitary operations—but chiefly from considerations of space—we do not treat further of complete lattices in this book.

Exercises

55. If a, b, c, d, e, f are any six elements of a chain, show that $\min [\max (a, b, c), \max (d, e, f)] \geqq \max [\min (a, d), \min (b, e), \min (c, f)]$.

56. Let a_{ij} ($i = 1, \ldots, m; j = 1, \ldots, n$) be $m \times n$ elements chosen at random from a lattice and set out in a rectangular array of m rows and n columns. Then if R_i denotes the join of all elements in the ith row and C_j the meet of all elements in the jth column, show that

$$R_1 \cdots R_m \geqq C_1 + \cdots + C_n.$$

(This is an example of the minimax inequality, after Birkhoff.)

57. If a, b, c are three elements of a chain, prove that

$$\min [\max (a, b), \max (b, c), \max (c, a)] \\ = \max [\min (a, b), \min (b, c), \min (c, a)]$$

and that this element is one of a, b, c.

58. If a, b, c are three natural numbers, prove that

$$\text{h.c.f. } [\text{l.c.m. } (a, b), \text{l.c.m. } (b, c), \text{l.c.m. } (c, a)] \\ = \text{l.c.m. } [\text{h.c.f. } (a, b), \text{h.c.f. } (b, c), \text{h.c.f. } (c, a)].$$

Is this number one of a, b, c?

59. If a subset A of a lattice consists of the elements $a_1, \ldots, a_n$, prove that $\inf A = a_1 \cdots a_n$ and that $\sup A = a_1 + \cdots + a_n$.

12. Length and Covering Conditions

Definition 25. For any pair of comparable elements a, b of a lattice L where $a \leqq b$, the subset X of L consisting of all elements x, $a \leqq x \leqq b$, is called the interval $[a, b]$.

Definition 26. Let K be a non-empty subset of elements of the interval $[a, b]$ of L such that any two elements of K are comparable and such that a, b belong to K; then K is a chain from a to b. If K is finite and consists of just n elements, the integer $n - 1$ is called the length of K. Thus if $a = b$, the interval consists of one element, there is only one chain K consisting of this same element, and the length of K is 0; if $a < b$, these two elements by themselves form a chain from a to b, of length 1; the chain $a = x_1 < x_2 < x_3 < x_4 = b$ is of length 3.

Definition 27. Let $a = x_1 < x_2 < \cdots < x_{n-1} < x_n = b$ be a finite chain K from a to b such that x_j is covered by x_{j+1} for $j = 1, \ldots, n-1$; then K is said to be maximal.

Definition 28. If all chains from a to b in a lattice are finite and if among the maximal chains there is one of greatest length n, the interval $[a, b]$ is said to be of length n, and we write

$$l\,[a, b] = n.$$

If L is a lattice with zero element o and unity element u, the interval $[o, u]$ is the entire lattice L; if $[o, u]$ is of length n, the integer n is called the length of the lattice, and L is said to be of finite length n.

Example 44. Every finite lattice is of finite length. An instance is given by Fig. 18, which shows the abstract "pentagonal" lattice of five elements. There are in all five chains from o to u, namely:

$$(1)\ o < u, \quad (2)\ o < a < u, \quad (3)\ o < b < u,$$
$$(4)\ o < c < u, \quad (5)\ o < b < a < u.$$

The chains (4) and (5) are maximal, of lengths 2 and 3 respectively; hence the lattice is of length 3.

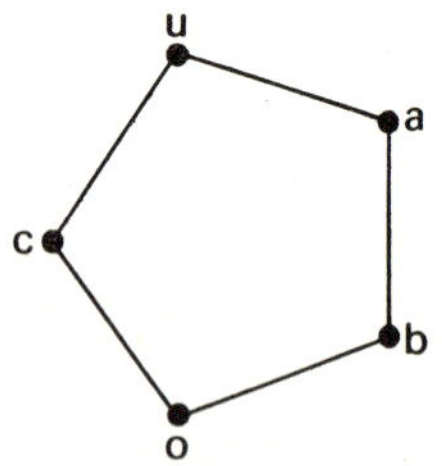

FIG. 18.

Example 45. An infinite lattice with zero and unity elements may be of finite length. If we take the following subsets of the set J of the integers:

J itself $\{0, \pm 1, \pm 2, ...\}$,
all one-element subsets of $J\{n\}$, $n = 0, \pm 1, \pm 2, ...$,
the empty set $\{\quad\}$,

and order these by set-inclusion, we have the lattice of Fig.19; in this lattice all maximal chains from the zero to the unity element have the same length 2, which is therefore the length of the lattice.

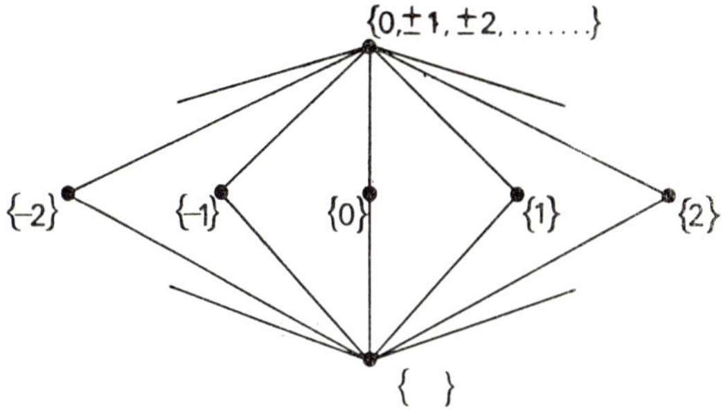

FIG. 19.

Example 46. An infinite lattice with o and u may have all chains from o to u finite but not be itself of finite length. As an example take the numbers 0, 1 and the fractions

$$\frac{m}{n}, \quad 0 < \frac{m}{n} < 1,$$

that is, the numbers

$$0, 1, \tfrac{1}{2}, \tfrac{1}{3}, \tfrac{2}{3}, \tfrac{1}{4}, \tfrac{2}{4}, \tfrac{3}{4}, \tfrac{1}{5}, \tfrac{2}{5}, \tfrac{3}{5}, \tfrac{4}{5}, \ldots.$$

Order as follows:

$$0 < \frac{m}{n} < 1 \quad \text{for all} \quad \frac{m}{n}; \quad \frac{m}{n} \leqq \frac{r}{n}$$

only if $\max(m, r) = r$; $\frac{m}{n}$, $\frac{r}{s}$ incomparable if $n \neq s$.

Figure 20 shows this lattice; all chains from 0 to 1 are finite, but there is no maximal chain of greatest length.

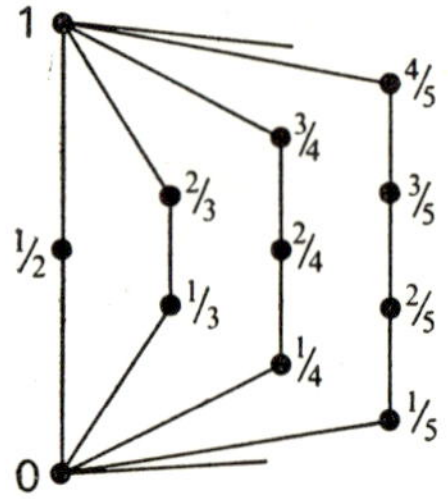

FIG. 20.

Definition 29. If a lattice L has the property that all chains connecting pairs of comparable elements are finite, we shall say that L is a lattice in which all terminated chains are finite. If further for every pair of elements a, b, $a \leqq b$, in such a lattice L the interval $[a, b]$ is of finite length, L will be said to be locally of finite length.

Example 47. The second property implies the first, but not conversely. In the lattice of Fig. 20 all terminated chains are finite, but the lattice is not locally of finite length, for the one interval [0, 1] fails in the matter of finite length. The chain of the natural numbers (Fig. 6b) and that of the integers (Fig. 6d) are locally of finite length;

in the chain of the rationals (Example 31) no chain connecting distinct elements can have element covering element so that there is a multitude of terminated chains which are infinite in this lattice. The direct products of Figs. 17a, b, c are all locally of finite length, that of Fig. 17d is not.

Definition 30. Let L be a lattice with o, being locally of finite length; then for any element x of L the interval $[o, x]$ has finite length, say n. We call this integer the height of x, writing

$$h(x) = l\,[o, x] = n.$$

Dually for L with u, $l\,[x, u]$ is the depth $d(x)$ of x.

THEOREM 45. Let L be a lattice with o, locally of finite length. If a, b are comparable elements, $a \leqq b$, we have

$$h(b) - h(a) = l\,[a, b].$$

In particular, if b covers a, $h(b) - h(a) = 1$.

Proof. Since $o \leqq a \leqq b$, we may calculate as follows in integers:

$$\begin{aligned} h(b) - h(a) &= l\,[o, b] - l\,[o, a] \\ &= l\,[o, a] + l\,[a, b] - l\,[o, a] \\ &= l\,[a, b]. \end{aligned}$$

If b covers a, by Def. 12, § 6, there is no element x in L such that $a < x < b$, so that $[a, b]$ is a two-element chain and $l\,[a, b] = 1$.

Definition 31. In a lattice with zero element o any element covering o is called an atom. If a is an atom, $h(a) = 1$. Dually, in a lattice with unity element u any element covered by u is called a dual atom. If b is a dual atom, $d(b) = 1$. Many writers use "point" for atom; for the dual atom some use "hyperplane" or "hyperatom" or "anti-atom"; H. B. Curry suggests the attractive names "point" and "counterpoint".

Example 48. The chain of the natural numbers has just one atom, the number 2; in the lattice of the natural numbers ordered by divisibility mentioned at the end of § 9 (3) all primes are atoms. A finite lattice with distinct o and u has at least one atom and one dual atom; an infinite lattice with o and u may or may not possess such elements; thus the chain of rationals from 0 to 1 has neither kind, but the lattice of fractions from 0 to 1 of Example 46 has a countable infinity of atoms and of dual atoms.

We now list eight conditions to do with lengths of intervals in lattices. The first four are called *covering conditions*; we denote them by C1–C4.

C1 If a covers ab, then $a + b$ covers b.
C2 If $a + b$ covers b, then a covers ab.
C3 If both a and b cover ab, then $a + b$ covers both a and b.
C4 If $a + b$ covers both a and b, then both a and b cover ab.

The fifth condition we call the *Jordan–Dedekind condition*; we denote it by the symbol JD.

JD A lattice will be said to satisfy this condition if for each pair of elements $a, b, a \leqq b$, all chains from a to b are finite and all maximal chains from a to b are of the same length $l\,[a, b]$.

We can see that the lattice of Fig. 19 satisfies this condition; those of Fig. 18 and Fig. 20 do not. A lattice satisfying this condition must of necessity be locally of finite length; but the converse is not true, for the "pentagonal" lattice of Fig. 18 even though finite does not satisfy the condition JD. Three further conditions which concern lengths of intervals suppose the integers in question to exist; we denote these *length conditions* by L1–L3.

L1 $l\,[xy, x] \geqq l\,[y, x + y]$.
L2 $l\,[xy, x] \leqq l\,[y, x + y]$.
L3 $l\,[xy, x] = l\,[y, x + y]$.

By Th. 45 in a lattice with zero, locally of finite length, L1 may be stated in terms of differences or sums of heights:

$$h(x) - h\,(x \cap y) \geqq h\,(x \cup y) - h(y)$$

or

$$h(x) + h(y) \geqq h\,(x \cap y) + h\,(x \cup y),$$

and there are similar versions for L2, L3. Dually, in a lattice with unity, locally of finite length, L1–3 may be stated in terms of depth.

THEOREM 46. If the elements of a lattice satisfy C1, they satisfy C3.

Proof. If both a and b cover ab, by C1 applied twice $a + b$ covers both b and a.

Dually we have

THEOREM 47. If the elements of a lattice satisfy C2, they satisfy C4.

A convenient abbreviation here will be to use the symbol for a condition to mean satisfaction of that condition; we can thus restate these theorems:

Th. 46 In any lattice
C1 implies C3.

Th. 47 In any lattice
C2 implies C4.

THEOREM 48. In any lattice in which all terminated chains are finite C3 implies JD.

Proof. Let p, q be any pair of comparable elements of the lattice, $p < q$, and let K_m, K_n be two maximal chains connecting p and q, of length m and n respectively. We have to prove that $m = n$ if C3 holds.

Let N be the set of those positive integers which give the lengths of intervals for which JD holds good. N is not empty for 1 belongs to it, since in this case q covers p and there is only one chain, and that of length 1, connecting p and q. Suppose that $k - 1$ belongs to N. (We can make this supposition, for there is at least one such k, namely $k = 2$.) Now let $[p, q]$ be an interval such that

$$p < x_1 < \cdots < x_k = q,$$

$$p < y_1 < \cdots < y_j = q$$

are maximal chains connecting p and q, of length k and j respectively. We shall prove that $j = k$ and hence that k belongs to N. Either $x_1 = y_1$ or $x_1 \neq y_1$.

If $x_1 = y_1 = s$, we have two maximal chains connecting s and q, of length $k - 1$, $j - 1$ respectively. By our supposition $j - 1 = k - 1$, whence $j = k$ (Fig. 21a).

If $x_1 \neq y_1$, then both x_1 and y_1 cover p, so that by C3 $x_1 + y_1 = t$ covers both x_1 and y_1. We have, of course, $x_1 < q$, $y_1 < q$; hence $t = x_1 + y_1 \leqq q$. Let

$$t < z_1 < \cdots < z_i = q$$

be a maximal chain, of length i, connecting t and q. Now

$$x_1 < x_2 < \cdots < x_k = q$$

and

$$x_1 < t < z_1 < \cdots z_i = q$$

are two maximal chains connecting x_1 and q, the first being of length $k - 1$. By our supposition the second must be of the same length; hence $i = k - 2$. Similarly the chains

$$y_1 < y_2 < \cdots < y_j = q$$

and

$$y_1 < t < z_1 < \cdots < z_i = q$$

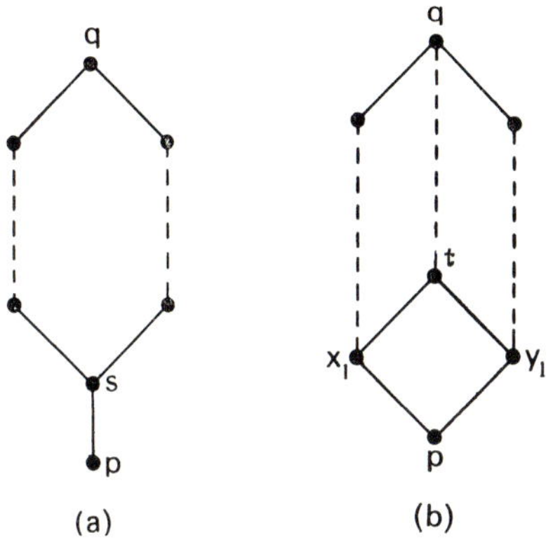

FIG. 21.

must be of the same length, and $i = j - 2$. Therefore $j - 2 = k - 2$ so that $j = k$ (Fig. 21b).

It follows that N contains all positive integers; in other words, JD holds for intervals of any length.

THEOREM 49. In any lattice in which all terminated chains are finite C4 implies JD.

Proof. In the proof above we worked upwards from the least lement p of the interval $[p, q]$; in the dual proof we work downwards from the greatest element p of the interval $[q, p]$. Note that the condition JD is self-dual in the sense that the length of a finite chain can be obtained by numbering off its elements in ascending or descending order.

THEOREM 50. In any lattice in which all terminated chains are finite C3 implies L1.

Proof. By Th. 48 JD is satisfied so that every interval in the lattice has a finite length and all maximal chains in an interval have the same length. We have to show now that for any elements p, q

$$l\,[pq, p] \geqq l\,[q, p+q].$$

Suppose p, q comparable, with $p \leqq q$; then $pq = p$, $p + q = q$ and $l\,[pq, p] = 0 = l\,[q, p+q]$. Suppose p, q incomparable; then $pq < p < p + q$, $pq < q < p + q$; therefore we have maximal chains

$$pq = x_0 < x_1 < \cdots < x_m = p \tag{1}$$

and

$$pq = y_0 < y_1 < \cdots < y_n = q. \tag{2}$$

By absorption $q = pq + q = x_0 + y_n$, and we have by Th. 34

$$q = x_0 + y_n \leqq x_1 + y_n \leqq x_2 + y_n \leqq \cdots \leqq x_m + y_n = p + q \tag{3}$$

which gives a chain from q to $p + q$. Our aim is to prove that in this chain (3) for $r = 1, \ldots, m$ each element $x_r + y_n$ either covers or equals the preceding term $x_{r-1} + y_n$; then the length of a maximal chain in $[q, p+q]$ cannot exceed m, which is the length of $[pq, p]$. Figure 22a shows the general situation.

Noting that if a and b cover c then $c = ab$, we restate C3:

If a and b cover c, then $a + b$ covers a and b.

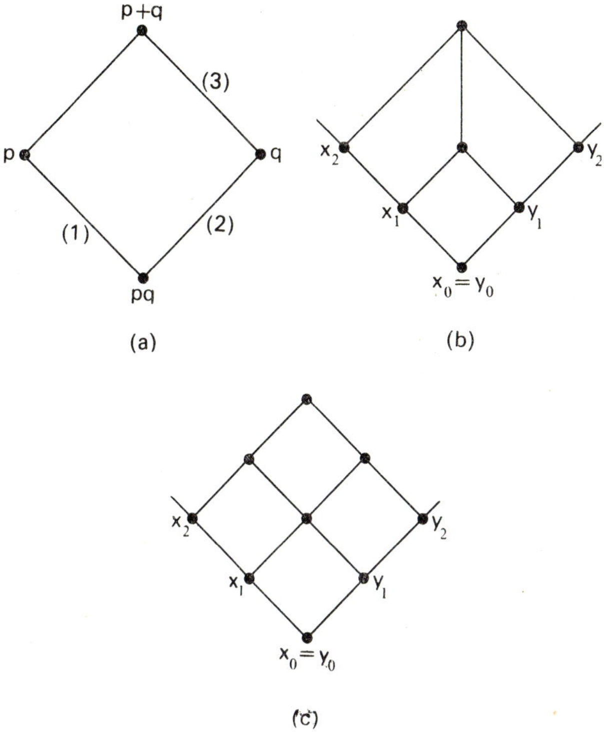

FIG. 22.

We have also the following:

If $a = c$ and b covers c, then $a + b$ covers a and equals b.
If a covers c and $b = c$, then $a + b$ equals a and covers b.
If $a = c$ and $b = c$, then $a + b$ equals a and equals b.

In summary form:

If $\left.\begin{matrix} a \\ b \end{matrix}\right\}$ covers/equals c, then $a + b$ covers/equals $\left\{\begin{matrix} a \\ b \end{matrix}\right.$.

Taking elements from chains (1) and (2) we put

$$a = x_{r-1} + y_s,$$

$$b = x_r + y_{s-1},$$

$$c = x_{r-1} + y_{s-1},$$

so that

$$a + b = x_{r-1} + y_s + x_r + y_{s-1}$$

$$= x_r + y_s,$$

and the expanded form of C3 gives:

$$\text{If } \left.\begin{matrix} x_{r-1} + y_s \\ x_r + y_{s-1}, \end{matrix}\right\} \text{ covers/equals } x_{r-1} + y_{s-1},$$

$$\text{then } x_r + y_s \text{ covers/equals } \left\{\begin{matrix} x_{r-1} + y_s \\ x_r + y_{s-1} \end{matrix}\right. . \qquad (4)$$

In fact

$$y_1 = x_0 + y_1 \text{ covers } x_1 y_1 = pq = x_0 + y_0,$$

and

$$x_1 = x_1 + y_0 \text{ likewise covers } x_0 + y_0;$$

therefore by (4) $x_1 + y_1$ covers/equals $x_0 + y_1$ (and $x_1 + y_0$). (5)
Also

$$y_2 = x_0 + y_2 \text{ covers } x_0 + y_1;$$

therefore by (4) $x_1 + y_2$ covers/equals $x_0 + y_2$ (and $x_1 + y_1$). (6)
Again

$$y_3 = x_0 + y_3 \text{ covers } x_0 + y_2;$$

therefore by (4) $x_1 + y_3$ covers/equals $x_0 + y_3$ (and $x_1 + y_2$).

Continuing to use the recurrence formula (4) in this way, we finally arrive at the result:

$$x_1 + y_n \text{ covers/equals } x_0 + y_n.$$

Starting again we have:

From (5)

$$x_1 + y_1 \text{ covers/equals } x_1 + y_0$$

and

$$x_2 = x_2 + y_0 \text{ covers } x_1 + y_0;$$

therefore by (4)

$$x_2 + y_1 \text{ covers/equals } x_1 + y_1 \text{ (and } x_2 + y_0).$$

Again from (6)

$$x_1 + y_2 \text{ covers/equals } x_1 + y_1;$$

therefore by (4)

$$x_2 + y_2 \text{ covers/equals } x_1 + y_2 \text{ (and } x_2 + y_1).$$

This process will eventually yield:

$$x_2 + y_n \text{ covers/equals } x_1 + y_n.$$

In similar fashion we prove:

$$x_r + y_n \text{ covers/equals } x_{r-1} + y_n$$

for the remaining values 3, ..., m of r. The theorem is thus established.

Figures 22b and 22c illustrate the necessity for the alternative "covers/equals" in assertion (4).

THEOREM 51. In any lattice in which all terminated chains are finite C4 implies L2.

Proof. Dual to the preceding; chains (1) and (2) now run downwards from $p + q$ to p and q, and chain (3) from q down to pq.

THEOREM 52. In any lattice in which all terminated chains are finite JD and L1 together imply C1.

Proof. Suppose JD and L1 satisfied in the lattice but that there exist elements a, b such that a covers ab whilst $a + b$ does not cover b. By hypothesis all chains from b to $a + b$ are finite, and by JD the maximals among these chains are all of the same length, namely $l\,[b, a + b]$. Now $b \leqq a + b$ but $a + b$ does not cover b; therefore there exists at least one element c such that $b < c < a + b$. Hence $l\,[b, a + b] \geqq 2$ whilst $l\,[ab, a] = 1$ in contradiction to L1.

Dually we have:

THEOREM 53. In any lattice in which all terminated chains are finite JD and L2 together imply C2.

THEOREM 54. In any lattice in which all terminated chains are finite C1 and C2 together imply JD and L3; and conversely.

Proof. We use & for "and" between joint conditions, and $\Longrightarrow$ for "implies" or "imply".

To prove the direct theorem we observe that in any lattice

$$\text{C1} \Longrightarrow \text{C3} \quad (\text{Th. }46); \quad \text{C2} \Longrightarrow \text{C4} \quad (\text{Th. }47);$$

whilst in any lattice in which all terminated chains are finite

$$\text{C3} \Longrightarrow \text{JD \& L1} \quad (\text{Ths. }48, 50); \quad \text{C4} \Longrightarrow \text{JD \& L2} \quad (\text{Ths. }49, 51).$$

Also by anti-symmetry in the partial order of the chain of the integers

$$\text{L1 \& L2} \Longrightarrow \text{L3}.$$

Therefore

$$\begin{aligned} \text{C1 \& C2} &\Longrightarrow \text{C3 \& C4} \\ &\Longrightarrow \text{JD \& L1 \& L2} \\ &\Longrightarrow \text{JD \& L3}. \end{aligned}$$

The converse theorem is proved as follows: In any lattice in which all terminated chains are finite JD & L1 $\Longrightarrow$ C1 (Th. 52), JD & L2 $\Longrightarrow$ C2 (Th. 53); whilst in the chain of the integers L3 $\Longrightarrow$ L1 & L2. Therefore JD & L3 $\Longrightarrow$ JD & L1 & L2 $\Longrightarrow$ C1 & C2.

The relations established between C1–C4, JD and L1–L3 are summarized in the schemes of implication given below. The letter f against an implication arrow means "in lattices in which all terminated chains are finite"; absence of this letter means "in any lattice".

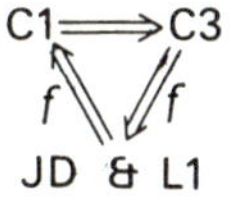

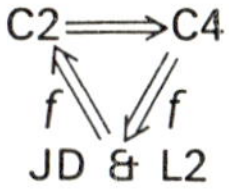

$$\text{L1 \& L2} \Longleftrightarrow \text{L3}$$

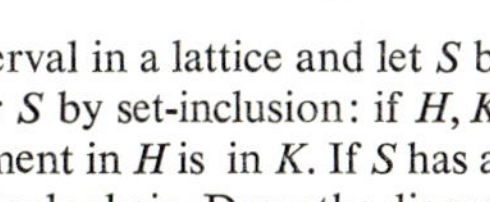

Exercises

60. Let $[a, b]$ be an interval in a lattice and let S be the set of all chains from a to b. Partially order S by set-inclusion: if H, K are two chains from a to b, $H \leq K$ if every element in H is in K. If S has a greatest member, show that $[a, b]$ consists of a single chain. Draw the diagram of the set S for the interval $[o, u]$ in the case of the lattices of Figs. 9b and 9d.
61. Discriminate between lattices
    (1) which are finite,
    (2) which are of finite length,

(3) which are locally of finite length,
(4) in which all terminated chains are finite,
(5) in which all chains are finite.
Order these five classes by set-inclusion to give the lattice of Fig. 9d.

62. (i) Of the lattices in the last exercise which must possess zero and unity elements?
(ii) State and prove the dual of Th. 45. Prove that in a lattice with o and u, which is locally of finite length, $h(u) = d(o)$.

63. Show that in the lattice of all subsets of a set of n objects ordered by set-inclusion there are precisely $\binom{n}{r}$ elements, each consisting of a subset of r objects and each of height r ($r = 0, 1, 2, \ldots, n$). See § 9 (2).

64. If x is a factor of the natural number a, show that the height of x in the lattice of the factors of a ordered by divisibility is equal to the sum of the exponents in the prime factorization of x. If a contains no square factor other than 1, show that the height of x is equal to the number of prime factors of x. See § 9 (3).

65. Let P be a partition in the lattice of all partitions of a set of n objects, ordered by refinement. If k is the number of blocks in P and the rank $r(P)$ of P is defined as $n - k$, show that $r(P) = h(P)$. How many atoms has the lattice? How many dual atoms? See § 9 (4).

66. (i) Prove that in any chain C1 and C2 are always satisfied.
(ii) Prove that in the lattice of Fig. 11b C1 and L1 are satisfied, but not C2 or L2.

67. In the lattice of Fig. 23 label the elements $x_r + y_s$ ($r = 0, 1, 2; s = 0, 1, 2$) as in the proof of Th. 50, and trace the "covers/equals" relation throughout.

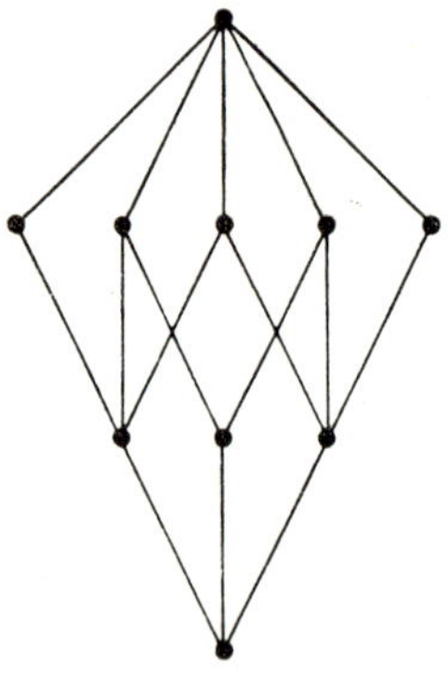

FIG. 23.

13. Complements

Definition 32. Let x be an element of the interval $[a, b]$ of a lattice L; if an element y exists in L such that

$$xy = a, \quad x + y = b,$$

y is called a complement of x relative to the interval $[a, b]$. We note that such a y must belong to the interval, for

$$a = xy \leqq y \leqq x + y = b;$$

and that the relation is symmetric, x being a complement of y relative to the interval. Each of a, b is the unique relative complement of the other; but if x is different from a and from b, y need not be unique. For example, in Fig. 11e both 6 and 12 are complements of 10 relative to [2, 60].

Definition 33. If every element x of an interval $[a, b]$ has at least one complement relative to $[a, b]$, the interval is said to be complemented. If every interval in a lattice is complemented, the lattice is said to be relatively complemented.

Definition 34. Let x be an element of a lattice L with zero element o and unity element u; if there exists in L an element y such that

$$xy = o, \quad x + y = u,$$

y is called a complement of x.

Definition 35. If every element x of a lattice with o and u has at least one complement, the lattice is said to be complemented. In other words, a lattice with o and u is complemented if the interval $[o, u]$ is complemented. It follows that a relatively complemented lattice with o and u is complemented; but a complemented lattice need not be relatively complemented. What was noted above about complements relative to an interval $[a, b]$ applies to complements in a complemented lattice L: if y is a complement of x, x is a complement of y; complements need not be unique, apart from o and u, each of which is the unique complement of the other.

Example 49. If A is a subset of a finite set U and A' is the set of members of U not in A, then A' is the unique complement of A in the lattice L of the subsets of U ordered by set-inclusion; for A and A' have nothing in common so that their intersection is empty, and between them they exhaust U which is therefore their union; thus $AA' = O$ and $A + A' = U$, and A' is a complement of A. If a subset B is a complement of A, then $AB = O$ implies that $B \leqq A'$ and $A + B = U$ implies that $A' \leqq B$ so that $B = A'$, which is therefore the unique complement of A. The lattice L is then a complemented lattice, in which as a matter of fact complements are unique. It is easy to prove that L is also relatively complemented.

Example 50. A glance at Fig. 19 is sufficient to establish that the lattice of Example 45 is complemented, each atom having infinitely many complements. Since the only interval with more than two elements is the lattice itself, the lattice is relatively complemented. The lattice of Example 46 (Fig. 20) is complemented, all elements except 0 and 1 possessing infinitely many complements; but this lattice is not relatively complemented, as can be seen from consideration of the interval $[\frac{1}{4}, \frac{3}{4}]$.

THEOREM 55. The direct product $L \times M$ of lattices L and M is relatively complemented if and only if L and M are relatively complemented. Again, $L \times M$ is complemented if and only if L and M are complemented.

Proof. First, let L and M be relatively complemented lattices. If

$$(a_1, a_2) \leqq (x_1, x_2) \leqq (b_1, b_2)$$

are elements of $L \times M$, then for $j = 1, 2$,

$$a_j \leqq x_j \leqq b_j.$$

By hypothesis x_j has a complement y_j relative to $[a_j, b_j]$; hence (y_1, y_2) is a complement of (x_1, x_2) relative to the interval $[(a_1, a_2), (b_1, b_2)]$.

Secondly, suppose the product $L \times M$ relatively complemented. If $[a_1, b_1]$, $[a_2, b_2]$ are intervals of L, M respectively with

$$a_1 \leqq x_1 \leqq b_1, \quad a_2 \leqq x_2 \leqq b_2,$$

then we have

$$(a_1, a_2) \leqq (x_1, x_2) \leqq (b_1, b_2) \quad \text{in } L \times M;$$

by hypothesis there exists (y_1, y_2) such that

$$(x_1, x_2)(y_1, y_2) = (a_1, a_2)$$

and

$$(x_1, x_2) + (y_1, y_2) = (b_1, b_2).$$

It follows that

$$x_1 y_1 = a_1 \quad \text{and} \quad x_1 + y_1 = b_1 \quad \text{in } L$$

and that

$$x_2 y_2 = a_2 \quad \text{and} \quad x_2 + y_2 = b_2 \quad \text{in } M;$$

therefore L and M are relatively complemented.

The proof of the second half of the theorem is left to the reader.

Example 51. In Example 41, § 9 (6) the component lattices and their product are all relatively complemented and complemented.

Exercises

68. Show that in any complemented lattice o and u are unique complements each of the other, and that if the lattice has two or more elements no element is its own complement.
69. Let L be the lattice of the factors of any square-free natural number ordered by divisibility; prove L relatively complemented and hence complemented.
70. Show that the five element lattice of Fig. 9b is complemented but not relatively complemented, that of Fig. 9d is neither, that of Fig. 9a is both.
71. Prove that a chain of three or more elements is neither relatively complemented nor complemented. Hence show that if a natural number contains a repeated prime factor, the lattice of its factors ordered by divisibility is neither relatively complemented nor complemented. See Example 42, § 9 (6).
72. In the lattice of the partitions of a set of four objects (and of five) ordered by refinement show that each atom has a dual atom for complement.
73. In a finite lattice which is complemented show that the unity element is either the zero element or the join of all atoms; in a finite lattice which is relatively complemented show that every non-zero element is the join of the atoms it contains. Hence prove the lattice of Fig. 12c neither complemented nor relatively complemented.

14. Sublattices

Definition 36. A non-empty subset S of elements of a lattice L which contains the meet and join of any two of its members is called a sublattice of L. Clearly L is a sublattice of itself; if S is a proper subset of L, S is called a proper sublattice of L.

Example 52. Take the lattice L of the fifteen partitions of a set of four objects, ordered by refinement; these partitions are listed in Example 7, § 4, and the diagram of the lattice is given in Fig. 13d. The subset of four singular partitions

$$P_3: (ac/b/d), \quad Q_1: (abc/d), \quad Q_2: (acd/b), \quad U: (abcd)$$

is a sublattice of L.

Example 53. Every non-empty subset H of a chain K is itself a chain and is called a subchain of K. H is a sublattice of K, for if a and b belong to H, since they are members of K they are comparable, with, say, $a \leqq b$; then $ab = a$ and $a + b = b$ belong to H.

Example 54. Let S be a subset of elements of a lattice L such that any two members of S are comparable; S is a chain lying in L and ordered with the partial ordering of L; clearly S is a sublattice of L. In particular, the trivial chain consisting of just one element of L is a sublattice of L.

THEOREM 56. Every interval $[a, b]$ of a lattice L is a sublattice of L.

Proof. Let $a \leqq x \leqq b$, $a \leqq y \leqq b$. Then by Ths. 33, 34

$$a \leqq xy \leqq x + y \leqq b$$

so that xy and $x + y$ belong to $[a, b]$. In particular the interval $[a, a]$, that is, each distinct element a of L is a sublattice of L.

THEOREM 57. Let a be some fixed element of a lattice L. If X is the set of all x in L which satisfy $x \leqq a$ and Y is the set of all y in L which satisfy $a \leqq y$, then X and Y are sublattices of L.

Proof. a belongs to both X and Y (being the only element they have in common) so that neither X nor Y is an empty subset of L. The reader can supply the rest of the proof, using Ths. 33 and 34 and idempotency.

Definition 37. A sublattice S of a lattice L is called convex if and only if for any pair of comparable elements a, b in S, $a \leqq b$, the entire interval $[a, b]$ belongs to S.

Example 55. The sublattice of Example 52 is not convex, since the partition R_2: (ac/bd) belongs to the interval $[P_3, U]$ but not to the sublattice. Obviously any interval of a lattice is a convex sublattice; so is each of the subsets X, Y of Th. 57. An alternative to Def. 37 is

Definition 38. A sublattice S of a lattice L is called convex if and only if it contains with any a and b not only ab and $a + b$ but also all x for which $ab \leqq x \leqq a + b$.

THEOREM 58. Definitions 37 and 38 are equivalent.

Proof. If a sublattice S is convex by Def. 37, for any elements a, b of S the comparable elements ab, $a + b$ belong to S (since S is a sublattice) and the entire interval $[ab, a + b]$ therefore belongs to S; that is, S contains all x for which $ab \leqq x \leqq a + b$. Thus

$$\text{Def. 37} \Longrightarrow \text{Def. 38}.$$

If a sublattice S is convex by Def. 38, and a, b are any pair of comparable elements, with, say, $a \leqq b$, then $ab = a$, $a + b = b$, so that the interval $[ab, a + b]$ which belongs to S by Def. 38 coincides with the interval $[a, b]$, and Def. 37 is satisfied. Thus

$$\text{Def. 38} \Longrightarrow \text{Def. 37}.$$

It is to be remarked that a subset T of a lattice L may be a lattice in its own right, preserving in T the order of the elements in L, and yet not be a sublattice of L.

Example 56. The twelve singular partitions of the lattice L of Example 52 above are a subset T of L; T may be made into a lattice as follows. Ordering T by refinement, define the meet $X \wedge Y$ of two singular partitions X, Y as the least refined singular partition contained in X and in Y; define their join $X \vee Y$ as the most refined singular partition containing X and Y. Then $X \wedge Y$ in T coincides with XY in L, but $X \vee Y$ in T may differ from $X + Y$ in L; for instance, we have

$$P_1: (ab/c/d), \quad P_2: (a/b/cd), \quad R_1: (ab/cd), \quad U: (abcd),$$

so that in T $P_1 \vee P_2 = U$ but in L $P_1 + P_2 = R_1$, which is non-singular. Thus the subset T of the singular partitions of L constitutes a lattice lying in L; the order of the elements in L is preserved in T; but T is not a sublattice of L. The same can be said of the twenty-seven singular partitions of the lattice of the fifty-two partitions of a set of five objects. (Cf. Fig. 13e and Frontispiece.) A sublattice then is a lattice within a lattice, both having the same ordering, meets being identical with meets, joins with joins, in the two lattices.

In the remainder of this section we deal with two special kinds of sublattice, introduced by M. H. Stone in 1934.

Definition 39. A non-empty subset X of a lattice L is called an ideal of L if and only if the following conditions are satisfied:

J1 For a in X, b in X, $a + b$ is in X.

J2 For a in X, c in L, ac is in X.

The name "ideal" has been borrowed from another branch of modern mathematics—the theory of rings—where there are subalgebras with analogous properties.

THEOREM 59. In an ideal X of a lattice L the following conditions are satisfied:

J3 If a is in X and $x \leqq a$, then x is in X.
J4 If $a + b$ is in X, then a is in X and b is in X.

Proof. If a is in X and $x \leqq a$, then $x = ax$ is in X by J2. If $a + b$ is in X, then $a \leqq a + b$ and a is in X by J3 just proved; b is in X for the same reasons.

THEOREM 60. A non-empty subset X of a lattice L is an ideal of L if the conditions of any one of the following combinations can be shown to be satisfied:

(i) J1 & J2, (ii) J1 & J3, (iii) J1 & J4.

Proof. (i) By Def. 39. (ii) We must prove that J3 implies J2. For any c, $ac \leqq a$; therefore a in X and c in L entail that ac is in X by J3. (iii) We must prove that J4 implies J2. For any c, $a = a + ac$ by absorption; therefore a in X means that $a + ac$ is in X and consequently ac in X by J4.

THEOREM 61. An ideal X of a lattice L is a convex sublattice of L.

Proof. For a, b in X ab is in X by J2 and $a + b$ in X by J1; hence X is a sublattice of L. If $ab \leqq x \leqq a + b$, then x in X by J3; hence X is convex.

The dual to Def. 39 runs:

Definition 40. A non-empty subset Y of a lattice L is called a dual ideal of L if and only if the following conditions are satisfied:

M1 For a in Y, b in Y, ab is in Y.
M2 For a in Y, c in L, $a + c$ is in Y.

Then we have

THEOREM 62. In a dual ideal Y of a lattice L the following conditions are satisfied:

M3 If a is in Y and $a \leqq y$, then y is in Y.
M4 If ab is in Y, then a is in Y and b is in Y.

THEOREM 63. As Th. 60, with Y for X, dual ideal for ideal, M1–M4 for J1–J4.

THEOREM 64. As Th. 61, with dual ideal Y for ideal X. Note that some authors call our X, characterized by J1–J4, a join-ideal, and our Y, characterized by M1–M4, a meet-ideal.

Example 57. In the lattice of the six factors of 18 illustrated in Fig. 24 the subset $\{1, 2, 3, 6\}$ is an ideal, the subset $\{3, 6, 9, 18\}$ is a dual ideal, the subset $\{1, 2, 9, 18\}$ is neither.

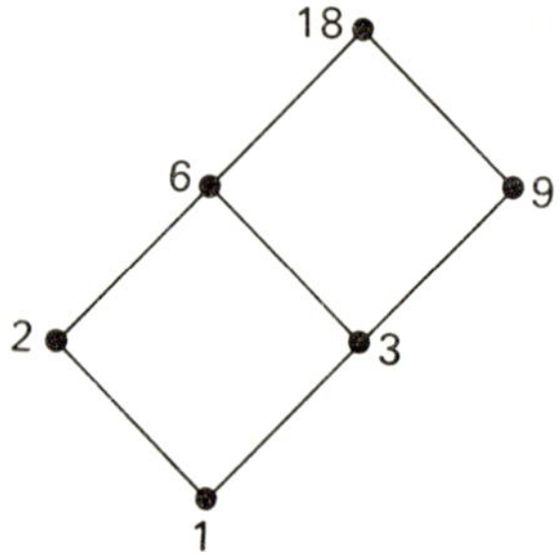

FIG. 24.

Example 58. In the lattice of all natural numbers ordered by divisibility the set of all powers of a fixed prime $\{p^r\ (r = 0, 1, 2, \ldots)\}$ is an ideal. The reader should verify that J2 is satisfied.

THEOREM 65. The ideals of a lattice ordered by set-inclusion constitute a lattice.

Proof. We notice to begin with that the set of ideals of a lattice is never empty, since to each element a there corresponds a sublattice X of elements $x \leqq a$ (Th. 57) easily shown to satisfy J2.

Let A, B be ideals of a lattice L. If every member of A is a member of B, we write $A \leqq B$. To prove the ideals of L form a lattice we shall show that for any ideals A, B there exists a greatest ideal contained in A, B and a least ideal containing A, B.

The greatest subset contained in A, B is of course their set-intersection AB. Neither A nor B is empty by Def. 39; let a belong to A, b to B. By J2 ab belongs to A and also to B, and hence to AB, which is thus not empty. If c and d belong to AB, they both belong to A and to B; hence by J1 $c + d$ belongs to A and to B and thus to AB. We have proved that J1 is satisfied in AB. If e belongs to AB (and so to each of A, B) and f is any element of L, by J2 ef belongs to A and also to B, and thus to AB. We have proved that J2 is satisfied in AB. Hence AB is an ideal; being the greatest subset contained in both A and B, AB is the greatest ideal contained in A and in B.

On the other hand the smallest subset containing A and B is their set-union $A + B$, which is not necessarily an ideal; for a in A and b in B give a and b in $A + B$, but do not imply $a + b$ in $A + B$. Consider the set C of all elements g of L such that $g \leqq a + b$ where a is some element of A, b of B. C is not empty, for it obviously contains every element of A and of B (and thus of $A + B$). Let $g_1 \leqq a_1 + b_1$, $g_2 \leqq a_2 + b_2$ with a_1, a_2 in A, b_1, b_2 in B. By J1 $a_1 + a_2$ is in A, $b_1 + b_2$ in B; hence $g_1 + g_2 \leqq (a_1 + a_2) + (b_1 + b_2)$ belongs to C, in which J1 is thus satisfied. For g in C, h in L, $gh \leqq g \leqq a + b$ for some a in A, b in B; hence gh is in C, and J2 is satisfied. Therefore C is an ideal. If X is any ideal containing A and B, by J1 X contains every join $a + b$ with a from A, b from B, and thus by J3 every element g of C; that is, X contains C, which is thus the least ideal containing A and B. We write $A \vee B$ for C. Hence the ideals of a lattice L ordered by set-inclusion form a lattice D where the meet of ideals A, B is their intersection AB but where their join is the ideal $A \vee B$ defined above.

THEOREM 66. Let S be a non-empty subset of elements of a lattice L. The elements contained by the joins of all finite subsets of S constitute an ideal G of L.

Proof. The proof that G is not empty and satisfies J1, J2 is left to the reader.

Definition 41. The ideal G of the last theorem is said to be generated by S (or from S). Thus the ideal $C = A \vee B$ in the proof of Th. 65 was generated by the set-union $A + B$. If S consists of a single element a, the ideal generated by this set $\{a\}$ is called the principal ideal generated by a; it consists of all $x \leqq a$, and will be denoted by $(a]$.

THEOREM 67. The principal ideals of a lattice L ordered by set-inclusion constitute a lattice P, where meet of $(a]$ and $(b]$ is $(ab]$ and join is $(a + b]$. P is a sublattice of the lattice D of all ideals of L.

Proof. Let A, B denote the principal ideals $(a]$, $(b]$. Since A and B are ideals their meet in D is their intersection AB. We prove that $AB = (ab]$. If x belongs to AB, it belongs to both A and B; hence $x \leqq a$, $x \leqq b$, so that $x \leqq ab$ and x belongs to $(ab]$. If y belongs to $(ab]$, $y \leqq ab \leqq a$ and y belongs to A; $y \leqq ab \leqq b$ and y belongs to B; hence y belongs to AB. It follows that $AB = (ab]$.

The join of A, B in D is the ideal $A \vee B$ of Th. 65. We prove that $A \vee B = (a + b]$. If x is in $A \vee B$, $x \leqq p + q$ for some p in A, q in B; then $p \leqq a$, $q \leqq b$, $x \leqq p + q \leqq a + b$, and x is in $(a + b]$. If y is in $(a + b]$, $y \leqq a + b$; but a is in A, b in B, and therefore y is in $A \vee B$. It follows that $A \vee B = (a + b]$.

Thus principal ideals of L have principal ideals for meet and join in D and therefore constitute a sublattice P of the lattice D; and P in itself is a lattice with

$$(a] \wedge (b] = (ab], \qquad (a] \vee (b] = (a + b].$$

THEOREM 68. In a finite lattice every ideal is principal.

Proof. Any ideal X of a finite lattice is itself a finite lattice (Th. 61) and therefore has a greatest member g (Th. 31, § 9). We prove that

$X = (g]$. If x is in X, $x \leqq g$ and so in $(g]$; hence $X \leqq (g]$. If y is in $(g]$, $y \leqq g$ and thus in X by J3; hence $(g] \leqq X$. It follows that $X = (g]$.

THEOREM 69. In a lattice of finite length every ideal is principal.

Proof. We recall from Def. 28 that in a lattice L of finite length all chains are finite. Any ideal X of L being non-empty must contain at least one chain K; K is finite and therefore by Th. 31 has a greatest element g, which is a maximal element of X considered as a partially ordered set (Def. 17, § 6). If h is a maximal element of X, by J1 $g + h$ is in in X. Now $g \leqq g + h$, $h \leqq g + h$; but g and h are maximal in X so that $g + h \leqq g$, $g + h \leqq h$; it follows that $g = g + h = h$. The proof now proceeds as in the last theorem, leading to $X = (g]$.

Dual to Th. 65 we have

THEOREM 70. The dual ideals of a lattice ordered by set-inclusion constitute a lattice.

Notice that we have retained set-inclusion as the ordering relation among the dual ideals; this entails that the dual ideals constitute a lattice D' where the meet of dual ideals A, B is their intersection AB but where their join is the dual ideal $A \vee B$ defined as follows: $A \vee B$ is the set of all elements h such that $h \geqq ab$ with a some element of A, b of B.

Theorem 66 becomes

THEOREM 71. Let S be a non-empty subset of elements of a lattice L. The elements containing the meets of all finite subsets of S constitute a dual ideal G' of L.

Corresponding to Def. 41 we have

Definition 42. The dual ideal G' of Th. 71 is said to be generated by S. Thus the dual ideal $A \vee B$ of Th. 70 was generated by the set-union $A + B$. If S consists of a single element a, the dual ideal generated by S is called the principal dual ideal generated by a; it consists of all $y \geqq a$, and will be denoted by $[a)$.

Dual to Th. 67 we have

THEOREM 72. The principal dual ideals of a lattice L ordered by set-inclusion constitute a lattice P' where meet and join of $[a)$, $[b)$ are given by

$$[a) \wedge [b) = [a + b), \qquad [a) \vee [b) = [ab).$$

P' is a sublattice of the lattice D' of all dual ideals of L.

Finally Th. 68 (69) gives

THEOREM 73 (74). In a finite lattice (in a lattice of finite length) every dual ideal is principal.

Example 59. The lattice of Fig. 25 contains the following ideals and dual ideals:

$$\begin{array}{ll} (u] = \{o, a, b, c, u\} & [u) = \{u\} \\ (c] = \{o, a, c\} & [c) = \{c, u\} \\ (b] = \{o, a, b\} & [b) = \{b, u\} \\ (a] = \{o, a\} & [a) = \{a, b, c, u\} \\ (o] = \{o\} & [o) = \{o, a, b, c, u\}. \end{array}$$

Here the lattice P of principal ideals coincides with the lattice D of all ideals, and P' coincides with D'. Since the ordering is by set-inclusion it is clear that P is isomorphic, P' dually isomorphic, with the original lattice.

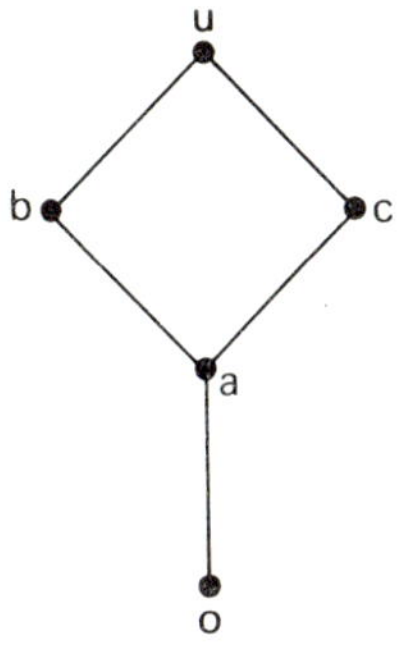

FIG. 25.

Exercises

74. Show that in the chain of the natural numbers the even numbers form a sublattice but neither an ideal nor a dual ideal; show that in the lattice of the natural numbers ordered by divisibility the even numbers form a convex sublattice which is a dual ideal.
75. Supply proofs for Ths. 57 and 66, and prove Th. 70 directly.
76. With the notation of Ths. 67 and 72 show that P is isomorphic, P' dually isomorphic, with L.
77. Let p, q be distinct prime numbers. Show that the set of all powers of p is an ideal of the lattice L of the natural numbers ordered by divisibility. If $A = \{p^r; r = 0, 1, \ldots\}$, $B = \{q^s; s = 0, 1, \ldots\}$ are ideals of this sort, determine $A \wedge B$ and $A \vee B$ in the lattice D of ideals of L. Show that $A \vee B$ contains just k principal ideals of length $k - 1$ for $k = 1, 2, \ldots$.
78. Let X be an ideal of a lattice L. Define a relation R as follows: aRb for a, b in L if and only if $a + x = b + x$ for some x in X. Prove that R is an equivalence relation over L. In the lattice of Example 59 find the five partitions arising in this way from the ideals and determine whether these partitions form a sublattice of the lattice of the fifty-two partitions of $\{o, a, b, c, u\}$.
79. (i) Prove that the only subset of a lattice L which is both ideal and dual ideal is L itself.

(ii) Prove that no ideal of a complemented lattice which is a proper sublattice can contain both an element and its complement.
(iii) Show that the lattice D of ideals of any lattice L has a unity element; find the restriction on L which ensures that D has a zero element.

Definition 43. An ideal X of a lattice L is said to be prime if and only if X is a proper subset of L and the following condition is satisfied:

J5 If ab is in X, then a is in X or b is in X.

Definition 44. A dual ideal Y of a lattice L is said to be prime if and only if Y is a proper subset of L and the following condition is satisfied:

M5 If $a + b$ is in Y, then a is in Y or b is in Y.

Example 60. The ideal mentioned in Example 57 is prime; that mentioned in Example 58 is not.

80. Prove that if a lattice is partitioned into subsets X and Y where X is an ideal and Y a dual ideal, then X and Y are prime. Prove that if a lattice is partitioned into subsets X and Y where X is a prime ideal, then Y is a prime dual ideal; alternatively, prove that if Y is a prime dual ideal, then X is a prime ideal.
81. Prove that in a chain all ideals are prime. Prove also the converse: A lattice in which every ideal is prime is a chain. Show that the set Q of rational numbers r such that $r^2 \leqq 2$ forms a prime ideal in the chain of the rational numbers.
82. Consider the lattice of the sixteen factors of 120 ordered by divisibility as in Example 38, § 9 (3) (Fig. 12c). Find the prime ideals and compare their number with the length of the lattice.
83. In the lattice of factors of any natural number n ordered by divisibility let $d_1, \ldots, d_k$ be the dual atoms. Prove that the ideals $(d_1], \ldots, (d_k]$ are prime; if n is square-free, prove that these are the only prime ideals.

15. Homomorphisms

We expand the definition of a dyadic relation in a set (Def. 2, § 3) as follows:

Definition 45. Let (S, T) be an ordered pair of sets of elements. Let θ denote a precisely specified set of ordered pairs (s, t) of elements where s is drawn from S, t from T. Then we describe θ as a dyadic relation in (S, T) between members of S and members of T, s being an antecedent, t a consequent in the relation; we may write $s\theta t$, $t = \theta(s)$ or $t = \theta s$. If T is the same set as S we are back at Def. 2.

Definition 46. If in the above relation θ

$$s\theta t_1 \quad \text{and} \quad s\theta t_2 \quad \text{imply} \quad t_1 = t_2,$$

that is, if any s appearing as antecedent in θ has just one consequent t, and if, moreover, every s of S does appear as antecedent, we say that the relation θ is a mapping of S *into* T; if $s\theta t$, we say that s is mapped on t. Note that in a mapping distinct antecedents may be mapped on the same consequent. If R is the subset of elements of T which appear as consequents in the mapping θ, R may be called the image of S under θ. If R coincides with T, that is if every element of T appears as consequent in θ, we say that θ is a mapping of S *onto* T.

Important types of mapping of set into set, where the sets in question are algebras with matched operations, are now defined for the case of lattice into lattice.

Definition 47. Let L, M be lattices and θ a mapping of L into M. If for all a, b in L we have in M

$$\theta\,(ab) = \theta(a)\,\theta(b),$$

θ is said to preserve meets and is called a meet-homomorphism. If for all a, b in L we have in M

$$\theta(a + b) = \theta(a) + \theta(b),$$

θ is said to preserve joins and is called a join-homomorphism. If θ preserves both meets and joins it is called a homomorphism (from L to M). The subset H of elements of M which appear as consequents in the mapping θ is called the homomorphic image of L. If M is the same lattice as L, the homomorphism is called an endomorphism.

Example 61. Let L be the "pentagonal" lattice, M the five-element chain in Fig. 26.

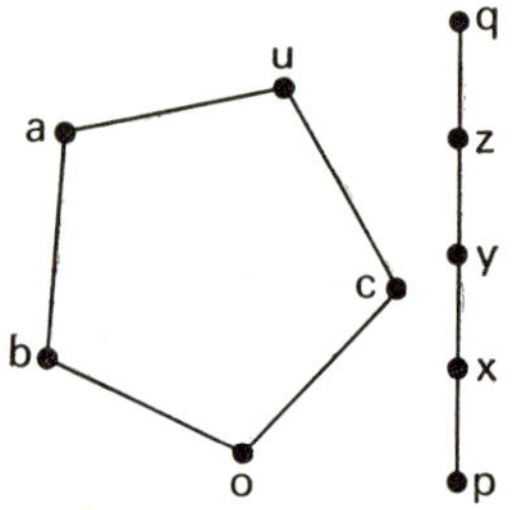

FIG. 26.

(i) If θ maps o, a, b, c on p and u on q, θ is a meet-homomorphism but not a join-homomorphism; for instance

$$\theta(bc) = \theta(o) = p = pp = \theta(b)\,\theta(c)$$

but

$$\theta(b + c) = \theta(u) = q \neq p = p + p = \theta(b) + \theta(c).$$

(ii) If φ maps o, a, b on p and c, u on q, φ is a homomorphism; $H = \{p, q\}$.

(iii) If ψ maps o, a, b on o and c, u on u, ψ is an endomorphism.

THEOREM 75. The homomorphic image H of L under θ is a sublattice of M.

Proof. Let a', b' be any elements of H; let a be an antecedent in L of a', b of b', so that $\theta(a) = a'$, $\theta(b) = b'$. Then

$$a'b' = \theta(a)\,\theta(b) = \theta\,(ab)$$

and

$$a' + b' = \theta(a) + \theta(b) = \theta\,(a + b).$$

The consequents of ab and $a + b$ exist in M and must lie in H; therefore H contains meet and join of every pair of its elements and is a sublattice of M.

In a homomorphism, as in any mapping according to our definition, every member of L has just one consequent in M; if the converse is true we have a special kind of homomorphism.

Definition 48. Let θ be a homomorphism from L onto M such that for a, b in L

$$\theta(a) = \theta(b) \text{ in } M \quad \text{implies} \quad a = b \text{ in } L,$$

that is, a homomorphism in which every member of M has one and only one antecedent in L; then θ is called an isomorphism. If M is the same lattice as L, θ is called an automorphism.

Example 62. Let L be the lattice of the eight factors of 30 ordered by divisibility and M that of the eight subsets of the set $\{2, 3, 5\}$ ordered by set-inclusion.

(i) If θ maps each number in L on the set of its prime factors in M, θ is an isomorphism.

(ii) If φ maps each element in L on its unique complement in L, 1, 2, 3, 5 being mapped on 30, 15, 10, 6 respectively, φ is an automorphism.

It is clear that a homomorphism is a many-to-one correspondence between all the elements of a lattice L and some of the elements of a lattice M which preserves the algebraic structure; here generally speaking H is a simplified version of L. An isomorphism is a one-to-one correspondence which again preserves the algebraic structure; here H coincides with M, which is an exact replica of L. Both types of mapping are obviously definable for any algebras with matching binary operations; it should be remarked that in modern mathematics algebras once proved isomorphic are thenceforward treated as identical. (The names of the mappings have been formed from Greek words: *μορφή (morphē)* means form, shape, for us algebraic structure; as for the prefixes, *homo-* means same, common; *endo-* means internal; *iso-* means equal, same; *auto-* means self.)

In Def. 48 we defined isomorphic lattices considered as algebras with meets and joins; but in Def. 13 (§ 6) we used the same word for isomorphic partially ordered sets. This ambiguity is justified by the following theorems:

THEOREM 76. Lattices isomorphic as algebras (Def. 48) are isomorphic as partially ordered sets (Def. 13).

Proof. Let L, M be lattices and θ an isomorphic mapping from L to M as defined by Def. 48. For a, b in L we have in M

$$\theta(ab) = \theta(a)\,\theta(b), \qquad \theta(a+b) = \theta(a) + \theta(b).$$

If $a \leqq b$ in L, then $a = ab$ in L so that $\theta(a) = \theta(ab) = \theta(a)\,\theta(b)$ in M; whence $\theta(a) \leqq \theta(b)$ in M. For c, d in M, there exist by hypothesis unique elements e, f in L such that $c = \theta(e), d = \theta(f)$. If $c \leqq d$ in M, then $c = cd$ in M, that is to say in M

$$\theta(e) = \theta(e)\,\theta(f) = \theta\,(ef).$$

But e is the unique antecedent in L of c; hence $e = ef \leqq f$ in L. Therefore θ is a one-to-one correspondence $a \sim \theta(a)$ between the elements of the partially ordered set L and those of the partially ordered set M such that

$$a \leqq b \text{ in } L \quad \text{if and only if} \quad \theta(a) \leqq \theta(b) \text{ in } M.$$

Definition 13 is thereby satisfied.

THEOREM 77. Lattices isomorphic as partially ordered sets (Def. 13) are isomorphic as algebras (Def. 48).

Proof. Let L, M be lattices and θ a one-to-one correspondence between their elements such that $a \sim \theta(a)$ and

$$a \leqq b \text{ in } L \quad \text{if and only if} \quad \theta(a) \leqq \theta(b) \text{ in } M.$$

For any elements a, b in L we have $ab \leqq a$, $ab \leqq b$. Consequently $\theta\,(ab) \leqq \theta(a)$, $\theta\,(ab) \leqq \theta(b)$ in M so that $\theta\,(ab)$ is a lower bound of $\theta(a), \theta(b)$. Let g be any element of M which is lower bound to $\theta(a)$, $\theta(b)$, and let h be the unique element in L such that $g = \theta(h)$; then $\theta(h) \leqq \theta(a), \theta(h) \leqq \theta(b)$ in M and hence from the hypothesis $h \leqq a$, $h \leqq b$ in L. Therefore, $h \leqq ab$ in L; this in turn yields $\theta(h) \leqq \theta\,(ab)$ in M, or $g \leqq \theta\,(ab)$ in M. Thus $\theta\,(ab)$ is greatest lower bound to $\theta(a)$, $\theta(b)$ in M, or

$$\theta\,(ab) = \theta(a)\,\theta(b).$$

Dually it may be shown that

$$\theta\,(a + b) = \theta(a) + \theta(b).$$

Definition 48 is thereby satisfied.

In Th. 76 we proved that an algebraic isomorphism maintains partial ordering; we will consider this matter of order a little further.

Definition 49. Let P, Q be partially ordered sets, and let θ be a mapping of P into Q such that if $a \leqq b$ in P, then $\theta(a) \leqq \theta(b)$ in Q; we say that θ preserves order.

THEOREM 78. Any meet-homomorphism or join-homomorphism preserves order.

Proof. For a meet-homomorphism see the first part of the proof of Th. 76. For a join-homomorphism dualize.

It is to be noted that a mapping of lattice into lattice which preserves order may preserve neither meets nor joins, even if the correspondence is one-to-one.

Example 63. Let L be the "pentagonal" lattice, M the chain in Fig. 26. If θ maps o, b, c, a, u on p, x, y, z, q, respectively, we have a one-to-one correspondence which preserves in M all the order relations of L; but in L, $ac = o$, $a + c = u$ whereas in M

$$\theta(a)\,\theta(c) = zy = y \neq p = \theta(o),$$

$$\theta(a) + \theta(c) = z + y = z \neq q = \theta(u).$$

Example 64. (In this example $a, b, c, \ldots$ denote natural numbers and $a + b$ means the arithmetic sum of a and b.) We revert to the construction of the integers in Example 8, § 5. There an algebra A

was defined of ordered pairs of natural numbers; the congruence relation C:

$$(p, q)\, C\, (r, s) \quad \text{if and only if} \quad p + s = q + r$$

gave a quotient algebra A/C the elements of which were the classes of congruent pairs. In A/C addition of classes was defined as follows. If X is the class containing (a, b), Y that containing (c, d), then $X + Y$ is the class containing $(a + c, b + d)$.

Consider now the class Z containing $(b + c, a + d)$; for given X, Y the class Z always exists in A/C and is unique. Noting that (c, d) and $(c + x, d + x)$ are congruent pairs we have

$$\begin{aligned} X + Z &= \{\text{class containing } (a + b + c, b + a + d)\} \\ &= \{\text{class containing } (c, d)\} \\ &= Y. \end{aligned}$$

In view of this equation we write $Z = Y - X$. Thus if X contains $(6, 10)$ and Y contains $(5, 8)$, then $Y - X$ contains $(10 + 5, 6 + 8)$, that is $(15, 14)$; in full we have

$$\begin{aligned} &\{\text{class containing } (5, 8)\} - \{\text{class containing } (6, 10)\} \\ &\quad = \{\text{class containing } (15, 14)\}. \end{aligned}$$

We recall that if X contains (a, b) and $a > b$ in the chain N of the natural numbers, X is called a positive integer and written $+(a - b)$ if $a < b$, a negative integer, written $-(b - a)$; if $a = b$, zero, written 0. The example of subtraction above becomes

$$(-3) - (-4) = +1.$$

The integers are ordered as a chain J in the following way:

$$X \leqq Y \quad \text{if and only if} \quad Y - X \text{ is positive or zero;}$$

that is,

$$X \leqq Y \quad \text{if and only if} \quad b + c \geqq a + d.$$

In the example above $15 > 14$; hence $-4 < -3$.

N' denoting the dual chain of the natural numbers, we institute a mapping φ of the direct product $N \times N'$ (Fig. 17b) onto the chain J of the integers (Fig. 6d) as follows:

For (a, b) in $N \times N'$, $\varphi(a, b) = \{\text{class containing } (a, b)\}$. Thus $(5, 8)$ is mapped on the integer -3. In this many-to-one mapping φ all antecedents in $N \times N'$ to the same integer in J lie at the same level in Fig. 17b; they constitute the class of congruent pairs which *is* the integer in question.

We prove that φ preserves order. Let $\varphi(a, b) = X$, $\varphi(c, d) = Y$. If $(a, b) \leqq (c, d)$ in $N \times N'$, then

$$(a, b) = (a, b) \cap (c, d) = [\min(a, c), \max(b, d)];$$

hence

$$a = \min(a, c) \quad \text{and} \quad b = \max(b, d),$$

so that $a \leqq c$ and $d \leqq b$ in the chain N of natural numbers. It follows from the arithmetic properties of addition (*not* by Th. 34) that $b + c \geqq a + d$. Therefore, $X \leqq Y$ in J.

But ϕ is neither meet- nor join-homomorphism.

In $N \times N'$

$$(5, 8) \cap (6, 10) = (5, 10) \quad \text{and} \quad \varphi(5, 10) = -5,$$

but in J

$$\varphi(5, 8) \cap \varphi(6, 10) = (-3) \cap (-4) = \min(-3, -4) = -4.$$

In $N \times N'$

$$(5, 8) \cup (6, 10) = (6, 8) \quad \text{and} \quad \varphi(6, 8) = -2,$$

but in J

$$\varphi(5, 8) \cup \varphi(6, 10) = (-3) \cup (-4) = \max(-3, -4) = -3.$$

If, however, for some fixed n we choose from $N \times N'$ the chain K

$$\cdots < (n, n + 2) < (n, n + 1) < (n, n) < (n + 1, n) < (n + 2, n) < \cdots$$

in which each element obviously covers the preceding, and map K on J as before—$(n, n+3)$, for instance, being mapped on -3— then the mapping is an isomorphism. For not only is it true that if $(a, b) \leqq (c, d)$ in K, then $X \leqq Y$ in J, but also that if $X \leqq Y$ in J, then $(a, b) \leqq (c, d)$ in K, as can easily be proved.

In Example 64 the algebra A and the lattice $N \times N'$ had the selfsame elements, namely all ordered pairs of natural numbers, but very different binary operations; the congruence relation C was defined with respect to the operations of A and not with respect to those of $N \times N'$. We now demonstrate an important connexion between homomorphisms and congruence relations defined over lattices.

THEOREM 79. Let L, M be lattices and θ a homomorphism of L into M. Then θ determines a congruence relation C over L, and the quotient lattice L/C is isomorphic with the homomorphic image H of L in M.

Proof. Define a dyadic relation C between elements a, b of L as follows:

$$aCb \quad \text{if and only if} \quad \theta(a) = \theta(b) \text{ in } M.$$

C is an equivalence relation; for

(i) aCa for every a in L, by Def. 46;
(ii) if aCb, then bCa;
(iii) if aCb and bCc, then $\theta(a) = \theta(b) = \theta(c)$, whence aCc.

Thus Def. 6, § 4, is satisfied.

To prove C a congruence relation, suppose a_1Cb_1, a_2Cb_2; then

$$\theta(a_1) = \theta(b_1) \quad \text{and} \quad \theta(a_2) = \theta(b_2);$$

therefore in M

$$\theta(a_1)\,\theta(a_2) = \theta(b_1)\,\theta(b_2).$$

But θ is a homomorphism so that $\theta(a_1)\theta(a_2) = \theta(a_1 a_2)$ and $\theta(b_1)\theta(b_2) = \theta(b_1 b_2)$; hence $\theta(a_1 a_2) = \theta(b_1 b_2)$. It follows that $a_1 a_2 C b_1 b_2$. Similarly it may be shown that $(a_1 + a_2) C (b_1 + b_2)$ and Def. 8, § 5, is satisfied.

The equivalence classes or blocks into which C partitions L by Th. 3, § 5, constitute a lattice —the quotient lattice L/C; in this lattice, if X and Y are two blocks respectively containing elements x and y of L,

the meet $X \wedge Y$ of X and Y is the block containing xy,
the join $X \vee Y$ of X and Y is the block containing $x + y$.

Consider the mapping φ which maps X in L/C on the element $\theta(x)$ in H. To each block X in L/C clearly corresponds just one element of H, namely that element of H on which θ maps all members of X; conversely if X and Y are mapped on the same element h of H by φ, there exist x in X and y in Y such that $\theta(x) = h = \theta(y)$; hence xCy which entails $X = Y$. Thus φ is one-to-one. We have further:

in H
$$\varphi(X \wedge Y) = \theta(xy) = \theta(x)\,\theta(y) = \varphi(X)\,\varphi(Y)$$
and
$$\varphi(X \vee Y) = \theta(x + y) = \theta(x) + \theta(y) = \varphi(X) + \varphi(Y).$$

The requirements of Defs. 47 and 48 being satisfied, L/C is proved isomorphic with H.

The converse also holds good:

THEOREM 80. Let C be a congruence relation defined over a lattice L. Then C determines a homomorphism γ from L onto L/C.

Proof. If x is any element of L, and X the unique block of L/C which contains x and all elements congruent to x, define a correspondence γ from L to L/C by

$$\gamma(x) = X.$$

Each element of L lies in just one block of L/C; hence γ is a mapping of L onto L/C (Def. 46). As above, $X \wedge Y$ is the block in L/C containing xy for any x in X, y in Y; similarly $X \vee Y$ is the block containing $x + y$. We have

$$\gamma(xy) = X \wedge Y = \gamma(x) \wedge \gamma(y),$$

$$\gamma(x + y) = X \vee Y = \gamma(x) \vee \gamma(y);$$

in words, γ preserves meets and joins and is therefore a homomorphism (Def. 47).

Definition 50. The congruence relation C of Th. 79 is called the congruence relation induced over L by the homomorphism θ. The homomorphism γ of Th. 80 is called the natural homomorphism determined by C.

The two theorems just proved have the effect of reducing the study of the homomorphisms of a lattice to that of the congruence relations over the lattice.

Definition 51. If the homomorphic image H of a lattice L under a homomorphism θ has a least element z, the subset of elements x of L such that $\theta(x) = z$ is called the kernel of the homomorphism; in words, the kernel consists of those elements of L which are mapped on the least element of H. If H has no least element, θ has no kernel. In Example 61 the kernel of φ is $\{o, a, b\}$, which we notice is the (principal) ideal $(a]$.

THEOREM 81. Let θ be a homomorphism of a lattice L such that the image H has a least element z. Then the kernel Z of θ is an ideal of L.

Proof. By definition of H (Def. 47) z in H must have at least one antecedent in L; therefore the kernel Z is not empty. If a and b are elements of L which belong to Z, then

$$\theta\,(a + b) = \theta(a) + \theta(b) = z + z = z,$$

and hence $a + b$ belongs to Z. If a is in Z and c in L, then

$$\theta\,(ac) = \theta(a)\,\theta(c) = z \cdot \theta(c) = z,$$

and hence ac is in Z. Conditions J1, J2 of Def. 39 are thus satisfied and Z is an ideal of L.

We remark that if L itself has a zero element o, by Th. 78 $\theta(o)$ is least element of H; then the kernel exists, and o belongs to it. Consequently, if θ is a homomorphism of a lattice L having a zero element and if C is the congruence relation induced over L by θ, the elements of L congruent to the zero element under C constitute an ideal of L.

Theorem 78 shows us that the order of the elements of a lattice L is reflected in the order of the elements of any homomorphic image H of L; working in reverse we have the following existence theorem:

THEOREM 82. Let H be the image of a lattice L under a homomorphism θ. If $x > y$ in H and if a is any element of L antecedent to x in θ, then there exists in L at least one element b antecedent to y and such that $a > b$ in L.

Proof. By Defs. 46 and 47 y must have at least one antecedent, say c, in L. Consider the element ac. We have

$$\theta\,(ac) = \theta(a)\,\theta(c) = xy = y.$$

Also $a \geqq ac$; if $a = ac$, $\theta(a) = \theta(ac)$, that is, $x = y$ contrary to hypothesis; therefore $a > ac$. Then writing b for ac, we have $\theta(b) = y$ with $a > b$ in L. Note that the dual assertion: "If $x < y$ in H ... such that $a < b$ in L" is proved by duality, $a + c$ replacing ac.

Homomorphisms preserve complements as well as meets and joins.

THEOREM 83. If a lattice L is relatively complemented or complemented, any homomorphic image H is so complemented.

Proof. Let $[a, b]$ be a complemented interval of L. If the homomorphism is denoted by θ, then by Th. 78 $[\theta(a), \theta(b)]$ is an interval of H. We show this interval to be complemented. Let h be any element of H such that $\theta(a) \leqq h \leqq \theta(b)$. There exists in L at least one element z antecedent to h so that $\theta(z) = h$. Consider the element $x = b(a + z)$ in L.

We have

$$\begin{aligned}\theta(x) &= \theta\,[b\,(a + z)]\\ &= \theta(b)\,\theta\,(a + z)\\ &= \theta(b)\,[\theta(a) + \theta(z)]\\ &= \theta(b)\,[\theta(a) + h]\\ &= \theta(b)\,h\\ &= h.\end{aligned}$$

Also

$$a \leqq b, \quad a \leqq a + z, \quad b\,(a + z) \leqq b$$

yield

$$a \leqq b\,(a + z) \leqq b,$$

that is

$$a \leqq x \leqq b.$$

By hypothesis there exists y in L such that

$$xy = a, \qquad x + y = b.$$

Then

$$\theta(x)\,\theta(y) = \theta(xy) = \theta(a)$$

and

$$\theta(x) + \theta(y) = \theta\,(x + y) = \theta(b).$$

Therefore $h = \theta(x)$ possesses at least one complement $\theta(y)$ relative to the interval $[\theta(a), \theta(b)]$.

It is to be noted that if $a \neq b$, then $x \neq y$; if θ identifies x and y, by which we mean that $\theta(x) = \theta(y)$, then from the above $\theta(a) = \theta(b)$. That is to say, if complements relative to an interval of L are mapped on the same element h of H, the whole interval is mapped on h.

Example 65. A chain of more than two elements cannot be a complemented lattice; therefore by Th. 83 a complemented lattice cannot be mapped homomorphically onto such a chain. Thus the mapping θ of Example 63 cannot be a homomorphism since the "pentagonal" lattice is complemented and the chain has five elements. Mappings of "Boolean" lattices on the chain of the two integers $0 < 1$ are of some importance in the sequel. Take the lattice of the sixteen factors of $210 = 2 \times 3 \times 5 \times 7$ ordered by divisibility; these numbers are

$$1, \quad 2, \quad 3, \quad 5, \quad 6, \quad 7, \quad 10, \quad 14$$

with their complements

$$210, \quad 105, \quad 70, \quad 42, \quad 35, \quad 30, \quad 21, \quad 15.$$

We will determine all the homomorphic mappings of this lattice onto the chain of two integers $0 < 1$. In view of Theorem 82 and to avoid mapping all sixteen factors on one element of the chain (Th.83) the factor 1 must be mapped on 0 and 210 must be mapped on the integer 1. The factors mapped on 0 constitute the kernel of the homomorphism (Def. 51) and an ideal of the lattice of factors (Th. 81). If the dual atoms of this lattice, namely 30, 42, 70, 105, were all mapped on the integer 1, their complements, namely the atoms 7, 5, 3, 2, would all belong to the kernel (Th. 83) which then by J1 would contain the join 210; hence the kernel contains at least one dual atom. If the kernel contained two dual atoms it would contain, again by J1, their join 210; hence the kernel must contain just one dual atom. Thus there are just four homomorphisms that satisfy our requirements; we display them as the partitions effected by the four induced congruence relations (Def. 50), the left-hand block being in each case the kernel:

(i) 1, 3, 5, 7, 15, 21, 35, 105 / 2, 6, 10, 14, 30, 42, 70, 210;
(ii) 1, 2, 5, 7, 10, 14, 35, 70 / 3, 6, 15, 21, 30, 42, 105, 210;
(iii) 1, 2, 3, 6, 7, 14, 21, 42 / 5, 10, 15, 30, 35, 70, 105, 210;
(iv) 1, 2, 3, 5, 6, 10, 15, 30 / 7, 14, 21, 35, 42, 70, 105, 210.

To complete this section we list some dual terms.

Definition 52. Let L, M be lattices and φ a mapping of L into M. If for all a, b in L we have in M

$$\varphi(ab) = \varphi(a) + \varphi(b)$$

φ is called a dual meet-homomorphism.

If for all a, b in L we have in M

$$\varphi(a + b) = \varphi(a)\,\varphi(b)$$

φ is called a dual join-homomorphism.

If φ has both these properties, φ is called a dual homomorphism.

A dual homomorphism in which the correspondence is one-to-one is called a dual isomorphism. The definitions of dual endomorphism and dual automorphism are obvious.

Definition 53. Let P, Q be partially ordered sets, and let φ be a mapping of P into Q such that if $a \leqq b$ in P, then $\varphi(a) \geqq \varphi(b)$ in Q; we say that φ inverts order.

THEOREM 84. Any dual meet- or join-homomorphism inverts order.

Proof. Dual to that of Th. 78.

Definitions 15 and 16 of § 6 can easily be shown to be compatible with the dual terms just defined. An example of a dual homomorphism is the following:

Example 66. Take the lattices of Example 65 and let φ be the mapping which maps the even factors of 210 on the integer 0, the odd factors on the integer 1. Then φ is a dual homomorphism, for meets and joins of factors are mapped respectively on joins and meets of chain elements; also order is inverted. We give three instances:

$$\varphi(15 \cap 70) = \varphi(5) = 1 = 1 \cup 0 = \varphi(15) \cup \varphi(70);$$

$$\varphi(15 \cup 70) = \varphi(210) = 0 = 1 \cap 0 = \varphi(15) \cap \varphi(70);$$

35 divides 70, but $\varphi(35) = 1 > 0 = \varphi(70)$.

Exercises

84. Show that any homomorphic image H of a lattice L with zero or unity element is similarly bounded. If L is of finite length k, show that H is of finite length $\leqq k$.
85. Let L be the lattice of the sixteen factors of 120 (Fig. 12c).
(i) If $x \neq 1$ is any element of L, denote by $\bar{x}$ the largest square-free factor of x; if $x = 1$, define $\bar{x}$ as 1. Map each x on $\bar{x}$ (for instance, 12 on 6, 8 on 2, 2

on 2); show that this mapping is an endomorphism of L onto a "Boolean' lattice of eight elements (Fig. 10d).

(ii) Two natural numbers are said to be coprime if their h.c.f. is 1. Denote by x^* the largest number in L which is coprime to x, where x is any element of L. Map each x on $(x^*)^*$. Show that this mapping is an endomorphism of L onto a lattice isomorphic with the image in (i).

86. A mapping (as defined in Def. 46) of a set S into or onto itself is sometimes called an operator of the set. Consulting Defs. 3, 5, § 3, show that the phrases "S is closed with respect to a unary operation θ" and "θ is an operator of S" mean the same thing. Let θ and φ be operators of a lattice L; for each element x of L define meet and join of θ and φ by

$$(\theta \cap \varphi)(x) = \theta(x)\,\varphi(x)$$

$$(\theta \cup \varphi)(x) = \theta(x) + \varphi(x).$$

Show that with these definitions the set of all operators of L form a lattice T where the relation of partial order is: $\theta \leqq \varphi$ in T if and only if $\theta(x) \leqq \varphi(x)$ in L for every x of L. If L has zero o and unity u, show that T has zero ζ and unity ν defined by

$$\zeta(x) = o, \quad \nu(x) = u \quad \text{for all } x \text{ in } L.$$

87. Show that the endomorphisms of a lattice L form a sublattice of the operator lattice T of the last exercise.

88. Let C be a congruence relation over a lattice L. Prove that
(i) aCb if and only if $(ab)\,C\,(a+b)$;
(ii) $(ab)\,C\,(a+b)$ if and only if xCy for any x, y which belong to the interval $[ab, a+b]$.

89. Determine the congruence relations over (i) a chain of three elements, (ii) a chain of four elements. In each case show that the congruence relations constitute a sublattice of the lattice of equivalence relations over the chain, ordered in the usual way by implication (or refinement of partitions).

90. Let L be the lattice of the factors of 18 ordered by divisibility. Determine the three prime ideals. Let P be the lattice of all subsets of this set of three ideals, ordered by set-inclusion. Map each element x of L on the subset of those prime ideals which do *not* contain x. Show that this mapping is a homomorphism of L into P, where the image H is isomorphic with L.

91. Let θ be a homomorphic mapping of any lattice onto the two-element chain $0 < 1$. Show that the elements mapped on 0 form a prime ideal, those mapped on 1 a prime dual ideal.

CHAPTER 4

MODULAR LATTICES

16. Modularity

The remaining chapters in this book treat of special lattices—first the class of modular lattices, then the wider class of semi-modular lattices, and lastly the narrower class of distributive lattices. The historical order would be:

(1) distributive (E. Schröder, 1890),
(2) modular (Dedekind, 1897),
(3) semi-modular (Birkhoff, 1933);

as we shall prove, the logical order is the exact opposite, for

$$\text{Class (1)} < \text{Class (2)} < \text{Class (3)};$$

but there are certain advantages in the order (2)–(3)–(1) in an introductory treatment.

The eight postulates of Def. 20, § 8, by which a lattice was defined, did not explicitly require either of the lattice operations of meet and join to be distributive with respect to the other, nor do they imply distributivity. We easily prove this by considering the lattice of five elements in Fig. 26 which we persist in calling "pentagonal"—in spite of the fact that it could be drawn equally well as a quadrilateral or triangle. In this lattice

$$a(b + c) = au = a,$$

$$ab + ac = b + o = b;$$

whence

$$a(b + c) \neq ab + ac.$$

It is perhaps worth remarking that this result is disconcerting only on account of the arithmetical notation used; no one is surprised when

$$a \cap (b \cup c) \neq (a \cap b) \cup (a \cap c).$$

However, we proved in Th. 41 that in every lattice

$$a(b + c) \geqq ab + ac \quad \text{(for any } a, b, c)$$

and in Th. 44 a weaker form of this result, namely that

$$a \geqq b \quad \text{implies} \quad a(b + c) \geqq b + ac \quad \text{(for any } c).$$

In this chapter we are going to discuss the lattices first studied by Dedekind where the following requirement is met:

Postulate V. For elements a, b, c of a lattice

$$a \geqq b \quad \text{implies} \quad a(b + c) = ab + ac = b + ac.$$

Notice that if we take $a \geqq c$ instead of $a \geqq b$ we get

$$a \geqq c \quad \text{implies} \quad a(b + c) = ab + c$$

which in the alternative notation assumes the striking form of an associativity:

$$a \geqq c \quad \text{implies} \quad a \cap (b \cup c) = (a \cap b) \cup c.$$

Postulates IB–IVB are duals of Postulates IA–IVA; but if we dualize Postulate V we have

$$a \leqq b \quad \text{implies} \quad a + bc = (a + b)(a + c) = b(a + c),$$

which is the same requirement with the roles of a and b interchanged; thus Postulate V is self-dual.

Definition 54. A lattice satisfying Postulate V is said to be modular.

Example 67. The modular formula of Postulate V holds good in any lattice where c is comparable to a or b. For instance, if $a \geqq b$ and $a \geqq c$, then $a \geqq b + c$ and $a(b + c) = b + c = b + ac$; the other possible cases are left to the reader. Since in a chain any two elements are comparable, all chains are modular.

Example 68. Note that if $a = b$ in Postulate V, both sides of the modular formula reduce to a by absorption; in view of this and of what was said above, when testing for the formula we need only look for $a > b$ with c comparable to neither. Thus the four-element lattice of Fig. 8e, which does not contain such a c, is modular. For the same reason the lattice of the five partitions of a set of three objects (Fig. 9a or 13c) is modular. On the other hand, the "pentagonal" lattice (Fig. 9b or 26) does contain such an element c and as we have seen is not modular. These small five-element lattices play a notable part in our theory.

THEOREM 85. A sublattice of a modular lattice is modular.

Proof. Let S be a sublattice of a modular lattice L; let a, b, c be elements of S with $a \geqq b$. Since L is modular, $a(b + c) = b + ac$; but this element belongs to S, for S is closed with respect to formation of meets and joins; therefore S is modular.

THEOREM 86. A non-modular lattice L must contain a sublattice isomorphic with the "pentagonal" lattice.

Proof. Being non-modular, L must contain elements p, q, r with $p \geqq q$ and $p(q + r) \neq q + pr$. In view of the remarks above (Examples 67, 68) we must have $p > q$, and r must be comparable to neither p nor q. In any lattice by Th. 44 $p \geqq q$ implies $p(q + r) \geqq q + pr$; here by hypothesis equality is excluded; therefore we have

$$p(q + r) > q + pr. \tag{1}$$

Consider the chain

$$pr \leqq q + pr < p(q + r) \leqq q + r.$$

If $pr = q + pr$, then $q \leqq pr$, $q + r \leqq pr + r = r \leqq q + r$, whence $r = q + r$ and $p(q + r) = pr = q + pr$ contrary to (1). It follows that

$$pr < q + pr.$$

If $p(q + r) = q + r$, then $p \geqq q + r$, $pr \geqq (q + r)r = r \geqq pr$, whence $r = pr$ and $q + pr = q + r = p(q + r)$ contrary to (1). It follows that

$$p(q + r) < q + r.$$

Next consider the chain

$$pr \leqq r \leqq q + r.$$

We have just seen that $r = q + r$ is incompatible with (1) and likewise $r = pr$. Thus in L we have two coterminous chains

$$pr < q + pr < p(q + r) < q + r \tag{2}$$

$$pr < r < q + r. \tag{3}$$

The element r cannot lie in the chain (2), for if $p(q + r) \leqq r$, then $p(q + r) = pp(q + r) \leqq pr$ contrary to (2), whilst if $p(q + r) > r$, then $p \geqq p(q + r) > r$ so that $pr = r$ contrary to (3). Therefore the chains (2) and (3) contain five distinct elements of L arranged as shown in Fig. 27.

This subset of five elements of L in itself is a lattice isomorphic with the "pentagonal" lattice, but we have still to prove that the subset forms a sublattice of L. It is easily verified that the subset contains join and meet, as defined in L, of any two of its elements.

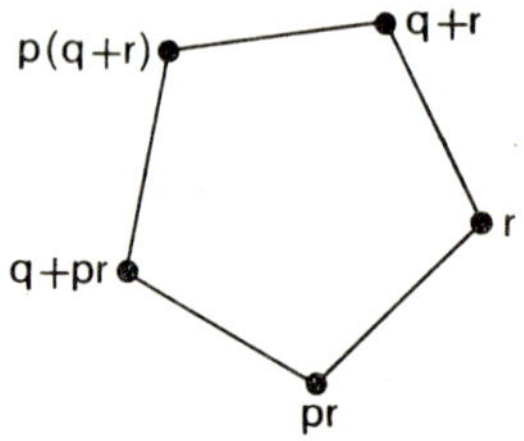

FIG. 27.

For instance,

$$[p(q+r)]r = p(q+r)r = pr;$$

whilst

$$p(q+r)+r \geqq (q+pr)+r = q+pr+r = q+r$$

and

$$p(q+r)+r \leqq (q+r)+r = q+r+r = q+r$$

give

$$p(q+r)+r = q+r.$$

Similarly it may be shown that

$$(q+pr)r = pr \quad \text{and} \quad (q+pr)+r = q+r.$$

The other joins and meets are of comparable elements. This completes the proof of the theorem.

Example 69. An example of a non-modular lattice to illustrate Th. 86 is given by the nine numbers 1, 2, 3, 6, 10, 12, 24, 60, 120 selected from the sixteen factors of 120 and ordered by divisibility as in Fig. 28. Here $p = 24$, $q = 3$, $r = 10$; we notice that p is a proper multiple of q, and that r is multiple or factor of neither. We have (using *lattice* notation)

$$pr = 2, \quad q + pr = 6, \quad p(q + r) = 12, \quad q + r = 60.$$

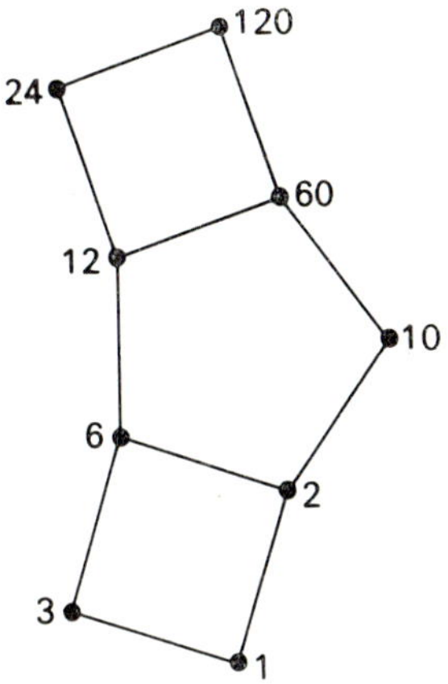

FIG. 28.

The chains (2) and (3) are:

2 which divides 6 which divides 12 which divides 60

and

2 which divides 10 which divides 60.

Notice that the "pentagonal" set {2, 6, 10, 12, 60} occurs also in the complete factorization lattice of all sixteen factors of 120 (Fig. 12c), and there also forms a "pentagonal" lattice in its own right; but the five numbers do not form a sublattice of the sixteen-element lattice, for in the larger lattice the join of 6 and 10 is 30 (not 60) and 30 does not belong to the "pentagonal" set. The sixteen-element lattice is in fact modular.

Example 70. The proof of the theorem, reinforced by Example 69, might suggest that the nine elements

$$p, \quad q,$$

$$pr, \quad q + pr, \quad r, \quad p(q + r), \quad q + r,$$

$$pqr, \quad p + q + r$$

are all distinct. This need not be the case: p may coincide with $p(q + r)$, q with $q + pr$. In the lattice of seven selected factors of 120 (Fig. 11e) $p = 12$, $q = 3$, $r = 10$, and the "pentagonal" set consists of the same five numbers as in Example 69, but here

$$p = p(q + r) \quad \text{and} \quad q + r = p + q + r;$$

in the lattice of five selected factors of 120 (Fig. 11d) $p = 12$, $q = 6$, $r = 10$, the same "pentagonal" set as before is on view, but

$$p = p(q + r) \quad \text{with} \quad q + r = p + q + r$$

and

$$q = q + pr \quad \text{with} \quad pr = pqr.$$

What we have proved in Th. 86 is that in a non-modular lattice the five "pentagonal" elements must exist, must be distinct and must form a sublattice. As a trivial consequence we have: A non-modular lattice contains at least five elements.

Example 71. Less artificial illustrations of Th. 86 are to found among the lattices of partitions of a set of n objects described in § 9 (4). For $n = 1, 2$ (Fig. 13a, b) the lattices contain fewer than five elements and so are modular. For $n = 3$ (Fig. 13c) the five-element lattice is modular, as we remarked in Example 68. For $n > 3$ the lattice is non-modular. Thus for $n = 4$ we have with the notation of Example 7, § 4,

$O:(a/b/c/d)$, $P_1:(ab/c/d)$, $Q_1:(abc/d)$, $R_2:(ac/bd)$, $U:(abcd)$

where

$$O < P_1 < Q_1 < U$$

and

$$O < R_2 < U;$$

these partitions form a "pentagonal" sublattice of the fifteen-element lattice. The general case with $n > 3$ will be taken up in the next chapter, where partition lattices properly belong.

A modular lattice by Th. 85 cannot contain a "pentagonal" sublattice, for this is non-modular; therefore in view of Th. 86 we may assert:

THEOREM 87. A lattice is modular if and only if it does not contain a sublattice isomorphic with the "pentagonal" lattice.

THEOREM 88. A lattice is modular if and only if for elements a, b, c the three relations

$$a \geqq b, \quad ac = bc, \quad a + c = b + c$$

jointly imply

$$a = b.$$

Proof. The condition is necessary. Suppose the lattice modular and that the three relations hold. Then

$$\begin{aligned} a &= a\,(a + c) \\ &= a\,(b + c) \\ &= b + ac \quad \text{by V} \\ &= b + bc \\ &= b. \end{aligned}$$

The condition is sufficient. Suppose the joint implication holds. This prevents the occurrence of a "pentagonal" sublattice

$$ac = bc < b < a < a + c = b + c$$

$$ac < c < a + c.$$

Therefore by Th. 87 the lattice is modular.

THEOREM 89. Any homomorphic image H of a modular lattice L is modular.

Proof. Let x, y, z be elements of such an image H. The remarks in Example 68 entail that we need prove only that

$$\text{if } x > y \text{ in } H, \text{ then} \quad x(y + z) = y + xz.$$

Denote the homomorphism by θ; let a, c in L be antecedents of x, z respectively. Thus $\theta(a) = x$, $\theta(c) = z$. If $x > y$ in H, then by Th. 82 there exists b in L such that $\theta(b) = y$ and $a > b$. Since L is modular, by V we have $a(b + c) = b + ac$.

Hence

$$\begin{aligned} x(y + z) &= \theta(a)[\theta(b) + \theta(c)] \\ &= \theta(a)\,\theta(b + c) \\ &= \theta[a(b + c)] \\ &= \theta(b + ac) \\ &= \theta(b) + \theta(ac) \\ &= \theta(b) + \theta(a)\,\theta(c) \\ &= y + xz. \end{aligned}$$

Therefore H is modular.

THEOREM 90. The direct product $L \times M$ of lattices L and M is modular if and only if L and M are modular.

Proof. First suppose L and M modular. If a_1, a_2, a_3 are elements of L, b_1, b_2, b_3 elements of M, and if $(a_1, b_1) \geqq (a_2, b_2)$ in $L \times M$, then $a_1 \geqq a_2$ in L and $b_1 \geqq b_2$ in M with the consequence that

$$a_1(a_2 + a_3) = a_2 + a_1 a_3$$

and

$$b_1(b_2 + b_3) = b_2 + b_1 b_3.$$

Hence

$$\begin{aligned}(a_1, b_1)\,[(a_2, b_2) + (a_3, b_3)] &= (a_1, b_1)\,(a_2 + a_3, b_2 + b_3)\\ &= [a_1(a_2 + a_3)\;\; b_1(b_2 + b_3)]\\ &= (a_2 + a_1 a_3, b_2 + b_1 b_3)\\ &= (a_2, b_2) + (a_1 a_3, b_1 b_3)\\ &= (a_2, b_2) + (a_1, b_1)\,(a_3, b_3).\end{aligned}$$

Therefore $L \times M$ is modular.

Secondly suppose $L \times M$ modular. We will prove L modular. Take a fixed element b in M, and let X be the subset of elements of $L \times M$ of the form (x, b) with x any element of L. If (a_1, b), (a_2, b) are elements of X, so are $(a_1 a_2, b)$, $(a_1 + a_2, b)$; hence X is a sublattice of $L \times M$. By Th. 85 X is modular. The correspondence $(x, b) \sim x$ between elements of X and elements of L is clearly one-to-one; if $(a_1, b) \leqq (a_2, b)$ in X, then $a_1 \leqq a_2$ in L and conversely; hence X, L are isomorphic lattices. Therefore by Th. 89 L is modular. M is proved modular in a similar manner.

Example 72. The product in Fig. 15 is modular since the component lattices are modular. From Examples 42 and 67 all complete factorization lattices are modular, being the products of chains; in particular, the sixteen factors of 120 form a modular lattice.

Exercises

92. Deal with the cases omitted in Example 67.
93. Prove that a lattice is modular if and only if for any elements a, b, c we have $ab + ac = a(ab + c)$.
94. If a, b, c are elements of a modular lattice with unity element u and if $a + b = ab + c = u$, show that $a + bc = b + ca = c + ab = u$.
95. Supply a proof of the formulae at the end of the proof of Th. 86.
96. Determine the "pentagonal" sublattices of the lattice of partitions of a set of four objects.
97. Decide whether the lattices of Figs. 11a, b are modular or not; determine whether or not these lattices are sublattices of the complete factorization lattice of 210.
98. Show that if a homomorphic image H of a lattice L contains a "pentagonal" sublattice, then L contains such a sublattice.

17. Length and Covering Conditions

We begin this section with a standard result for modular lattices.

THEOREM 91 *(Isomorphism Theorem)*. Let a, b be any elements of a modular lattice L. Then the intervals $[ab, a]$ and $[b, a + b]$ are isomorphic sublattices of L.

Proof. Since intervals are sublattices (Th. 56), only the isomorphism needs proof.

To each x in $[ab, a]$ make correspond the unique element $b + x$ in L. Call this mapping ψ; then $\psi(x) = b + x$. Since $b \leqq a + b$ and $x \leqq a$, we have $b \leqq b + x \leqq a + b$, so that to each x in $[ab, a]$ there corresponds just one y in $[b, a + b]$, namely $y = b + x$.

For any element y in $[b, a + b]$ consider the element ay in L.

Since $ab \leqq a$ and $b \leqq y$, we have $ab \leqq ay \leqq a$, so that ay is in $[ab, a]$; also, since $y \leqq a + b$, we have $y = y(b + a)$, and since $y \geqq b$ and L is modular, we have by V

$$y = y(b + a) = b + ay.$$

Hence each y in $[b, a + b]$ is the consequent of at least one antecedent, namely ay, in the correspondence ψ. Let x_1, x_2 be elements of $[ab, a]$; then $x_1 = x_1 + ab$ and $x_2 = x_2 + ab$. Also, since $a \geqq x_1$, $a \geqq x_2$ and L is modular, we have by V

$$a(b + x_1) = x_1 + ab = x_1,$$

$$a(b + x_2) = x_2 + ab = x_2.$$

Now suppose x_1, x_2 have the same consequent y in the correspondence ψ; then

$$b + x_1 = y = b + x_2$$

so that

$$a(b + x_1) = ay = a(b + x_2),$$

that is,

$$x_1 = ay = x_2.$$

Hence to each y in $[b, a + b]$ there corresponds just one x in $[ab, a]$; therefore ψ is one-to-one.

Finally, if $x_1 \leqq x_2$ in $[ab, a]$, we have $y_1 = b + x_1 \leqq b + x_2 = y_2$ in $[b, a + b]$, whilst if $y_1 \leqq y_2$ in $[b, a + b]$ we have $x_1 = ay_1 \leqq ay_2 = x_2$ in $[ab, a]$; therefore ψ is an isomorphism.

With the help of this theorem we are able to determine the connexions between modularity (Postulate V) and the length and covering conditions of § 12.

THEOREM 92. If in a modular lattice a covers ab, then $a + b$ covers b; in symbols, V $\Longrightarrow$ C1.

Proof. If a covers ab in a modular lattice, the interval $[ab, a]$ is a chain of two elements; hence the isomorphic interval $[b, a + b]$ is a chain of two elements, or $a + b$ covers b.

THEOREM 93. If in a modular lattice $a + b$ covers b, then a covers ab; in symbols, V $\Longrightarrow$ C2.

Proof. Interchange the intervals in the last proof.

THEOREM 94. If in a modular lattice a and b cover ab, then $a + b$ covers a and b; in symbols, V $\Longrightarrow$ C3.

Proof. By Ths. 92 and 46 V $\Longrightarrow$ C1 $\Longrightarrow$ C3.

THEOREM 95. If in a modular lattice $a + b$ covers a and b, then a and b cover ab; in symbols, V $\Longrightarrow$ C4.

Proof. By Ths. 93 and 47 V $\Longrightarrow$ C2 $\Longrightarrow$ C4.

The conditions C3 and C4 are very obviously satisfied in the modular lattice of five partitions (Fig. 9a or 13c) and very obviously not satisfied in the standard non-modular "pentagon" (Fig. 9b or 26). We recall that our formulation of the Jordan–Dedekind condition JD entailed that in a lattice where this condition is satisfied not only for any x, y with $x \leqq y$ has the interval $[x, y]$ a length n, say, but also all maximal chains in that interval are of length n. The length condition L3 was: $l\,[xy, x] = l\,[y, x + y]$, supposing the integers in question to exist.

THEOREM 96. In a modular lattice in which all terminated chains are finite the conditions JD and L3 are satisfied; in symbols, $\mathrm{V} \overset{f}{\Longrightarrow} \mathrm{JD}$ & L3.

Proof. By Ths. 92 and 93 and then by Th. 54 $\mathrm{V} \Longrightarrow \mathrm{C1}$ & C2 $\overset{f}{\Longrightarrow}$ JD & L3.

THEOREM 97. If in a lattice in which all terminated chains are finite the conditions JD and L3 are satisfied, then the lattice is modular; in symbols, JD & L3 $\overset{f}{\Longrightarrow}$ V.

Proof. If the lattice were not modular, by Th. 86 it would contain five distinct elements a, b, c, s, t related as follows:

$$s < b < a < t$$

$$ac = bc = s \qquad\qquad t = a + c = b + c$$

$$s < c < t$$

with c comparable to neither a nor b. If x, y are any pair of comparable elements, say $x \leqq y$, the condition JD ensures that the length $l\,[x, y]$ exists; then by L3 we should have

$$l\,[ac, a] = l\,[c, a + c], \quad \text{that is,} \quad l\,[s, a] = l\,[c, t]$$

and

$$l\,[bc, b] = l\,[c, b + c], \quad \text{that is,} \quad l\,[s, b] = l\,[c, t];$$

hence $l\,[s, a] = l\,[s, b]$, an equality incompatible with $b < a$. Therefore the lattice must be modular.

We summarize what we have proved in this section and incorporate results from § 12 in the following scheme of implication:

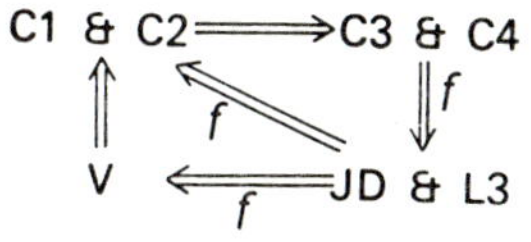

From this scheme, for lattices in which all terminated chains are finite we may read off these results:

$$\mathrm{V} \overset{f}{\Longleftrightarrow} \mathrm{C1}\ \&\ \mathrm{C2}$$
$$\mathrm{V} \overset{f}{\Longleftrightarrow} \mathrm{C3}\ \&\ \mathrm{C4}$$
$$\mathrm{V} \overset{f}{\Longleftrightarrow} \mathrm{JD}\ \&\ \mathrm{L3}$$

Exercises

99. Prove that in a finite modular lattice

$$h(a) + h(b) = h(ab) + h(a + b).$$

Show that this formula is true in a lattice with zero, locally of finite length. Dualize in both cases.

100. Prove that if x' is a complement of x in a modular lattice of finite length, then the length of the lattice is $h(x) + h(x')$.
101. Show that the lattice of Fig. 14 does not satisfy the Jordan–Dedekind condition but is modular.
102. Show that in the lattice of Fig. 17d the conditions C1–C4 are satisfied.
103. Show that in the lattice of partitions of a set of five objects the condition JD is satisfied but not the condition L3.
104. Show that if the lattice of Th. 97 is locally of finite length, the condition JD is superfluous.

18. Irreducible Elements

In number theory we are interested in prime factorization; thus $210 = 6 \times 35 = 2 \times 3 \times 5 \times 7$ displays the number 210 as a product of two composite numbers and then of four primes; the primes cannot be factorized further in any non-trivial way. An analogous question is raised in lattice theory. Let a be an element of a lattice; consider the equation $a = xy$. Since xy is contained in x and in y, any elements satisfying this equation must contain a. An obvious solution is $x = a$, $y = b$ for any $b \geqq a$. More interesting will be a solution with elements b, c such that $a = bc$ where $b \neq a$, $c \neq a$, that is, where $b > a$, $c > a$. These and the dual considerations lead us to formulate

Definition 55. An element a of a lattice is said to be meet-reducible if elements b and c can be found such that $a = bc$ with $b > a$, $c > a$. If such elements cannot be found, a is said to be meet-irreducible. If elements d and e can be found such that $a = d + e$ with $d < a$, $e < a$, a is said to be join-reducible, otherwise join-irreducible. Another form of the definitions is given by

THEOREM 98. If $a = bc$ and a is meet-irreducible, then $a = b$ or $a = c$.

THEOREM 99. If $a = d + e$ and a is join-irreducible, then $a = d$ or $a = e$.

Proof (Th. 99). We have $d \leqq d + e = a$, $e \leqq d + e = a$. Since $a = d + e$ and a is join-irreducible, by Def. 55 one of the statements $d < a$, $e < a$ is false; but $d \leqq a$, $e \leqq a$. Therefore one of the statements $d = a$, $e = a$ is true.

In the case of lattices where a diagram can profitably be drawn it is easy to distinguish reducible and irreducible elements: an element is meet-reducible if from it *rise* two or more connecting lines, meet-irreducible if there rises only one or none; dually, an element is join-reducible if two or more lines *descend* from it, join-irreducible if only one or none. It follows that the zero element and the atoms—if such elements exist—are always join-irreducible, the unity element and the dual atoms—with the same proviso—always meet-irreducible.

Example 73. In the direct product $N \times N$ of Examples 3 and 43 (Fig. 17a) where N is the chain of the natural numbers, every element is meet-reducible. For if (m, n) is any element of this lattice, choose a number k which exceeds both m and n, for instance their arithmetic sum. Then

$$(m, k)(k, n) = [\min(m, k), \min(k, n)] = (m, n)$$

whilst

$$(m, n) < (m, k), \quad (m, n) < (k, n).$$

THEOREM 100. If $a = b_1 \cdots b_n$ and a is meet-irreducible, $a = b_i$ for some subscript i.

THEOREM 101. If $a = c_1 + \cdots + c_n$ and a is join-irreducible, $a = c_i$ for some subscript i.

Proof (Th. 101). Since $a = c_1 + (c_2 + \cdots + c_n)$, by Th. 99

$$\text{either} \quad a = c_1 \quad \text{or} \quad a = c_2 + \cdots + c_n.$$

In the latter case

$$\text{either} \quad a = c_2 \quad \text{or} \quad a = c_3 + \cdots + c_n.$$

It is clear that at most $n - 1$ applications of Th. 99 will determine that for some subscript i

$$a = c_i.$$

Definition 56. If in a lattice we have

$$a = x_1 x_2 \cdots x_n \tag{1}$$

where the x_i are all meet-irreducible

and $$a = x_2 x_3 \cdots x_n,$$

we say that x_1 is redundant in the decomposition (1).

If no x_i is redundant in eqn. (1) we shall say the decomposition is without redundancy.

Dually, if in a lattice we have

$$a = y_1 + y_2 + \cdots + y_n \tag{2}$$

where the y_j are all join-irreducible and

$$a = y_2 + y_3 + \cdots + y_n$$

we say that y_1 is redundant in the decomposition (2).

If no y_j is redundant in eqn. (2) we shall say the decomposition is without redundancy. (Some authors speak of a reduction, or representation; a decomposition without redundancy is generally said to be irredundant.) For simplicity we adopt the convention that if the right-hand side of eqn.(1) or (2) consists of a single element (which cannot then be redundant) we still refer to it as a meet or join.

In view of the duality of all terms and theorems, for the remainder of this section we shall work with join-reducible and join-irreducible elements only, dropping the prefix when convenient.

THEOREM 102. In a finite lattice every element can be represented in at least one way and without redundancy as the join of a subset of the join-irreducible elements contained by that element. And dually.

Proof. Let a be an element of a finite lattice and let

$$a = x_0, x_1, \ldots, x_r$$

be the finite set of elements contained in a so that $x_i \leqq a$ for every i. Then

$$a = x_0 + x_1 + \cdots + x_r. \tag{3}$$

Examine each element in turn. Since a join-reducible element contains the components of any of its reductions, if any x_i is reducible the components of all its reductions will be found on the right in eqn. (3). Thus deletion of any reducible x_i does not affect the equality, and we are left with a representation of a as a join of irreducibles, namely all irreducibles contained in a. Removal of redundant terms now gives one or more decompositions without redundancy.

Example 74. In the lattice of Fig. 29 we will carry out this reduction for the unity element u. We express u as join of all the elements it contains:

$$u = u + a + b + c + d + e + f + g + h + o.$$

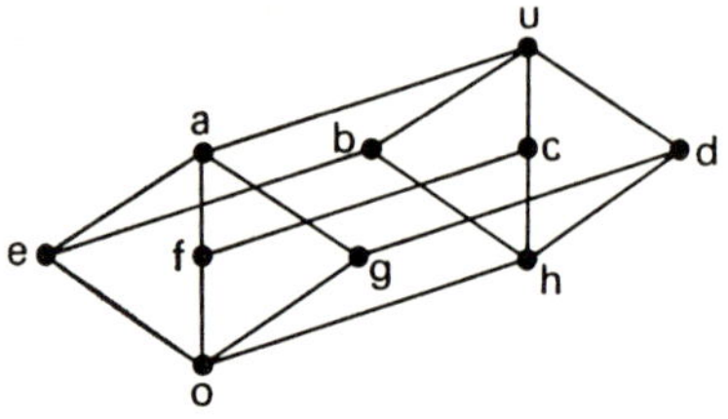

FIG. 29.

u, a, b, c, d are all reducible in terms of elements occurring later in the join; for instance $a = e + f$. Deleting all reducible elements in turn, we are left with

$$u = e + f + g + h + o,$$

which gives u as join of irreducibles. In the join o and any one of e, f, g are redundant; thus we have finally three irredundant decompositions:

$$u = e + f + h = f + g + h = e + g + h.$$

In infinite lattices the number of irreducibles may be infinite and the procedure of the last theorem impossible. In this regard we have

THEOREM 103. In a lattice in which all chains are finite every element can be represented in at least one way and without redundancy as the join of a finite subset of the join-irreducible elements contained by that element. And dually.

Proof. Let L be a lattice in which all chains are finite, and let S be the subset of elements of L for which the assertion is false. We must prove S empty. S is a partially ordered set, ordered with the ordering of L; if S is not empty, it must contain at least one chain which lying in L must be finite and therefore by Th. 31 possess a least element x; x is minimal in S (see Def. 17). If x were irreducible it could be represented as the (conventional) join of one irreducible, namely itself; but x is in S. Hence x is reducible; consequently there exist y and z in L such that

$$x = y + z, \quad y < x, \quad z < x.$$

But x is minimal in S; therefore neither y nor z belong to S, and each of y, z is the join of a finite number of irreducibles, contained in y, z respectively; x contains all that y and z contain; therefore $x = y + z$ is the join of a finite subset of irreducibles contained in x; casting out redundant elements from this finite subset, we have x an element of L for which the assertion is true; hence x does not belong to S. The hypothesis that S is not empty has led to contradiction, and the theorem is proved.

Returning to modular lattices we now demonstrate one of the classical theorems of lattice theory. The lattice of Example 74 is modular (by Th. 90) and the final decompositions of u each contain three irreducibles; there is a causal connexion here, for what we are going to prove is that any two distinct decompositions into irreducibles of an element of a modular lattice, provided they are without redundancy, must contain the same number of elements. This theorem originates from a particular case proved in 1921 by Emmy Noether, the greatest of women mathematicians; as a theorem of lattice theory it was proved about 1935 by the distinguished Russian mathematician A. G. Kurosh and independently by the American Oystein Ore; consequently it is known as the Kurosh–Ore Theorem. With the modest resources at our command we can establish the result; what we cannot do adequately is show the importance for modern algebra of modular lattices, and in particular of the Kurosh–Ore Theorem; for this the names cited will be sufficient guarantee.

We begin with a preliminary observation.

THEOREM 104. Let X, Y be isomorphic lattices, and x, y elements of X, Y respectively which correspond in the isomorphism so that $x \sim y$. Then if x is irreducible in X, y is irreducible in Y.

Proof. Isomorphism preserves joins and partial order, and distinct elements are mapped on distinct elements. Suppose y reducible then $y = y_1 + y_2$ with $y_1 < y$, $y_2 < y$. If $x_1 \sim y_1$, $x_2 \sim y_2$ in the isomorphism, we have $x = x_1 + x_2$ with $x_1 < x$, $x_2 < x$; thus x is reducible in X and the hypothesis of the theorem is contradicted.

Next we establish that it is permissible to replace elements in one decomposition by elements from another.

THEOREM 105. *Replacement Theorem.*
Let

$$a = p_1 + \cdots + p_m \tag{4}$$

and

$$a = q_1 + \cdots + q_n \tag{5}$$

be two representations of an element a of a modular lattice L as join of irreducibles without redundant elements. Then for each p_j an element q_k can be found such that

$$a = p_1 + \cdots + p_{j-1} + q_k + p_{j+1} + \cdots + p_m, \tag{6}$$

that is, any element of the first representation can be replaced by a suitable element from the second; and the resulting representation is a join of irreducibles without redundancy.

Proof. Choose some element p_j and let

$$P_j = p_1 + \cdots + p_{j-1} + p_{j+1} + \cdots + p_m$$

so that

$$a = P_j + p_j.$$

We have $P_j \leqq a$; but p_j is not redundant in (4), whence $P_j \neq a$ and therefore $P_j < a$.

The interval $[P_j, a]$ or $[P_j, P_j + p_j]$ is a sublattice of L.

Again, $P_j p_j \leqq p_j$; from $P_j p_j = p_j$ would follow $P_j + p_j = P_j$ and p_j would be redundant in (4); hence $P_j p_j < p_j$ and the interval $[P_j p_j, p_j]$ is a sublattice of L.

Let $Q_k = P_j + q_k$ for $k = 1, \ldots, n$. Since for each k $q_k \leqq a$ and since as proved above $P_j < a$, we have

$$Q_k = P_j + q_k \leqq a.$$

Also $P_j \leqq Q_k$; hence for each k we have

$$P_j \leqq Q_k \leqq a,$$

and consequently the elements Q_k lie in the interval $[P_j, a]$. Each $q_k \leqq P_j + q_k = Q_k$; but each $Q_k \leqq a$; hence

$$a = q_1 + \cdots + q_n \leqq Q_1 + \cdots + Q_n \leqq a$$

and consequently

$$a = Q_1 + \cdots + Q_n.$$

Since L is modular and $a = P_j + p_j$, the intervals

$$[P_j p_j, p_j] \quad \text{and} \quad [P_j, a]$$

are isomorphic sublattices of L (Th. 91); in an isomorphism order is preserved, so that here greatest element must correspond to greatest element and we have

$$p_j \sim a.$$

By hypothesis p_j is irreducible in L and consequently in the sublattice $[P_j p_j, p_j]$; by Th. 104 it follows that a is irreducible in $[P_j, a]$. But from above

$$a = Q_1 + \cdots + Q_n$$

where each $Q_k \leqq a$ and all Q_k lie in $[P_j, a]$. Therefore by Th. 101 for some value of k

$$a = Q_k = P_j + q_k,$$

that is,

$$a = p_1 + \cdots + p_{j-1} + q_k + p_{j+1} + \cdots + p_m$$

which is (6).

To complete the proof we must show that (6) is without redundancy. Since $a \neq P_j$, q_k is not redundant; since $a \neq q_k$, we cannot delete P_j *en bloc*; but if P_j has two or more constituent elements, might not some of these have become redundant owing to the intrusion of q_k? To appreciate this difficulty consider the non-modular lattice of Fig. 30. Here the atoms a, b, c, s, t are join-irreducible, and

$$\text{(i) } u = a + b + c, \qquad \text{(ii) } u = s + t$$

are two distinct representations of u as join of irreducibles without redundancy. By inspection (not by the half-theorem so far proved) we may replace c in (i) by t from (ii), obtaining

$$\text{(iii) } u = a + b + t.$$

Since $u \neq a + b$, t is not redundant; since $u \neq t$, $a + b$ cannot be deleted; but $u = a + t$ so that the constituent b of the join $a + b$ becomes redundant in (iii) owing to the advent of t. We must show

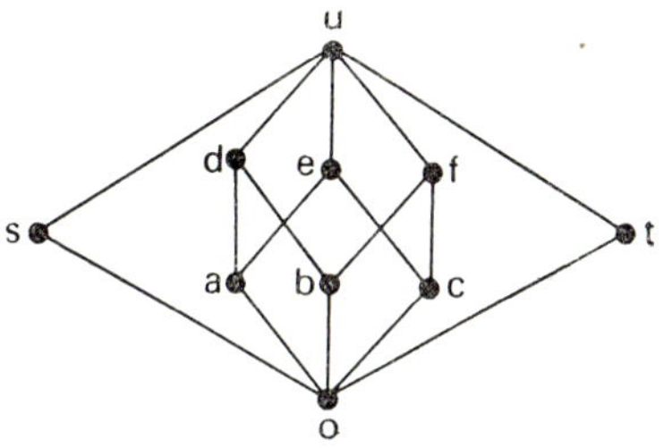

FIG. 30.

that this cannot happen in the circumstances of our theorem. Let R denote the join of such constituents of P_j as remain when we have deleted those which have become redundant in (6) through the intrusion of q_k; then

$$a = R + q_k, \tag{7}$$

which is a representation of a as join of irreducibles without redundancy. Now apply the procedure of the first part of the theorem, replacing q_k in (7) by an element p_i from (4). We shall obtain

$$a = R + p_i. \tag{8}$$

Since the representation (8) consists of elements from (4) only, and (4) is without redundancy, these representations must be identical, $R = P_j$, and (6) is without redundancy.

We are now in a position to prove the main theorem.

THEOREM 106. *Kurosh–Ore Theorem.*

Let

$$a = p_1 + \cdots + p_m \tag{4}$$

and

$$a = q_1 + \cdots + q_n \tag{5}$$

be two representations of an element a of a modular lattice as join of irreducibles without redundant elements. Then $m = n$.

Proof. Starting with eqn. (4) we use Th. 105 to replace p_1 by some q_{k_1} from eqn. (5) and obtain

$$a = q_{k_1} + p_2 + \cdots + p_m.$$

Applying the replacement theorem to this decomposition we obtain

$$a = q_{k_1} + q_{k_2} + p_3 + \cdots + p_m.$$

Continuing in this way we finally arrive at

$$a = q_{k_1} + \cdots + q_{k_m}. \tag{9}$$

After each replacement we are left with a representation of a as join of m irreducibles, without redundancy. Hence eqn. (9) contains just m members of the set of n elements $q_1, \ldots, q_n$. If $m < n$, eqn. (5) would contain redundant elements, contrary to hypothesis; if $m > n$, eqn. (9) would contain redundant elements, but we have proved the contrary; therefore $m = n$.

We remind the reader that duality gives theorems parallel to Ths. 104–6, in terms of meet-irreducibles.

Example 75. The lattice of Fig. 30 is non-modular by Th. 87. The elements o, s, a, b, c, t are join-irreducible; d, e, f each have a unique irredundant decomposition; but u has one such decomposition with three irreducibles and six with two irreducibles. Thus the assertion of Th. 106 does not apply to decompositions in this lattice. The reason for this is not the non-modularity; for consider the lattice of Fig. 31, which again is not modular. Here u is the only join-reducible, and its five irredundant decompositions are all joins of two elements. This example shows that modularity is a sufficient but not necessary condition in Th. 106. Note also that Th. 106 is

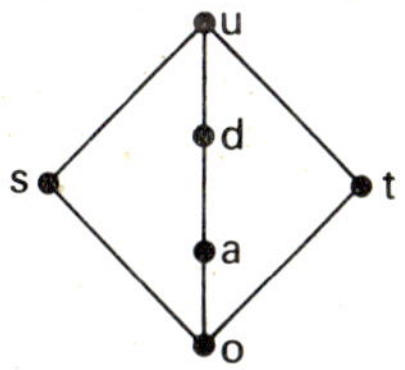

FIG. 31.

conditional, not existential: *if* an element of a modular lattice has distinct irredundant representations, *then* these contain the same number of elements. The lattice dual to $N \times N$ (Example 73) is modular (by Th. 90) and contains no join-irreducibles at all, so that there does not exist a single decomposition into join-irreducibles.

Exercises

105. Show that in the lattice of the natural numbers ordered by divisibility an element is join-irreducible if and only if it is of the form p^r $(r = 0, 1, \ldots)$ where p is prime.
106. J denoting the chain of the integers, show that every element of $J \times J$ (Fig. 17c) is both meet- and join-reducible.
107. Prove that every element of a finite chain is both meet- and join-irreducible. What can be said about the irreducible elements of the product of two such chains?
108. With the help of Ths. 103 and 106, give an existence theorem for decompositions in modular lattices of finite length.

19. Complements

Reference to Defs. 32–35, § 13, will remind the reader that a complemented lattice must have zero element o and unity element u, the interval $[o, u]$ being complemented; in a relatively complemented lattice all intervals are complemented. In the special case of modular lattices with o and u, if $[o, u]$ is complemented, then all intervals are complemented.

THEOREM 107. A complemented modular lattice is relatively complemented.

Proof. Let $[a, b]$ be any interval of a complemented modular lattice, and x any element such that $a \leqq x \leqq b$; we must prove the existence of an element y such that $xy = a$, $x + y = b$. Take the element $a + bx'$ where x' is a complement of x in the lattice. We have

$$\begin{aligned} x(a + bx') &= a + bx'x \quad \text{by V} \\ &= a + bo \\ &= a + o \\ &= a, \end{aligned}$$

whilst

$$\begin{aligned} x + (a + bx') &= (x + a) + bx' \\ &= x + bx' \\ &= b(x + x') \quad \text{by V} \\ &= bu \\ &= b. \end{aligned}$$

Hence $y = a + bx'$ is a complement of x relative to the interval $[a, b]$. Note that since $b \geqq a$, V gives an alternative form for y:

$$y = a + bx' = (a + x')b.$$

In the six theorems that follow we establish connexions between complementation and reducibility; we do not require the lattices in question to be modular.

THEOREMS 108–11. Let L be a finite lattice of more than one element. Then:

THEOREM 108. If L is complemented, the unity element is join of all atoms.

THEOREM 109. If L is relatively complemented, every non-zero element is join of the atoms it contains.

THEOREM 110. If L is relatively complemented, the only join-irreducible elements are the atoms and zero.

THEOREM 111. If L is relatively complemented, every non-zero element can be represented in at least one way as join of a subset of atoms without redundancy.

Proof (Th. 108). L has at least two elements and therefore at least one atom. Let $p_1, \ldots, p_n$ be the atoms and let

$$v = p_1 + \cdots + p_n.$$

Choose any element w from L which contains at least one atom, say $w \geqq p_k$. Then

$$vw = (p_1 + \cdots + p_n)\, w \geqq p_k p_k = p_k > o.$$

If v' is a complement of v, we have $vv' = o$; hence v' cannot be an element which contains at least one atom; it follows that $v' = o$ and $u = v + v' = v + o = v$.

Proof (Th. 109). Let $x > o$ be any non-zero element of L; by hypothesis the interval $[o, x]$ is a complemented lattice. Apply Th. 108 to this interval.

Proof (Th. 110). An element $x > o$ contains at least one atom; let x contain the atoms $p_1, \ldots, p_k$. By Th. 109

$$x = p_1 + \cdots + p_k.$$

If x is join-irreducible in L, by Th. 101 $x = p_i$ for some i.

Proof (Th. 111). By Ths. 102 and 110.

Theorems 110 and 111 can be extended as follows:

THEOREMS 112 and 113. Let L be a lattice of finite length $\geqq 1$. Then:

THEOREM 112. If L is relatively complemented, the only join-irreducible elements are the atoms and zero.

THEOREM 113. If L is relatively complemented, every non-zero element can be represented in at least one way as join of a finite subset of atoms without redundancy.

Proof (Th. 112). Let $x > o$ be join-irreducible in L. From the hypothesis of finite length there is at least one maximal finite chain from o to x, lying in the interval $[o, x]$; this chain must contain an atom p, for $x > o$; we have then $o < p \leqq x$. Since $[o, x]$ is complemented, there exists q such that

$$o = pq \leqq q \leqq p + q = x$$

$$o = pq < p \leqq p + q = x.$$

Since $x = p + q$ and x is join-irreducible, by Th. 99

$$x = p \quad \text{or} \quad x = q.$$

If $x = p + q = q, p = pq = o$, which is false, for $p > o$ is an atom; therefore $x = p$ and thus is an atom.

Proof (Th. 113). If L is of finite length, all its chains are finite. Then by Ths. 103 and 112.

Example 76. The "pentagonal" lattice of Fig. 26 with atoms b, c and join-irreducibles a, b, c, o is complemented, so that $u = b + c$, but not relatively complemented for a is neither atom nor zero. The sixteen-element factorization lattice of the number 210 with the primes 2, 3, 5, 7 for atoms is relatively complemented, each element $\neq 1$ being the l.c.m. of some subset of these primes. The sixteen-element factorization lattice of 120 has atoms 2, 3, 5 and join-irreducibles 1, 2, 3, 4, 5, 8; this lattice cannot be complemented for $120 \neq$ l.c.m. $(2, 3, 5) = 30$; the prime powers 4 and 8 are irreducible but neither atoms nor zero element.

Our final theorem characterizes a class of modular lattices of some importance. Figure 29 will serve as illustration.

THEOREM 114. In a complemented modular lattice L of finite length ($\geqq 1$):

(i) every interval is complemented;
(ii) every non-zero element x can be represented in at least one way and without redundancy as the join of a finite subset of atoms;
(iii) any two such representations of x contain the same number m of atoms;
(iv) the number m of atoms is the height of x in L.

Proof (i) By Th. 107. (ii) By Ths. 107 and 113. (iii) By Ths. 106 and 112. There remains (iv). Let

$$x = p_1 + \cdots + p_m \tag{1}$$

be an irredundant representation of a non-zero element x of L as join of the m atoms p_i. Since (1) contains no redundant element, we must have

$$o < p_1 < p_1 + p_2 < p_1 + p_2 + p_3 < \cdots < p_1 + \cdots + p_m = x \quad (2)$$

without equality signs intervening. Let

$$p_1 + \cdots + p_k$$

be any element of the chain (2) other than the first or last. We have

$$(p_1 + \cdots + p_k)\, p_{k+1} \leqq p_{k+1};$$

but if

$$(p_1 + \cdots + p_k)\, p_{k+1} = p_{k+1},$$

then

$$(p_1 + \cdots + p_k) + p_{k+1} = p_1 + \cdots + p_k,$$

which renders p_{k+1} redundant in (1).

Therefore

$$(p_1 + \cdots + p_k)\, p_{k+1} < p_{k+1};$$

but p_{k+1} is an atom; hence

$$(p_1 + \cdots + p_k)\, p_{k+1} = 0$$

and p_{k+1} covers $(p_1 + \cdots + p_k)\, p_{k+1}$.

L being modular, C1 is satisfied therein (Th. 92); it follows that $p_1 + \cdots + p_k + p_{k+1}$ covers $p_1 + \cdots + p_k$. Hence each term in (2) covers its predecessor; that is, the chain (2) is maximal and of length m. The lattice satisfies the finitary condition of Th. 96, all chains being finite; hence the Jordan–Dedekind condition is satisfied, and the length of the interval $[o, x]$ is m; that is to say

$$h(x) = h(p_1 + \cdots + p_m) = m.$$

Theorems 108–14 can all be dualized; to effect this, we must interchange u and o, and replace atom by dual atom, join-irreducible by meet-irreducible, height by depth, C1 by C2.

Exercises

109. State the dual to Th. 114; prove the last part of your theorem.
110. Let a complemented modular lattice of length 4 be given. Name each non-zero element x according to the number m of atoms its irredundant representations contain as follows: if $m = 1$, a point; if $m = 2$, a line; if $m = 3$, a plane; if $m = 4$, a space. Call $m - 1$ the dimension of the element. Interpret "comparable with" as "is incident with". Give geometrical meanings to C1–C4 and Th. 106; give examples of complements. Interpret the lattice of Fig. 10f in this way.

20. Groups and Modules

In this section we make an algebraic excursion in the course of which we shall come across the best-known example of a modular lattice.

We begin with a comparison of the integers and the positive rationals. From the constructions described in § 5 it is easy to show that:

(1) for any integers m, n there is defined a unique integer

$$m + n$$

called their sum;

(2) for any integers k, m, n

$$k + (m + n) = (k + m) + n;$$

(3) there is a unique integer 0 such that for any integer n

$$n + 0 = 0 + n = n;$$

(1) for any positive rationals r, s there is defined a unique positive rational

$$rs$$

called their product;

(2) for any positive rationals q, r, s

$$q(rs) = (qr)s;$$

(3) there is a unique positive rational 1 such that for any positive rational r

$$1r = r \cdot 1 = r;$$

(4) each integer n has a unique inverse n' such that

$$n + n' = n' + n = 0;$$

n' is written $-n$;

(5) for any integers m, n

$$m + n = n + m.$$

(4) each positive rational r has a unique inverse r' such that

$$rr' = r'r = 1;$$

r' is written r^{-1};

(5) for any positive rationals r, s

$$rs = sr.$$

It is clear that the two sets of numbers have the properties (1)–(5) in common, the only difference between the two columns being one of notation. We are led to the following definition:

Let there be given over a set G a binary operation denoted for elements a, b of G by $a \circ b$. If

(1) G is closed with respect to the operation,
(2) the operation is associative,
(3) there exists in G a unique identity element e such that $e \circ x = x \circ e = x$ for every x in G,
(4) for each x in G there exists a unique inverse element x' such that $x \circ x' = x' \circ x = e$,

then G is called a group. If further

(5) the operation is commutative,

then G is called an Abelian group (after the great Norwegian N.H. Abel, one of the pioneers of group theory).

Example 77. Above we have two infinite groups, the additive group of the integers, the multiplicative group of the positive rationals. Here is an additive Abelian group of only five elements. Classify the natural numbers by the remainders they leave on division by 5 into the five classes

$$\omega: 5, 10, \ldots; \quad \nu: 1, 6, \ldots; \quad \varkappa: 2, 7, \ldots; \quad \lambda: 3, 8, \ldots; \quad \mu: 4, 9, \ldots$$

To add these classes add remainders and reduce modulo 5, obtaining the tables:

+	0	1	2	3	4
0	0	1	2	3	4
1	1	2	3	4	0
2	2	3	4	0	1
3	3	4	0	1	2
4	4	0	1	2	3

+	ω	ν	$\varkappa$	λ	μ
ω	ω	ν	$\varkappa$	λ	μ
ν	ν	$\varkappa$	λ	μ	ω
$\varkappa$	$\varkappa$	λ	μ	ω	ν
λ	λ	μ	ω	ν	$\varkappa$
μ	μ	ω	ν	$\varkappa$	λ

Thus $\lambda + \mu = \varkappa$.

Example 78. Here is a multiplicative group, also Abelian, with eight elements. Classify the natural numbers into remainder classes this time dividing by 15. Select and name the eight classes shown:

Remainder	1	2	4	8	11	7	14	13
Class	e	a	b	c	d	f	g	h

To multiply these classes multiply corresponding remainders and reduce modulo 15; this gives the following multiplication table:

$\times$	e	a	b	c	d	f	g	h
e	e	a	b	c	d	f	g	h
a	a	b	c	e	f	g	h	d
b	b	c	e	a	g	h	d	f
c	c	e	a	b	h	d	f	g
d	d	f	g	h	e	a	b	c
f	f	g	h	d	a	b	c	e
g	g	h	d	f	b	c	e	a
h	h	d	f	g	c	e	a	b

The inverse elements are given by:

Element	e	a	b	c	d	f	g	h
Inverse	e	c	b	a	d	h	g	f

Before proceeding further we note that the work we did in § 11 on associativity applies to the operation of a group, and prove a useful formula. In any group $(ab)' = b'a'$, for we have

$$(b'a')(ab)(ab)' = b'(a'a)\,b\,(ab)' = b'b\,(ab)' = (ab)'$$

and

$$(b'a')(ab)(ab)' = (b'a')\,e = b'a'.$$

We have used the convenient multiplicative notation here, as is usual in group theory.

A non-empty subset H of a group G is called a subgroup of G if and only if the requirements (1), (3) and (4) are met by H with respect to the group operation of G; thus if H is to be a subgroup, for any x, y in H we must have $x \circ y$, $y \circ x$, e, x', y' in H.

Example 79. G is a subgroup, and the identity element e on its own is a subgroup; these are the only subgroups of the five-element group of Example 77. The even integers are a non-trivial subgroup of the additive group of the integers. In the group of Example 78 the elements e, a, b, c form a subgroup, the elements e, f, g, h do not, as a glance at the multiplication table shows.

If H is a subgroup of a group G and g is a fixed element of G, the subset consisting of all elements of the form $g \circ h$ with h in H is called a left coset of H and written gH; a right coset Hg is similarly defined. Thus if G is the group of Example 78 and H the subgroup consisting of e, a, b, c, then dH consists of the elements d, f, g, h. If H is a subgroup of a group G and if for each x in G

$$xH = Hx,$$

that is, the sets xH, Hx have precisely the same membership, then H is said to be a normal subgroup of G. Obviously in an Abelian group all subgroups are normal; in any group the group consisting of the identity element alone is a normal subgroup, and so is the entire group considered as a subgroup.

We have now arrived at our classic example of a modular lattice. We assert:

The normal subgroups of a group ordered by set-inclusion form a modular lattice.

Proof. In this proof we use the multiplicative notation for the group operation; note that this need not be commutative.

Let A, B be normal subgroups of a group G. By (3) e belongs to both A and B and thus to their set-intersection AB, which is accordingly a non-empty subset of G. If a, b are in A and also in B, then by (1) ab is in A and likewise in B and consequently in AB. If c is in AB, c is in A and in B; hence by (4) c' is in A and likewise in B and consequently in AB. Thus AB satisfies (3), (1) and (4) and is therefore a subgroup of G.

Note that if H is a normal subgroup of G, then $xH = Hx$ for each x in G and hence $xH \leqq Hx$, $Hx \leqq xH$; consequently for p in H there exist q, r in H such that $xp = qx$, $px = xr$. Conversely, if H is a subgroup and for p in H, x in G, elements q, r can be found in H such that $xp = qx$, $px = xr$, then $xH \leqq Hx$, $Hx \leqq xH$, so that $xH = Hx$ and H is normal.

If c is in AB, c is in A, which is normal; hence for x in G an element d can be found in A such that $xc = dx$; c is also in B and for the same reason an element d_1 can be found in B such that $xc = d_1x$; then $d = dxx' = xcx' = d_1xx' = d_1$ so that d is in AB. In the same way an element f can be found in AB such that $cx = xf$. Therefore AB is normal. Being the intersection of A and B, AB is thus the largest normal subgroup contained by A and B.

Consider the subset C of G consisting of elements of the form ab with a from A, b from B. C is not empty but indeed contains $Ae = A$ and $eB = B$ and incidentally $ee = e$. If $p = a_1b_1$, $q = a_2b_2$ are elements of C (with a_1, a_2 in A, b_1, b_2 in B), then since A is normal $b_1a_2 = a_3b_1$ for some a_3 in A with the consequence that

$$pq = a_1b_1a_2b_2 = a_1a_3b_1b_2 = (a_1a_3)(b_1b_2)$$

which is in C. If $r = ab$ is in C, $r' = (ab)' = b'a'$ as proved earlier. A is normal and contains a'; therefore $b'a' = a_4b'$ for some a_4 in A; also we have b' in B; hence r' is in C. Thus C satisfies (3), (1) and (4) and is therefore a subgroup of G containing A and B. If D is any subgroup containing A and B, D contains all elements of the form ab with a from A, b from B, and hence contains C. Therefore C is the smallest subgroup of G which contains A and B.

Since A and B are normal, for x in G, a in A, b in B we have $xa = a_1x$ for some a_1 in A, $xb = b_1x$ for some b_1 in B; then $s = a_1b_1$ is in C; hence if $r = ab$ in C,

$$xr = xab = a_1xb = a_1b_1x = sx.$$

Similarly, t can be found in C such that $rx = xt$. Therefore C is normal.

We have proved that the normal subgroups of a group, ordered by set-inclusion, satisfy the requirements of Def. 22 and so form a lattice with AB for meet $A \wedge B$ and C for join $A \vee B$.

Let X, Y, Z be normal subgroups of G. In view of the modular inequality (Th. 44) we prove the lattice modular if we show that:

$$X \geqq Y \text{ implies } X(Y \vee Z) \leqq Y \vee XZ.$$

If a group element g is in $X(Y \vee Z)$, then g is in X and in $Y \vee Z$. This last means that $g = yz$ with y in Y, z in Z. If $X \geqq Y$, y is in X and therefore y' is in X. Then g in X and y' in X give

$$y'g = y'yz = ez = z \text{ in } X.$$

Since z is in Z and in X, z is in XZ. Thus we have $g = yz$ with y in Y and z in XZ; hence g belongs to $Y \vee XZ$. It follows that

$$X(Y \vee Z) \leqq Y \vee XZ.$$

Before completing the comparison between integers and rationals with which we began we need to define another term. Let R be an Abelian group with the group operation written additively; if R is closed with respect to a second associative operation, written multiplicatively, such that for all a, b, c in R

$$a(b + c) = ab + ac, \quad (a + b)\,c = ac + bc,$$

then R is called a ring. If R has an element u such that $ua = au = a$ for every a in R, u can be proved unique in R and is called the unity element.

Example 80. The integers with ordinary addition and multiplication form a ring with unity 1. The group of Example 77 can be made into a ring if we define multiplication of classes as multiplication of corresponding remainders with reduction modulo 5. This gives the tables:

×	0	1	2	3	4
0	0	0	0	0	0
1	0	1	2	3	4
2	0	2	4	1	3
3	0	3	1	4	2
4	0	4	3	2	1

×	ω	ν	$\varkappa$	λ	μ
ω	ω	ω	ω	ω	ω
ν	ω	ν	$\varkappa$	λ	μ
$\varkappa$	ω	$\varkappa$	μ	ν	λ
λ	ω	λ	ν	μ	$\varkappa$
μ	ω	μ	λ	$\varkappa$	ν

Defining integer exponents for the positive rationals thus: $r^0 = 1$, $r^1 = r$, $r^n = (r^{n-1})\,r$, $r^{-n} = (r^n)^{-1}$, we continue the comparison.

Let p, q be any integers.

(6) pm is a unique integer;	(6) r^p is a unique positive rational;
(7) $(p + q)\,m = pm + qm$;	(7) $r^{q+p} = r^q r^p$;
(8) $p\,(m + n) = pm + pn$;	(8) $(rs)^p = r^p s^p$;
(9) $(pq)\,m = p\,(qm)$;	(9) $r^{qp} = (r^q)^p$;
(10) $1m = m$.	(10) $r^1 = r$.

The notable parallelism of the two columns leads us to a final algebraic system. Let G be an Abelian group with elements $a, b, c, \dots$, the group operation for a, b being denoted by $a \circ b$. Let R be a ring with elements $\alpha, \beta, \gamma, \dots$, the ring operations for α, β being written $\alpha + \beta, \alpha\beta$ as is customary; let R have a unity element ν so that $\nu\theta = \theta\nu = \theta$ for every θ in R.

If for every x, y in G
and for every θ, φ in R

(6) θx is a uniquely determined element of G;
(7) $(\theta + \varphi)\, x = \theta x \circ \varphi x$,
(8) $\theta\,(x \circ y) = \theta x \circ \theta y$,
(9) $(\theta\varphi)\, x = \theta\,(\varphi x)$,
(10) $\nu x = x$,

we say that G with R applied thus is a left R-module with unity.

A submodule of a left R-module is a subgroup of G which with x contains θx for all θ in R.

(6) $x\theta$ is a uniquely determined element of G;
(7) $x\,(\varphi + \theta) = x\varphi \circ x\theta$,
(8) $(x \circ y)\,\theta = x\theta \circ y\theta$,
(9) $x\,(\varphi\theta) = (x\varphi)\,\theta$,
(10) $x\nu = x$,

we say that G with R applied thus is a right R-module with unity.

A submodule of a right R-module is a subgroup of G which with x contains $x\theta$ for all θ in R.

Example 81. We have been comparing a left and a right module.

Take for G the additive group of the integers, for R the ring of the integers; define θx as the arithmetic product of the two integers.

Take for G the multiplicative group of the positive rationals, for R the ring of the integers; define $x\theta$ as the power x^θ. For instance, if $x = \frac{2}{3}$, $\theta = -3$, $x\theta = \frac{27}{8}$.

In an Abelian group G all subgroups are normal, and the modular lattice L of normal subgroups contains all subgroups; if G is a module, by definition the submodules constitute a subset M of L; we prove M a sublattice of L. Let G be a left R-module where the identity element of G is e (so that $x \circ e = x$ for all x in G). First we show that M is not empty. The element e alone is a normal subgroup of G; by (8) for all θ in R and any x in G

$$\theta x = \theta(x \circ e) = \theta x \circ \theta e;$$

but e is the unique identity element of G; hence $\theta e = e$ for all θ in R; hence e alone constitutes a submodule of G. Also by (6) G itself is a submodule. If X, Y are submodules of G, their meet XY in L is a normal subgroup; if z is in XY, z is in X and in Y; X and Y being submodules, θz is in X and in Y and therefore in XY, for all θ in R; hence XY is a submodule. If w is in $X \vee Y$, then $w = x \circ y$ with x in X, y in Y; by (8) for all θ in R

$$w = \theta(x \circ y) = \theta x \circ \theta y;$$

X and Y being submodules, θx is in X, θy is in Y; hence θw is in $X \vee Y$ for all θ in R; therefore the join $X \vee Y$ is a submodule. Thus M is a sublattice of L; L is modular and therefore by Th. 85 M is modular.

This last result was established by Dedekind; working with a set of modules he discovered the structural principle:

$$X \geqq Y \text{ implies that } X(Y \vee Z) = Y \vee XZ,$$

which in the context he called the *modular* law. Translated into abstract terms, this law becomes our Postulate V; now we understand why "a lattice satisfying Postulate V is said to be modular".

Example 82. Let G be the eight-element group of Example 78, R the five-element ring of Examples 77 and 80. Apply R to G thus: for x in G, $x\omega = x^0 = e$, $x\nu = x^1 = x$, $x\varkappa = x^2$, $x\lambda = x^3$, $x\mu = x^4$ (where $x^2 = xx$, etc.), obtaining the table

x	e	a	b	c	d	f	g	h
$x\omega$	e	e	e	e	e	e	e	e
$x\nu$	e	a	b	c	d	f	g	h
$x\varkappa$	e	b	e	b	e	b	e	b
$x\lambda$	e	c	b	a	d	h	g	f
$x\mu$	e	e	e	e	e	e	e	e

The modular lattice L consists of the eight subgroups of the group G:

$$\{G\},$$

$$\{e, b, d, g\}, \quad \{e, a, b, c\}, \quad \{e, b, f, h\},$$

$$\{e, d\}, \quad \{e, g\}, \quad \{e, b\},$$

$$\{e\}.$$

These are all submodules of the right R-module G; here M coincides with L (Fig. 32).

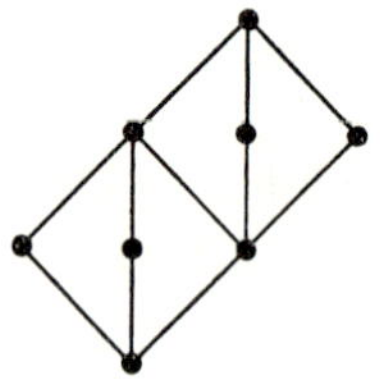

FIG. 32.

Example 83. Take the "Boolean" lattice of the factors 1, 2, 3, 6 of the square-free number 6, ordered by divisibility; call this lattice B.

With the warning that x' here means lattice complement and *not* group inverse of x, we convert B into a ring R as follows:

ring product of x and y = lattice meet of x and y;
but ring sum of x and y = lattice join of xy' and $x'y$.

This conversion gives the following tables.

Ring addition

	1	2	3	6
1	1	2	3	6
2	2	1	6	3
3	3	6	1	2
6	6	3	2	1

Lattice join

	1	2	3	6
1	1	2	3	6
2	2	2	6	6
3	3	6	3	6
6	6	6	6	6

Product or meet

	1	2	3	6
1	1	1	1	1
2	1	2	1	2
3	1	1	3	3
6	1	2	3	6

The ring addition table displays the ring in its capacity as Abelian group, with the number 1 for identity element and each element its own additive inverse; call this group G. The subgroups of G are five in number:

$$\{1\}, \quad \{1, 2\}, \quad \{1, 3\}, \quad \{1, 6\}, \quad \{1, 2, 3, 6\};$$

these subgroups, ordered by set-inclusion, constitute the modular lattice L, which is isomorphic with the lattice of five partitions of a set of three objects (Fig. 9a or 13c). The ring R has a unity element, namely the number 6; we apply R to G, that is to itself, by defining θx for θ in R, x in G, as the ring product of θ and x. This gives G as a (left) R-module. Of the five subgroups of G only four are submodules; $\{1, 6\}$ is not a submodule, as a glance at the product or meet table shows. The four submodules constitute the modular lattice M, which in this instance is a proper sublattice of L.

Exercises

111. Show that the group of Example 77 has only trivial subgroups forming a two-element chain.

112. Construct the multiplicative group of the classes which correspond to the remainders 1, 3, 5, 7 when the natural numbers are divided by 8. Apply the integers as exponents. Determine the lattice of submodules and show that this coincides with the lattice of subgroups. Do the same for the remainder classes corresponding to 1, 2, 3, 4 upon division by 5.

113. Show that in a (left) R-module G there exists an element ω in R such that $\omega x = e$ for all x in G.

114. Show that in the (left) module of the integers of Example 81 each sub module consists of all multiples of some fixed positive integer. Prove directly that the submodules, ordered by set-inclusion, form a lattice which is modular.

CHAPTER 5

SEMI-MODULAR LATTICES

21. Semi-modularity

It was shown in § 17 that modular lattices in which all terminated chains are finite are characterized by C3 and C4:

$$\text{C3 \& C4} \xrightarrow[\text{Th.54}]{f} \text{JD \& L3} \xrightarrow[\text{Th.97}]{f} \text{V}.$$

A fortiori modular lattices of finite length are characterized by C3 and C4. In 1933 Birkhoff introduced lattices of finite length characterized by C3 alone; he called them "semi-modular" lattices. We notice that

$$\text{C3} \xrightarrow[\text{Ths.48,50}]{f} \text{JD \& L1} \xrightarrow[\text{Th.52}]{f} \text{C1}.$$

The scope of the definition of semi-modular lattices was widened in 1951 by the French mathematician R. Croisot, and it is one of his skilfully designed formulations that we shall follow. We recall that a "pentagonal" subset of elements cannot appear as a sublattice in a modular lattice, and clearly the "pentagonal" lattice does not satisfy C3 or C1. Croisot's definition is so framed that

(i) lattices satisfying the requirements of the definition need not be of finite length;
(ii) it is satisfied by all modular lattices;
(iii) lattices in which the "pentagon" occurs as sublattice may yet satisfy the requirements;

(iv) C1 and C3 are satisfied in any lattice conforming to the definition.

Definition 57. A lattice L is said to be semi-modular if and only if the following postulate is satisfied:

Postulate VI A. If a, b, c are any three elements of L such that

(1) a and c are incomparable,
(2) $ac < b < a$,

then there exists in L an element d such that

(3) $ac < d \leqq c$,
(4) $a(b + d) = b$.

This intricate postulate is conditional:

if there exist elements a, b, c satisfying (1) and (2),
then there exists element d satisfying (3) and (4).

Suppose elements a, b, c of a lattice are given satisfying (1) and (2). By (1) a and c are distinct; by (2) a and b are distinct; b is comparable with a and so distinct from c; hence a, b, c are distinct.

(1) entails that $ac < a < a + c$, $ac < c < a + c$;
(2) entails that $ac < b < a + c$;

hence the five elements $ac, b, c, a, a + c$ are distinct.

From (2)

$$ac \leqq bc \leqq ac; \quad \text{hence} \quad ac = bc.$$

It follows that b, c are not only distinct but incomparable;

for if $b < c$, then $ac = bc = b$, which contradicts (2),
and if $c < b$, then $ac = bc = c$, which contradicts (1).

Hence

$$bc < b < b + c, \quad bc < c < b + c.$$

Also, from (2)

$$b + c \leqq a + c.$$

Now consider the element $a_1 = a(b + c) \leqq a$.
From $b < a$ and $b < b + c$ we have $b \leqq a_1 \leqq a$.

If $a_1 \leqq c$, then $a_1 = a_1 c = a(b + c)\,c = ac$ by absorption; but $ac < b$;

if $a_1 > c$, then $c = a_1 c = ac < a$, which contradicts (1); hence a_1 and c are distinct and incomparable.

Finally, $a_1 = a(b + c) \leqq b + c$; if $a_1 = b + c$, then $c < b + c = a_1$, but a_1 and c are incomparable; hence $a_1 < b + c$.

To sum up our analysis so far:
If elements a, b, c of a lattice are such that (1) and (2) are satisfied, then there exist seven elements

$$ac, b, c, a, a + c \quad \text{and} \quad a_1 = a(b + c), b + c,$$

the first five being all distinct, and $a_1 < b + c$. They lie in the lattice with this ordering:

$$ac = bc < b \leqq a_1 \leqq a < a + c,$$

$$ac = bc < b \leqq a_1 < b + c \leqq a + c,$$

$$ac = bc < c < b + c \leqq a + c.$$

The elements $ac, b, c, a, a + c$ constitute a "pentagonal" subset; Fig. 33a (six elements), Fig. 33b (five elements), Fig. 33c (seven elements) show all possible positions of a_1 and $b + c$. We notice that Fig. 33b constitutes a "pentagonal" sublattice, Fig. 33c properly contains such a sublattice.

Definition 57 may now be paraphrased:

A lattice is semi-modular if the existence of a "pentagonal" subset $ac, b, c, a, a + c$ entails the existence of an element d satisfying (3) and (4).

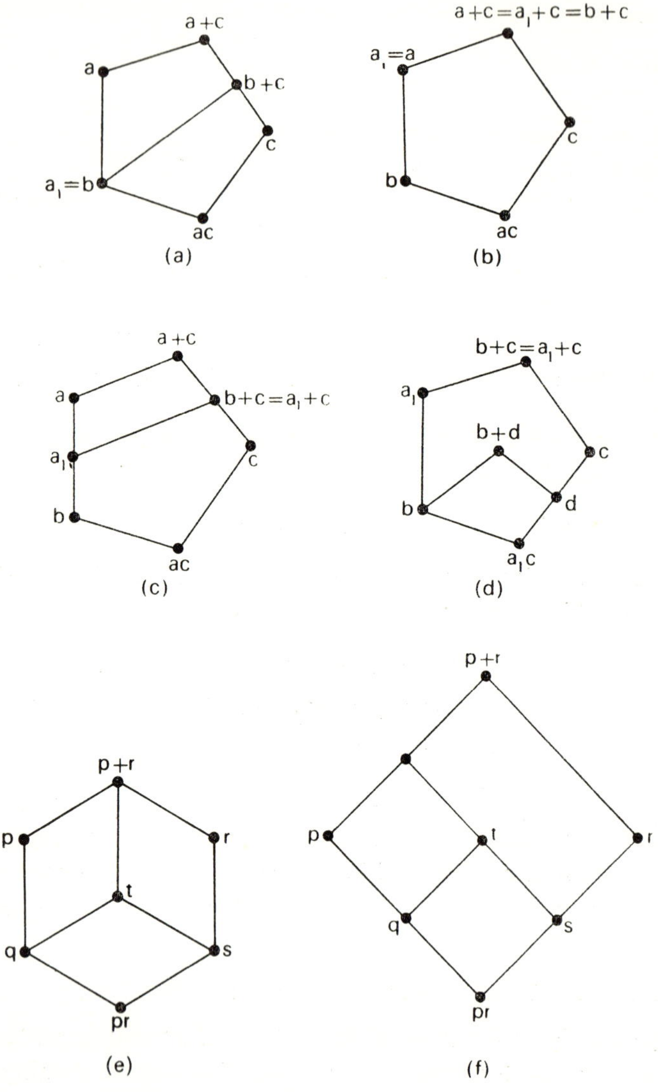
a+c
a
b+c
c
a₁=b
ac
(a)
a+c=a₁+c=b+c
a₁=a
c
b
ac
(b)
a+c
a
b+c=a₁+c
a₁
c
b
ac
(c)
b+c=a₁+c
a₁
b+d
c
b
d
a₁c
(d)
p+r
p
r
t
q
s
pr
(e)
p+r
p
t
r
q
s
pr
(f)

FIG. 33.

THEOREM 115. Every modular lattice is semi-modular.

Proof. Let L be a modular lattice. If L contains no "pentagonal" subset, VIA is satisfied vacuously and L is semi-modular. If L does contain such a subset, by Th. 87 the arrangements of Figs. 33b, 33c are ruled out, and we must have the arrangement of Fig. 33a. To satisfy VIA we take $d = c$; (3) allows this. Then by V

$$a(b + d) = a(b + c) = b + ac = b + bc = b$$

and (4) is satisfied.

Suppose now a lattice L to be non-modular. By Th. 86 L contains at least one "pentagonal" sublattice. Suppose further that a, b, c are present in L satisfying (1) and (2); the presence of these elements entails the presence of the elements

$$ac, \quad b, \quad c, \quad a, \quad a + c \quad \text{and} \quad a_1, \quad b + c$$

in one of the arrangements of Figs. 33a, 33b, 33c. If L is semi-modular, there must exist in L an element d satisfying (3) and (4). If the arrangement is that of Fig. 33a $d = c$ satisfies (3) and (4); if either of the arrangements 33b, 33c obtains, so that the elements

$$a_1c, \quad b, \quad c, \quad a_1, \quad a_1 + c$$

form a "pentagonal" sublattice, we cannot have $d = c$, for this would give $b + d = b + c$ and so $a(b + d) = a(b + c) = a_1 \neq b$, which contradicts (4). Therefore in either of these cases there is present an element d such that

$$(3')\ ac < d < c \quad \text{and} \quad (4)\ a(b + d) = b.$$

Since $a_1c = a(b + c)c = ac$ and by (4) $a_1(b + d) = a(b + c)(b + d) = b(b + c) = b$, we may rewrite the properties of d as

$$(3'')\ a_1c < d < c \quad \text{and} \quad (4')\ a_1(b + d) = b.$$

From (3″) $a_1c = (a_1c)\,d = (bc)\,d = b\,(cd) = bd$; hence b, d are distinct and incomparable (for $bd < b$, $bd < d$), and we have $b < b + d$, $d < b + d$. Since $b < b + d$, $b < a_1$, (4′) entails that a_1 and $b + d$ are incomparable; in particular $a_1 < a_1 + b + d$. From (3″) $b + d \leqq b + c$; as we have seen, equality is ruled out here so that $b + d < b + c$. If $b + d \leqq c$, then $a_1(b + d) \leqq a_1c$, which is impossible; if $c < b + d$, then $b + c \leqq b + d$; hence c and $b + d$ are incomparable. Therefore the elements d and $b + d$ must be positioned as shown in Fig. 33d. We note that

$$b + d < a_1 + b + d$$

with

$$a_1 < a_1 + b + d = a_1 + b + c = b + c$$

or with

$$a_1 < a_1 + b + d < a_1 + b + c = b + c$$

allows $b + d$ to be connected to $b + c$ in one of two ways. But the join of $b + d$ and c cannot lie between c and $b + c$, for $b + d + c = b + c$.

THEOREM 116. A non-modular lattice L is semi-modular if and only if for each "pentagonal" sublattice

$$pr < q < p < p + r$$

$$pr < r < p + r$$

occurring in L there can be found two elements s, t, distinct from one another and from the five given, situated as shown in Fig. 33e or Fig. 33f.

Proof. We have just proved the necessity of the condition; its sufficiency is obvious.

We state without proof

THEOREM 117. A non-modular lattice which is semi-modular contains at least seven elements.

Example 84. The numbers 1, 2, 3, 6, 10, 15, 30 ordered by divisibility give an example of the smallest non-modular lattice which is semi-modular; 1, 2, 15, 10, 30 form a "pentagonal" sublattice with 3 and 6 as the extra elements required; likewise 1, 3, 10, 15, 30 with 2 and 6. See Fig. 33e for a diagram.

Example 85. Let L be the interval $[(0, 1), (\omega, 3)]$ taken from the direct product of Fig. 17d, § 9 (6), with the element $(\omega, 2)$ deleted. L is not modular; indeed it contains an infinity of "pentagonal" sublattices, but VIA is satisfied in every case; for any finite $n = 0, 1, 2, \ldots$ we have a "pentagonal" sublattice

$$(n, 1) < (n, 2) < (n, 3) < (\omega, 3)$$

$$(n, 1) < (\omega, 1) < (\omega, 3)$$

and as the extra elements required by Th. 116 we may take $(n + k, 1)$ and $(n + k, 2)$ for any finite $k = 1, 2, 3, \ldots$. To give the explicit fulfilment of Postulate VIA in this instance:

In L there are elements $(n, 3)$, $(n, 2)$, $(\omega, 1)$ such that

(1) $(n, 3)$ and $(\omega, 1)$ are incomparable,

(2) $(n, 1) < (n, 2) < (n, 3)$;

and there exists in L an element $(n + 1, 1)$ such that

(3) $(n, 1) < (n + 1, 1) \leqq (\omega, 1)$,

(4) $(n, 3)\,[(n, 2) + (n + 1, 1)]$

$= (n, 3)\,(n + 1, 2)$

$= (n, 2)$.

In this example we have a multiple repetition of the situation of Fig. 33f.

THEOREM 118. The dual of a semi-modular lattice need not be semi-modular.

Proof. The dual of the lattice of Example 84 orders the same numbers by multiplicity; the numbers 30, 10, 15, 2, 1 still form a "pentagonal" sublattice but the requirements of Th. 116 are no longer met. See Fig. 34.

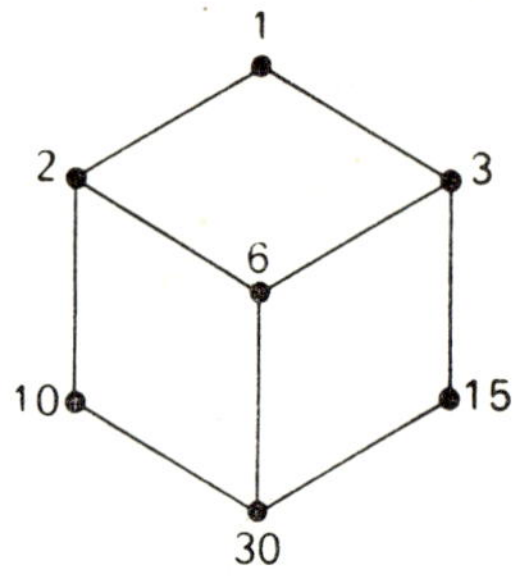

FIG. 34.

THEOREM 119. A sublattice of a semi-modular lattice need not be semi-modular.

Proof. A semi-modular lattice which is not modular contains a sublattice of five elements which is not modular; apply Th. 117.

THEOREM 120. A convex sublattice of a semi-modular lattice is semi-modular.

Proof. Let a, b, c be elements of a semi-modular lattice L which satisfy (1) and (2) of VIA; then by Def. 57 there exists in L an element d satisfying (3) and (4). In Def. 57 and our subsequent discussion at most ten elements are mentioned—the seven of Fig. 33c together with $d, b + d, a_1 + b + d$; all without exception belong to the interval $[ac, a + c]$. If a, b, c belong to a convex sublattice X of L, by Def. 38 all elements of the interval $[ac, a + c]$ belong to X; hence all elements required for the fulfilment of VIA belong to X, and X is semi-modular.

THEOREM 121. The direct product of two semi-modular lattices is semi-modular. Conversely, if the direct product of two lattices is semi-modular, so is each constituent.

Proof. Denote the elements of a lattice L by $a, b, c, \ldots$, those of a lattice M by $\alpha, \beta, \gamma, \ldots$, those of the product $L \times M$ by $A, B, C, \ldots$, where $A = (a, \alpha)$, etc. We shall give only an outline of the proof of the first part of the theorem, leaving details to the patient reader. Let L, M be semi-modular and let A, B, C be elements of $L \times M$ such that

(5) A, C are incomparable, (6) $AC < B < A$.

We must prove the existence of an element $D = (d, \delta)$ in $L \times M$ such that

(7) $AC < D \leqq C$, (8) $A(B + D) = B$.

From the discussion of Def. 57 we have in $L \times M$ seven elements

$$AC, B, C, A, A + C \quad \text{and} \quad A_1 = A(B + C), B + C,$$

disposed in one of the arrangements of Figs. 33a, 33b, 33c.

Case 33a. Take $D = C$ as before.

Case 33b. Here $A + C = B + C$ so that

$$(9)\ a + c = b + c \text{ in } L, \quad (10)\ \alpha + \gamma = \beta + \gamma \text{ in } M.$$

We remind the reader that $(b, \beta) \leqq (a, \alpha)$ entails $b \leqq a$, $\beta \leqq \alpha$; hence $(b, \beta) < (a, \alpha)$ in (6) entails

$$\text{either (i) } b < a, \quad \text{or (ii) } \beta < \alpha.$$

If (i) holds, using (9) we show that

$$(11)\ a, c \text{ are incomparable in } L, \quad (12)\ ac < b < a \text{ in } L,$$

this last emerging from the fact that in $L \times M$

$$(ac, \alpha\gamma) < (b, \alpha\gamma) < (a, \alpha\gamma).$$

Therefore there exists in L the element d of Def. 57, and $D = (d, \alpha\gamma)$ exists in $L \times M$, satisfying (7) and (8).

If (ii) holds, using (10) we are led in the same way to an element δ in M, and $D = (ac, \delta)$ is the element required.

Case 33c. Here $A_1 + C = B + C$ so that

$$a_1 + c = b + c \text{ in } L, \quad \alpha_1 + \gamma = \beta + \gamma \text{ in } M.$$

Using the first of these with $b < a_1$ we are led to $D = (d, \alpha_1\gamma)$; or using the second with $\beta < \alpha_1$, to $D = (a_1c, \delta)$.

To prove the converse, let $L \times M$ be semi-modular, and let a, b, c be elements of L such that a, c are incomparable and $ac < b < a$. For any element μ of M we have then (a, μ), (c, μ) incomparable in $L \times M$, and $(ac, \mu) < (b, \mu) < (a, \mu)$; therefore there exists (d, δ) such that

$$(ac, \mu) < (d, \delta) \leqq (c, \mu) \tag{13}$$

and

$$(a, \mu)\,[(b, \mu) + (d, \delta)] = (b, \delta). \tag{14}$$

From (13) $\mu \leqq \delta \leqq \mu$; hence $\delta = \mu$, so that (13) becomes

$$(ac, \mu) < (d, \mu) < (c, \mu) \quad \text{in } L \times M,$$

whence $ac < d < c$ in L. Also (14) reduces to $[a(b + d), \mu] = (b, \mu)$, whence $a(b + d) = b$. Therefore L is semi-modular. The proof for M is similar.

Semi-modularity need not be preserved under a homomorphism.

Example 86. Map the lattice L of Example 85 into itself as follows:

$$\text{for } x \neq \omega, \quad \text{map } (x, j) \text{ on } (0, j), \quad j = 1, 2, 3;$$
$$\text{map } (\omega, 1) \text{ on itself and } (\omega, 3) \text{ on itself.}$$

The resulting endomorphic image is a "pentagonal" lattice.

THEOREM 122. If L is a semi-modular lattice in which all chains are finite, any homomorphic image H of L is semi-modular.

Proof. Here we follow Croisot, but our theorem is not as general as his. Let H be the image of L under a homomorphism θ; let α, β, γ be elements of H satisfying (1) and (2) of VIA; we must prove the existence in H of an element δ satisfying (3) and (4) of the same. Let X denote the set of all elements of L mapped under θ on $\alpha\gamma$. X is not empty by Def. 46 and is a partially ordered set with the ordering of L; hence X contains at least one maximal finite chain K; being finite, K has a greatest element e, which is maximal in X. For x in X we have $\theta(x) = \alpha\gamma$, and $x \not> e$; it follows that $x \leqq e$, for if x were incomparable with e we should have

$$e < e + x \quad \text{and} \quad \theta(e + x) = \theta(e) + \theta(x) = \alpha\gamma + \alpha\gamma = \alpha\gamma$$

which would entail $e + x$ in X and hence e not maximal in X. Then $x \leqq e$, and e is not only a maximal but the greatest element of X. Now $\alpha\gamma < \beta, \alpha\gamma < \gamma$ in H and $\theta(e) = \alpha\gamma$; consequently by the dual to Th. 82 there exist in L elements b and c such that

$$\theta(b) = \beta, \quad \theta(c) = \gamma, \quad \text{and} \quad e < b, \quad e < c;$$

hence $e \leqq bc$; but $\theta(bc) = \theta(b)\,\theta(c) = \beta\gamma = \alpha\gamma$ so that bc is in X and therefore $bc = e$. Again, $\beta < \alpha$ in H and $\theta(b) = \beta$ entail by the same dual theorem that there exists in L an element a such that $\theta(a) = \alpha$ and $b < a$. Hence $bc \leqq ac$; also, since $\theta(ac) = \theta(a)\,\theta(c) = \alpha\gamma$, ac belongs to X, $ac \leqq e = bc$, and hence $ac = bc$. Thus we have elements a, b, c in L such that $ac < b < a$, $ac < c$ and therefore a, c incomparable. L being semi-modular, by VIA there exists an element d in L such that $ac < d \leqq c$, $a(b + d) = b$. Let $\theta(d) = \delta$. Then in H we have $\alpha\gamma \leqq \delta \leqq \gamma$; from $\alpha\gamma = \delta$ would follow d in X and $d \leqq e = ac$; hence $\alpha\gamma < \delta \leqq \gamma$. Finally, in H

$$\alpha(\beta + \delta) = \theta(a)\,[\theta(b) + \theta(d)] = \theta(a)\,\theta(b + d)$$
$$= \theta[a(b + d)] = \theta(b) = \beta;$$

therefore H is semi-modular.

Theorem 118 shows that VIA is not self-dual. We therefore lay down

Definition 58. A lattice L is said to be dually semi-modular if and only if the following postulate is satisfied:

Postulate VIB. If a, b, c are any three elements of L such that

(1) a and c are incomparable,

(2) $a < b < a + c$,

then there exists in L an element d such that

$$(3)\ c \leqq d < a + c,$$

$$(4)\ a + bd = b.$$

Note that theorems corresponding to all results obtained in this section may be proved for dually semi-modular lattices; in particular all modular lattices are dually semi-modular.

THEOREM 123. V $\Longrightarrow$ VIA & VIB but not conversely.

Proof. The first part is proved by Th. 116 and its dual. To prove the second part consider this example. Form the direct product $J_\omega \times J_\omega$ where J_ω is the augmented chain of the integers

$$-\omega < \cdots < -1 < 0 < 1 < \cdots < \omega$$

of Fig. 14 (Example 40), and delete the elements $(-\omega, 0)$ and $(\omega, 1)$. This lattice satisfies VIA and VIB but not V. It is significant that this lattice contains infinite terminated chains.

Exercises

115. Prove the lattices of Figs. 11b (§ 9), 13d (§ 9), 23 (§ 12) semi-modular but not modular.
116. Complete the proof of Th. 121.
117. Show that if the element $(\omega, 2)$ is reinstated in the lattice of Example 85 the lattice remains semi-modular.

22. Length and Covering Conditions

The main purpose of Postulate VIA is to ensure that though a semi-modular lattice may contain a "pentagonal" sublattice, yet elements will be present in the lattice to guarantee the satisfaction of C1 and so of C3.

THEOREM 124. VIA $\Longrightarrow$ C1 $\Longrightarrow$ C3.

THEOREM 125. VIB $\Longrightarrow$ C2 $\Longrightarrow$ C4.

Proof (Th. 124). Since C1 holds everywhere for comparable elements, we have to prove that if b, c are incomparable elements of a semi-modular lattice L and c covers bc, then $b + c$ covers b. Suppose that b, c are such elements and that c covers bc, but that $b + c$ does not cover b; then there exists a in L such that

$$b + c > a > b. \tag{1}$$

Then

$$b + c \geqq a + c \geqq b + c \quad \text{so that} \quad a + c = b + c. \tag{2}$$

Also from (1)

$$c = c(b + c) \geqq ac \geqq bc.$$

Since c covers bc, either

$$c = ac \quad \text{and} \quad ac > bc$$

or

$$c > ac \quad \text{and} \quad ac = bc. \tag{3}$$

If $c = ac$, from (2) $b + c = a + c = a$, which contradicts (1). Therefore (3) holds.

If $c = a + c$, from (2) $c = b + c$, but b, c are incomparable. Therefore a, c are incomparable, since

$$ac < c < a + c. \tag{4}$$

Since b, c are incomparable, $bc < b$, which with (1) and (3) gives

$$ac < b < a. \tag{5}$$

Since L is semi-modular, (4) and (5) entail the existence in L of an element d such that

$$ac < d \leqq c, \tag{6}$$

$$a(b + d) = b. \tag{7}$$

Since c covers bc and from (3) $bc = ac$, we must have in (6) $d = c$. Then (7) becomes

$$a(b + c) = b.$$

But from (2)

$$a(b + c) = a > b.$$

In view of this contradiction $b + c$ must cover b. Theorem 46 completes the proof.

In lattices in which all terminated chains are finite we may now prove the converse to Th. 123.

THEOREM 126. VIA & VIB $\xrightarrow{f}$ V.

Proof. By Ths. 124 and 125 VIA & VIB $\Longrightarrow$ C3 & C4; then by Ths. 54 and 97.

In the same restricted class of lattices we can prove

THEOREM 127. C1 $\xrightarrow{f}$ VIA.

THEOREM 128. C2 $\xrightarrow{f}$ VIB.

Proof (Th. 127). Let L be a lattice in which all terminated chains are finite and in which C1 is satisfied. We remark that in any lattice $a > b$ implies $a(b + d) \geqq ab = b$. Suppose L not semi-modular but with elements a, b, c such that a, c are incomparable and

$$ac < b < a; \tag{8}$$

then for all d such that

$$ac < d \leqq c \tag{9}$$

we cannot have $a(b + d) = b$ and therefore must have

$$a(b + d) > b.$$

From (9) $c > ac$; hence there is at least one finite chain connecting c to ac; descending this chain we must arrive at an element d_1 covering ac and such that

$$ac < d_1 \leqq c, \tag{10}$$

$$a(b + d_1) > b. \tag{11}$$

From (8) and (10) $ac = bac = bc \geqq bd_1 \geqq bac = ac$; hence $ac = bd_1$. Thus d_1 covers bd_1 and therefore by C1 $b + d_1$ covers b. Now from (11)

$$b + d_1 \geqq a(b + d_1) > b;$$

hence $b + d_1 = a(b + d_1)$; it follows that

$$d_1 = d_1 c \leqq (b + d_1)c = a(b + d_1)c \leqq ac,$$

which contradicts (10). Therefore L is semi-modular.

Combining the results of this and the previous sections with those of §§ 12 and 17 we have the following scheme of implication:

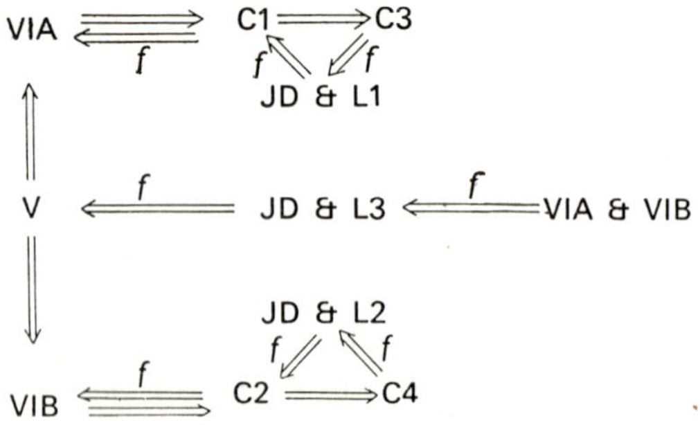

Exercises

118. Let L be a semi-modular lattice of finite length; let $p_1, \ldots, p_n$ be a set of atoms of L such that no one of these is contained in the join of any selection of the others. If $p_1, \ldots, p_k$ is a selection of k of these atoms, show that the element $p_1 + \cdots + p_k$ is of height k.
119. Prove that a lattice of finite length in which every element has a unique representation as meet of meet-irreducible elements without redundancy is semi-modular.

23. Complements and Atoms

In the last chapter we saw that a complemented modular lattice is necessarily relatively complemented; this theorem does not hold for complemented semi-modular lattices, as witness the lattice of Fig. 23, § 12.

Theorem 113 of § 19 stated that in a relatively complemented lattice of finite length ($\geqq 1$) the unity element u and every other non-zero element can be represented as join of a finite number of atoms. The full converse that if in a lattice of finite length ($\geqq 1$) every non-zero element can be represented as join of a finite subset of atoms, then the lattice is relatively complemented (every interval complemented) is not generally true; nor is the partial converse that if u is join of a finite subset of atoms, then the lattice is complemented (the one interval $[o, u]$ complemented). Counter-examples will be exhibited at the end of this section. However, in the case of semi-modular lattices of finite length—sometimes called "Birkhoff" lattices—both the weak and the strong converse theorems hold.

THEOREM 129. A semi-modular lattice L of finite length in which the unity element u is join of a finite subset of atoms is complemented.

Proof. Let $u = p_1 + \cdots + p_n$, the p_i being atoms of L. In any lattice with o, u each of these elements is complement of the other.

If L contains elements other than these, let x be any element such that

$$o < x < u.$$

If x contained p_i for every i, we should have

$$u = p_1 + \cdots + p_n \leqq x;$$

therefore there must be at least one atom among the p_i which is not contained in x; designate such an atom as q_1 so that

$$q_1 \nleqq x \quad \text{and} \quad q_1 \text{ covers } o.$$

If $xq_1 = q_1$, $q_1 \leqq x$; hence $xq_1 < q_1$; but q_1 is an atom so that

$$xq_1 = o \quad \text{and} \quad q_1 \text{ covers } xq_1.$$

Hence by C1 $x + q_1$ covers x. If $x + q_1$ contains p_i for every i, then as above $x + q_1 = u$; otherwise among the p_i there exists an atom not contained in $x + q_1$; designate this atom as q_2. Obviously $q_2 \neq q_1$. As above, we show that q_2 covers $(x + q_1)\, q_2 = o$ and hence that $x + q_1 + q_2$ covers $x + q_1$. Proceeding in this manner, we build up a chain

$$x < x + q_1 < x + q_1 + q_2 < \cdots,$$

where each element is covered by its successor. Since L is of finite length, we must eventually arrive at u through the maximal chain

$$x < x + q_1 < \cdots < x + q_1 + \cdots + q_k = u$$

where $1 \leqq k \leqq n$. By JD

$$h(u) = h(x) + k. \tag{1}$$

Now consider the chain

$$o < q_1 \leqq q_1 + q_2 \leqq \cdots \leqq q_1 + \cdots + q_k. \tag{2}$$

If q_r were contained in $q_1 + \cdots + q_{r-1}$, it would also be contained in $x + q_1 + \cdots + q_{r-1}$, which is impossible in view of the manner of designation of q_r, so that $q_r \nleqq q_1 + \cdots + q_{r-1}$. Hence

$$q_r(q_1 + \cdots + q_{r-1}) < q_r;$$

but q_r is an atom; hence q_r covers $q_r(q_1 + \cdots + q_{r-1}) = o$; it follows by C1 that $q_1 + \cdots + q_r$ covers $q_1 + \cdots + q_{r-1}$, and the chain (2) is maximal.

Let $y = q_1 + \cdots + q_k$; then by JD

$$h(y) = k. \tag{3}$$

We have

$$x + y = x + q_1 + \cdots + q_k = u.$$

By L1

$$l[xy, x] \geqq l[y, x + y] = l[y, u],$$

that is,

$$\begin{aligned} h(x) - h(xy) &\geqq h(u) - h(y) \\ &= h(x) + k - k \qquad \text{from (1), (3)} \\ &= h(x). \end{aligned}$$

It follows that $h(xy) = 0$ and hence $xy = o$.

Thus for any x, $o < x < u$, there exists a complement y, and the theorem is proved.

THEOREM 130. A semi-modular lattice L of finite length in which every non-zero element is join of a finite subset of atoms is relatively complemented.

Proof. Let $[a, b]$ be any interval of L where $a < b$. Let

$$b = a + b = p_1 + \cdots + p_k,$$

where the p_i are atoms of L. Then

$$b = (a + p_1) + (a + p_2) + \cdots + (a + p_k). \tag{4}$$

If $p_i \leqq a$, $a + p_i = a$. If $p_i \nleqq a$, then $ap_i \neq p_i$, and $p_i > ap_i = o$; hence p_i covers ap_i so that by C1 $a + p_i$ covers a. If $a + p_i = a$ for every i, then (4) gives $b = a$; but $b > a$; hence some $a + p_i$ must cover a. Thus discarding otiose terms from (4) we are left with a representation of b as join of a finite number of elements which cover a. The interval $[a, b]$ is a convex sublattice of L and therefore by Th. 120 semi-modular; L being of finite length, $[a, b]$ cannot be otherwise; hence by the last theorem $[a, b]$ is complemented. Thus in L every interval is complemented.

Example 87. We illustrate the various possibilities touched on in this section by comparing six finite lattices previously encountered. All are non-modular.

Fig. no. of lattice	34	33b	30	33e	23	11b
Semi-modular	no	no	no	yes	yes	yes
Complemented	no	yes	yes	no	yes	yes
u = join of atoms	yes	yes	yes	no	yes	yes
Rel. complemented	no	no	yes	no	no	yes
x = join of atoms	yes	no	yes	no	no	yes

Exercises

120. Check the thirty assertions made in the table of Example 87. (For small finite lattices the quickest check on semi-modularity is C3; to test for relative complements look for three-element intervals.)
121. By adding an extra atom to Fig. 34 make the lattice complemented but still not relatively so. Add an extra element to Fig. 33b so that the return becomes "no" on all counts.

24. Partitions

The lattices of partitions or equivalence relations of a finite set S of n objects described in §§ 4 and 9 provide excellent examples of semi-modular lattices. We recall that if X and Y are partitions of S, $X \leqq Y$ means that X is a refinement of Y, each block of X being wholly contained in some block of Y; if E_X and E_Y are the corresponding equivalence relations, $E_X \leqq E_Y$ means that E_X implies E_Y, that is to say, if a, b are objects of S and aE_Xb, then aE_Yb; in view of the exact correspondence we shall simplify the notation and write aXb for aE_Xb, and the isomorphic lattices of partitions and relations for a set of n objects will both be denoted by $\Pi(n)$.

In Example 71 it was pointed out that for $n = 1, 2, 3$ $\Pi(n)$ is modular; we now prove that for $n \geqq 4$, $\Pi(n)$ is semi-modular but not modular.

Proof. Since $\Pi(n)$ is finite, it will suffice to show that C3 is satisfied but that for $n \geqq 4$ C4 is not. (See the scheme of implication at the end of § 22.) A partition X covers a partition Z if and only if one block of X is set-union of two blocks of Z whilst the remaining blocks of X coincide exactly with the remaining blocks of Z; for instance, in $\Pi(5)$ $(abc/d/e)$ covers $(ab/c/d/e)$, $(bc/a/d/e)$ and $(ac/b/d/e)$. Let X, Y be incomparable partitions of $\Pi(n)$, both covering their meet XY. Let XY consist of the blocks $A/B/C/D/ \cdots /K$. Since for $n < 4$ $\Pi(n)$ has been proved modular, we may ignore the cases where our hypotheses cannot be fulfilled. Then X, Y must have at least two blocks each and hence XY must have at least three. Suppose XY has just three blocks, being of the form $A/B/C$, and let X (which covers XY) be of the form $A + B/C$; then since Y is incomparable with X and covers XY, Y must be $A/B + C$. The join $X + Y$ is consequently the unity partition $A + B + C$, which covers each of the dual atoms X and Y, and C3 is satisfied. Now let XY contain at least four blocks A, B, C, D and let X be $A + B/C/D/ \cdots /K$. Then Y must take one of the forms

$$\text{(i) } A/B + C/D/ \cdots /K, \quad \text{(ii) } A/B/C + D/ \cdots /K.$$

In case (i) the join $X + Y$ is $A + B + C/D/ \cdots /K$;
in case (ii) the join $X + Y$ is $A + B/C + D/ \cdots /K$.
In either case $X + Y$ covers X and Y so that C3 is satisfied.

On the other hand, C4 is not satisfied if $n \geqq 4$. For then there exists in the lattice at least one partition T of the form

$$A + B + C + D/E/ \cdots /K$$

where none of A, B, C, D are empty sets. T covers

$$V \text{ of the form } A + B/C + D/E/ \cdots /K,$$
$$W \text{ of the form } A + C/B + D/E/ \cdots /K;$$

hence $T = V + W$ covers V and W. But VW is of the form

$$A/B/C/D/E/ \cdots /K,$$

which is covered by neither V nor W. Hence for $n \geqq 4$ C4 does not hold.

Next we proceed to prove $\Pi(n)$ relatively complemented.

Proof. Let X be any non-zero partition of a set S of n objects, $n > 1$. Let R be the set-union of all blocks of X which contain two or more objects; R is not empty, for X is non-zero and contains at least one such block. From R (which is, of course, finite) take all possible two-object sets, say $A_1, \ldots, A_k$; convert each A_j into an atom of the lattice by adjoining the $n - 2$ objects not in A_j as single-object blocks, denoting each atomic partition so formed by Y_j. Then

$$X = Y_1 + \cdots + Y_k$$

where the Y_j are atoms; $\Pi(n)$ being finite, Th. 130 applies, and the lattice is relatively complemented.

As an example of the construction above take

$$X = (abc/d/e) \text{ in } \Pi(5); \quad R = \{a, b, c\}, \quad Y_1 = (ab/c/d/e),$$

$$Y_2 = (ac/b/d/e), \quad Y_3 = (bc/a/d/e), \quad \text{and} \quad X = Y_1 + Y_2 + Y_3.$$

In § 4 we defined join $P + Q$ of equivalence relations P, Q over a finite set S as meet of all equivalence relations over S which contain both P and Q. We take up now the suggestion of Exercise 27 regarding an alternative definition. Let R be the dyadic relation: for a, b in S aRb if and only if there exists a finite sequence $x_1, \ldots, x_{2n-1}$ in S such that alternately

$$aPx_1, \quad x_1Qx_2, \ldots, \quad x_{2n-1}Qb.$$

Since aPa, aQa for all a in S, R is over S and reflexive. If aRb, the sequence of x_i in reverse and the symmetry of P, Q give

$$bQx_{2n-1}, \ldots, \quad x_1Pa,$$

which with bPb in front and aQa behind gives bRa. If aRb with sequence x_i and bRc with sequence y_j, then the x_i followed by the y_j will clearly give aRc. Thus R is an equivalence relation (Def. 6). From $P \leqq P + Q$, $Q \leqq P + Q$ we have

$$aPx_1 \text{ implies } aP + Qx_1,$$

$$x_1Qx_2 \text{ implies } x_1P + Qx_2, \text{ etc.,}$$

so that

$$aRb \text{ implies } aP + Qb; \text{ hence } R \leqq P + Q.$$

If aPb, then aPb, bQb give aRb, so that $P \leqq R$; similarly we can prove that $Q \leqq R$. Hence $P + Q \leqq R$. Therefore $R = P + Q$.

We end this section with a theorem about lattices susceptible of extensive generalization.

THEOREM 131. The congruence relations over a finite lattice L of n elements constitute a sublattice of the lattice $\Pi(n)$ of all equivalence relations over L.

Proof. The set of congruence relations over L is not empty, for the zero partition puts every element of L in a class by itself, the unity partition lumps all elements together, and these partitions clearly give rise to congruence relations rightly termed trivial. Let P, Q be congruence relations over L with meet PQ and join $P + Q$ in $\Pi(n)$.

If $aPQb$, $cPQd$, then aPb, aQb, cPd, cQd; from the first and third of these equivalences we have $acPbd$, from the second and fourth $acQbd$; hence $acPQbd$. Therefore PQ is a congruence relation with respect to meets in L. The proof for joins is the same.

If $aP + Qb$, $cP + Qd$, then there exist sequences x_i, y_j in L such that

$$aPx_1, \ldots, x_{2n-1}Qb,$$

$$cPy_1, \ldots, y_{2m-1}Qd;$$

if $n = m$, these trains of equivalences are of the same length; if $n < m$, fill out in the obvious way with $b = x_{2n} = \cdots = x_{2m-1}$; if $n > m$, with $d = y_{2m} = \cdots = y_{2n-1}$. Thus we obtain

$$aPx_1, \ldots, \quad x_{r-1}Px_r, \ldots, \quad x_{s-1}Qx_s, \ldots, \quad x_tQb,$$

$$cPy_1, \ldots, \quad y_{r-1}Py_r, \ldots, \quad y_{s-1}Qy_s, \ldots, \quad y_tQd$$

where $t = \max(2n - 1, 2m - 1)$. P and Q being congruence relations, we have

$$acPx_1y_1, \ldots, \quad x_ty_tQbd.$$

Hence $acP + Qbd$, and $P + Q$ is a congruence relation with respect to meets in L. The proof for joins is the same. Therefore meet PQ and join $P + Q$ of congruence relations P, Q are themselves congruence relations, and the theorem is proved.

Exercises

122. Show that in $\Pi(n)$ complements of partitions other than zero and unity are not unique.
123. (i) In $\Pi(n)$ show that the partitions contained by a singular dual atom constitute an ideal isomorphic with $\Pi\ (n - 1)$.
(ii) In $\Pi(5)$ show that the partitions contained by a non-singular dual atom constitute an ideal isomorphic with Fig. 29.
124. Interpret $\Pi(4)$ geometrically, calling atoms points, the joins of points lines, and so on. Show that this interpretation gives a complete plane quadrilateral of 6 points and 7 lines—4 "sides" each containing 3 points and 3 "diagonals" each containing 2 points. In the figure find a set T of 4 triangles such that each point belongs to just 2 triangles in T; determine a lattice isomorphism between the partitions of T and the points, lines and plane of the figure.
125. Interpret $\Pi(5)$ as in the last exercise. Show that this geometrical interpretation gives a three-dimensional figure of 10 points, 25 lines (10 lines containing 3 points each, 15 lines containing 2 points each), 15 planes (5 planes with 6 points each, 10 planes with 4 points each). Show that if we ignore items corresponding to the non-singular partitions we have 10 pairs of perspective triangles, that is, so situated that joins of vertices are concurrent, meets of sides collinear—this is Desargues' configuration, of importance in projective geometry. Determine a set T of 5 tetrahedra such that each of the 10 points belongs to just 2 of these tetrahedra, and obtain a lattice isomorphism between the partitions of T and the points, lines, planes and solid of the original figure. See Fig. 37 (p. 280).
126. With the geometrical interpretation of the last exercise re-examine Exercise 123 (taking $n = 5$ in (i)).
127. (This exercise requires a little familiarity with group theory.) Show that to each subgroup H of a finite group G of n elements there corresponds a partition of $\Pi(n)$. (*Hint:* consider the coset xH for each x in G.) Hence show that the lattice of subgroups of G ordered by set-inclusion is isomorphic with a sublattice of $\Pi(n)$. Show that the congruence relations over G correspond to the normal subgroups of G. Exemplify with the additive group G of Example 83; prove that the lattice of congruence relations over this group G is not isomorphic with the lattice of congruence relations over the lattice B of the same example.

CHAPTER 6

DISTRIBUTIVE LATTICES

25. Distributivity

Though lattices, of a specialized sort, appear in inchoate form in the work of Boole (1847), they were first effectively distinguished as algebraic systems by Ernst Schröder in his monumental treatise on the algebra of logic (Volume I, 1890); he dealt particularly with the lattices we now call distributive.

Definition 59. A lattice is said to be distributive if and only if it satisfies the following postulate:

Postulate VII. For any elements a, b, c in the lattice

$$a(b + c) = ab + ac.$$

Example 88. The lattice of subsets of a set ordered by set-inclusion is distributive. See formula (3) of § 1.

Example 89. All chains are distributive. Formula (7) of § 2 was proved in view of this assertion. The proofs in § 2 refer specifically to the chain of the natural numbers in their usual order of succession, but apply unaltered to chains in general.

Example 90. The complete factorization lattices of § 9 are distributive, in view of formula (11) of § 2.

It follows from Def. 59 and the associativity discussed in § 11 that for elements of a distributive lattice

$$\begin{aligned} a(b_1 + \cdots + b_n) &= ab_1 + a(b_2 + \cdots + b_n) \\ &= ab_1 + ab_2 + a(b_3 + \cdots + b_n) \\ &= ab_1 + \cdots + ab_n \quad \text{after } n - 1 \text{ steps.} \end{aligned}$$

Formulae (4) of § 1, (8) and (12) of § 2 show that the dual of VII holds good in the three examples cited; in the general case we have

THEOREM 132. In a distributive lattice, for any a, b, c

$$a + bc = (a + b)(a + c).$$

Proof

$$\begin{aligned} (a + b)(a + c) &= (a + b)a + (a + b)c \\ &= a + (ac + bc) \\ &= (a + ac) + bc \\ &= a + bc. \end{aligned}$$

THEOREM 133. If in a lattice for any a, b, c

$$a + bc = (a + b)(a + c),$$

the lattice is distributive.

Proof

$$\begin{aligned} ab + ac &= (ab + a)(ab + c) \\ &= a(ab + c) \\ &= a(a + c)(b + c) \\ &= a(b + c). \end{aligned}$$

These theorems show that VII implies its dual and is implied by its dual. Consequently

THEOREM 134. The dual of a distributive lattice is distributive.

The dual distributive formula can be extended thus: for elements of a distributive lattice

$$\begin{aligned} a + b_1 \cdots b_n &= (a + b_1)(a + b_2 \cdots b_n) \\ &= (a + b_1)(a + b_2)(a + b_3 \cdots b_n) \\ &= (a + b_1) \cdots (a + b_n) \quad \text{after } n - 1 \text{ steps.} \end{aligned}$$

THEOREM 135. In a distributive lattice, for any a, b, c

$$(a + b)(b + c)(c + a) = ab + bc + ca.$$

Proof.

$$\begin{aligned} (a + b)(b + c)(c + a) &= a(b + c)(c + a) + b(b + c)(c + a) \\ &= a(b + c) + b(c + a) \\ &= ab + ac + bc + ba \\ &= ab + bc + ca. \end{aligned}$$

THEOREM 136. If in a lattice for any a, b, c

$$(a + b)(b + c)(c + a) = ab + bc + ca,$$

the lattice is distributive.

Proof. We begin by proving the lattice modular. Let p, q, r be elements of the lattice with $q \geqq p$. Then $p = pq$, $q = p + q$ so that

$$\begin{aligned} q(r + p) &= q(q + r)(r + p) \\ &= (p + q)(q + r)(r + p) \\ &= pq + qr + rp \qquad \text{by hypothesis} \\ &= p + qr + rp \\ &= p + qr. \end{aligned}$$

To prove the lattice distributive:

$$\begin{aligned} a(b + c) &= a(a + b)\,a(c + a)(b + c) \\ &= a(a + b)(b + c)(c + a) \\ &= a(ab + bc + ca) \qquad \text{by hypothesis} \\ &= a[bc + (ab + ca)]. \end{aligned}$$

From $a \geqq ab$, $a \geqq ca$ we have $a \geqq ab + ca$; hence by the modular formula just proved

$$\begin{aligned} a(b + c) &= (ab + ca) + a(bc) \\ &= ab + ca + (ca)\,b \\ &= ab + ac. \end{aligned}$$

THEOREM 137. Every sublattice of a distributive lattice is distributive.

Proof. For any elements a, b, c of a sublattice of a distributive lattice, the elements $b + c$, ab, ac and consequently $a(b + c)$, $ab + ac$ belong to the sublattice, so that VII is met within the sublattice.

THEORFM 138. A distributive lattice cannot contain a sublattice isomorphic with the "pentagonal" lattice nor with the five-element partition lattice $\Pi(3)$.

Proof. Neither "pentagonal" nor partition lattice is distributive.

THEOREM 139. A modular lattice is non-distributive if and only if it contains a sublattice isomorphic with $\Pi(3)$.

Proof. The condition is clearly sufficient, by the last theorem. To prove the necessity of the condition, let L be a lattice which is modular but not distributive. Then by Th. 135 there must exist in L at least one set of elements a, b, c such that

$$(a + b)(b + c)(c + a) \neq ab + bc + ca.$$

By Th. 43 in any lattice

$$(a + b)(b + c)(c + a) \geqq ab + bc + ca;$$

therefore we must have in L

$$(a + b)(b + c)(c + a) > ab + bc + ca.$$

Let $p = (a + b)(b + c)(c + a)$ and $q = ab + bc + ca$ so that $p > q$. Consider the elements r, s, t of L where

$r = (b + c)(a + bc) = a(b + c) + bc$ (by V, for $b + c \geqq bc$),

$s = (c + a)(b + ca) = b(c + a) + ca$ (similarly by V),

$t = (a + b)(c + ab) = c(a + b) + ab$ (similarly by V).

From $ab + bc \leqq a(b + c) + bc$ and $ca \leqq (b + c)a \leqq a(b + c) + bc$ we have

$$q \leqq r;$$

from $(b + c)(a + bc) \leqq (b + c)(a + b)$ and $(b + c)(a + bc) \leqq (b + c)(a + c)$ we have

$$r \leqq p.$$

Similar considerations apply to s, t; thus we have

$$q \leqq r \leqq p, \quad q \leqq s \leqq p, \quad q \leqq t \leqq p.$$

From $a + bc \leqq a + c$ follows $(a + bc)(a + c) = a + bc$;
from $b + ca \leqq b + c$ follows $(b + ca)(b + c) = b + ca$;

hence

$$\begin{aligned} rs &= (b + c)(a + bc)(c + a)(b + ca) \\ &= (a + bc)(b + ca) \\ &= (a + bc)b + ca && \text{(by V, for } a + bc \geqq a \geqq ca) \\ &= ab + bc + ca && \text{(by V, for } b \geqq bc) \\ &= q. \end{aligned}$$

A precisely dual argument yields

$$r + s = p.$$

Since $rs = q < p = r + s$, r and s must be distinct. Symmetry gives similar results for s, t and for t, r; therefore we have

$$rs = st = tr = q < p = r + s = s + t = t + r \qquad (1)$$

with

$$r, s, t \text{ all distinct.} \qquad (2)$$

If $r = p$, then $q = rs = ps = s$, $q = tr = tp = t$, but $s \neq t$; if $r = q$, then $p = r + s = q + s = s$, $p = t + r = t + q = t$, which again contradicts $s \neq t$; thus

$$q < r < p;$$

by symmetry

$$q < s < p$$

and

$$q < t < p.$$

These results with (1) and (2) give five distinct elements p, q, r, s, t in L forming a sublattice isomorphic with $\Pi(3)$.

We may now assert

THEOREM 140. A lattice is distributive if and only if it does not contain a sublattice isomorphic with the "pentagonal" lattice or with the five-element partition lattice $\Pi(3)$.

Proof. Theorem 138 shows the necessity of the condition; its sufficiency is proved by Th. 87, which ensures the lattice is modular, and Th. 139, which then ensures distributivity.

THEOREM 141. Every distributive lattice is modular, semi-modular and dually semi-modular.

Proof. By Ths. 140 and 87; then by Th. 115 and its dual.

THEOREM 142. A lattice is distributive if and only if for elements a, b, c the two equations

$$ac = bc, \quad a + c = b + c$$

jointly imply

$$a = b.$$

Proof. Suppose the lattice distributive and that the two equations hold. Then

$$a = a(a + c) = a(b + c) = ab + ac = ab + bc = b(a + c)$$
$$= b(b + c) = b.$$

On the other hand, suppose that in a lattice L the joint implication holds. Since the implication holds for all a, b, c, it holds for a, b, c with $a \geqq b$; therefore by Th. 88 L is modular. With the notation of Th. 139, if L were not distributive, L would contain the sublattice p, q, r, s, t with $rt = st$, $r + t = s + t$, but $r \neq s$; therefore L must be distributive.

THEOREM 143. The direct product $L \times M$ of distributive lattices L, M is distributive. Conversely, if a product $L \times M$ is distributive, so is each constituent.

Proof. Let L have elements $a, b, c, \ldots$, and M elements $\alpha, \beta, \gamma, \ldots$. If L, M are distributive, then

$$\begin{aligned}(a, \alpha)[(b, \beta) + (c, \gamma)] &= (a, \alpha)(b + c, \beta + \gamma) \\ &= [a(b + c), \alpha(\beta + \gamma)] \\ &= (ab + ac, \alpha\beta + \alpha\gamma) \\ &= (ab, \alpha\beta) + (ac, \alpha\gamma) \\ &= (a, \alpha)(b, \beta) + (a, \alpha)(c, \gamma).\end{aligned}$$

Conversely, if $L \times M$ is distributive, then

$$(a, \alpha)\,[(b, \beta) + (c, \gamma)] = (a, \alpha)\,(b, \beta) + (a, \alpha)\,(c, \gamma),$$

that is,

$$[a\,(b + c), \alpha\,(\beta + \gamma)] = (ab + ac, \alpha\beta + \alpha\gamma).$$

Hence $a\,(b + c) = ab + ac$ in L and $\alpha\,(\beta + \gamma) = \alpha\beta + \alpha\gamma$ in M, so that L, M are distributive.

Example 91. The lattice $N \times N$, where N is the chain of the natural numbers, is distributive. This lattice was introduced as Example 3 in § 3; equations (15) and (16) are, of course, the distributive and dual distributive formulae.

The theorem can obviously be extended to a product of any finite number of lattices; note particularly that the product of a finite number of chains is distributive.

THEOREM 144. Any homomorphic image H of a distributive lattice L is itself distributive.

Proof. Let α, β, γ be any elements of the image H of L under a homomorphism θ. Then there exists at least one set of elements a, b, c in L such that $\theta(a) = \alpha$, $\theta(b) = \beta$, $\theta(c) = \gamma$. It follows that

$$\begin{aligned}
\alpha\,(\beta + \gamma) &= \theta(a)\,[\theta(b) + \theta(c)] \\
&= \theta(a)\,\theta\,(b + c) \\
&= \theta\,[a\,(b + c)] \\
&= \theta\,(ab + ac) \qquad \text{by VII in } L \\
&= \theta\,(ab) + \theta\,(ac) \\
&= \theta(a)\,\theta(b) + \theta(a)\,\theta(c) \\
&= \alpha\beta + a\gamma.
\end{aligned}$$

Therefore H is distributive.

We end this section with a remark about length and covering conditions.

THEOREM 145. In any distributive lattice C1–C4 are satisfied; if in the lattice all terminated chains are finite, then JD and L3 are satisfied.

Proof. By Ths. 141, 92–95, and for the second part Th. 96.

Exercises

128. Let

$$\bigvee a_r = a_1 + \cdots + a_m, \quad \bigvee b_s = b_1 + \cdots + b_n,$$

$$\bigwedge a_r = a_1 \cdots a_m, \qquad \bigwedge b_s = b_1 \cdots b_n,$$

where the a_r, b_s are elements of a distributive lattice. Prove that

$$\bigwedge a_r + \bigwedge b_s = \bigwedge (a_r + b_s),$$

$$(\bigvee a_r)(\bigvee b_s) = \bigvee (a_r b_s),$$

the right-hand meet and join being taken over all r, s.

129. (After E. Pitcher and M. F. Smiley.) Show that a lattice L is distributive if and only if for every set of elements a, b, c in L the inequalities

$$ac \leqq b \leqq a + c$$

imply that

$$ab + bc = b = (a + b)(b + c).$$

130. Classify the fifteen abstract lattices with six elements as semi-modular, modular, distributive or none of these.

131. Construct the lattice L of the twenty-seven factors of the number 900 ordered by divisibility. Determine the smallest sublattice D of L which contains the numbers 12, 45, 50 and show that D may be represented by Fig. 35.

(The lattice shown in this diagram is called "the free distributive lattice generated by three elements".)

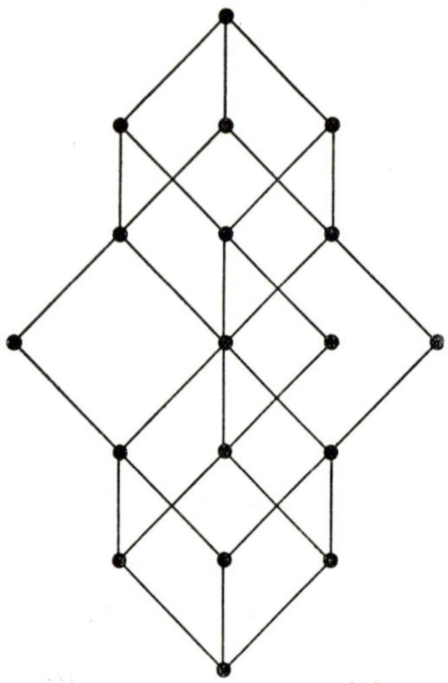

FIG. 35.

26. Irreducible Elements

The Kurosh–Ore Theorem (Th. 106) stated that if an element of a modular lattice has two irredundant representations as join (or dually as meet) of irreducibles, the same number of irreducibles appears in both; for a distributive lattice we have the stronger theorem that the same irreducibles appear in both. This classical result was published by Birkhoff in 1937.

THEOREM 146. If an element of a distributive lattice can be represented as the join without redundancy of a finite set of join-irreducibles, the representation is unique.

Proof. Let a be an element of a distributive lattice L, and let $p_1, \ldots, p_m$ and $q_1, \ldots, q_n$ be two sets of join-irreducible elements such that

$$a = p_1 + \cdots + p_m = q_1 + \cdots + q_n$$

where neither join has redundant components. By Th. 141 L is modular; hence by Th. 106 $m = n$.

Choose any one element p_i from the first set. Then

$$p_i \leqq a = q_1 + \cdots + q_n$$

so that

$$p_i = p_i(q_1 + \cdots + q_n)$$
$$= p_iq_1 + \cdots + p_iq_n \qquad \text{by VII.}$$

But p_i is join-irreducible; therefore by Th. 101 for some subscript j

$$p_i = p_iq_j \quad \text{and hence} \quad p_i \leqq q_j.$$

Starting again with q_j, we prove in exactly the same way that for some subscript k

$$q_j = q_jp_k \quad \text{and hence} \quad q_j \leqq p_k.$$

Combining the two results we have

$$p_i \leqq q_j \leqq p_k \quad \text{and hence} \quad p_i \leqq p_k.$$

It follows that

$$p_i + p_k = p_k;$$

but the representation $a = p_1 + \cdots + p_n$ is without redundancy; hence we must have $i = k, p_i = p_k$, and consequently $p_i = q_j$. Thus we can show that each element of the set $p_1, \ldots, p_n$ belongs to the set $q_1, \ldots, q_n$; in the same way we can prove that each element of the second set is a member of the first; therefore the two sequences $p_1, \ldots, p_n$ and $q_1, \ldots, q_n$ are identical as sets, although they may differ in the order of their terms.

The formulation of the dual theorem for meets of meet-irreducibles is left to the reader.

Example 92. The factors of any natural number n ordered by divisibility constitute a finite distributive lattice, in which the join-irreducibles apart from 1 are primes and their powers. By Th. 102 n can be represented in at least one way as join without redundancy of prime powers which divide n; by Th. 146 this representation is unique. This does not mean that we have exhibited the unique factorization theorem for natural numbers as a simple corollary to Th. 146; in fact we used unique factorization into prime powers to establish the distributivity of our lattice of factors. See formulae (11) and (12) of § 2.

For the remainder of this section we confine our attention to distributive lattices of finite length. For this restricted class of lattice we have by Ths. 103 and 146 the result: every element can be represented as irredundant join of a unique finite subset of the join-irreducibles which that element contains; and dually. The following theorem should be compared with Th. 114 (ii)–(iv).

THEOREM 147. In a distributive lattice L of finite length n an element of height k contains just k non-zero join-irreducibles and is their join, with or without redundancy, and dually. Consequently the lattice contains just n non-zero join-irreducibles and just n non-unity meet-irreducibles.

Proof. We prove the theorem for join-irreducibles only, and disregard the trivial case of the lattice of one element only. If $n \geqq 1$, L contains at least one non-zero join-irreducible, to wit an atom, and every non-zero element contains at least one atom. Suppose an element x of height $k \geqq 1$ contains m distinct non-zero irreducibles

$$s_1, \ldots, s_m;$$

classify these elements s_i in batches according to ascending height, renaming and renumbering them as

$$t_1, \dots, t_m$$

in such a way that if $i < j$, then $h(t_i) \leqq h(t_j)$.

It follows that t_1 is an atom and we have a chain

$$o < t_1 \leqq t_1 + t_2 \leqq \cdots \leqq t_1 + \cdots + t_m \leqq x. \tag{1}$$

If any equality save the last held good, say

$$t_1 + \cdots + t_{r-1} = t_1 + \cdots + t_r = (t_1 + \cdots + t_{r-1}) + t_r,$$

we should have

$$\begin{aligned} t_r &= (t_1 + \cdots + t_{r-1})\, t_r \\ &= t_1 t_r + \cdots + t_{r-1} t_r \qquad \text{by VII.} \end{aligned}$$

But t_r is irreducible; hence by Th. 101 we should have for some subscript $j < r$

$$t_r = t_j t_r;$$

from this would follow

$$t_r \leqq t_j$$

and consequently

$$h(t_r) \leqq h(t_j);$$

but $j < r$ would entail $h(t_j) \leqq h(t_r)$ from the method of numbering; thus we should have t_r, t_j of the same height and also comparable; hence we should have $t_r = t_j$ with $j \neq r$, which contradicts the hypothesis that the t_i (or s_i) are distinct. Therefore the chain (1) may be written

$$o < t_1 < t_1 + t_2 < \cdots < t_1 + \cdots + t_m \leqq x. \tag{2}$$

By Th. 145 the condition JD is satisfied in L; since x is of height k, by JD every maximal chain from o to x is of length k; hence the greatest possible value of m in (2) is k. We have shown that an element of height $k \geqq 1$ must contain one and cannot contain more than k non-zero irreducibles.

We continue the proof by observing that if x is of height 1, x is an atom, which contains just one non-zero irreducible, namely itself, and x is the (conventional) join of this one irreducible. If then $n = 1$, in which case L reduces to a two-element chain, the theorem is proved. Let $n > 1$, and let H be the set of those integers h, $1 \leqq h \leqq n$, such that if an element x is of height g, $1 \leqq g \leqq h$, then x contains and is the join of just g distinct non-zero irreducibles. H is not empty, for 1 belongs to H. Let $k < n$ belong to H; we prove that $k + 1$ belongs to H. Suppose y is an element of height $k + 1$ in L; then y must cover some element x of height k; since k belongs to H, we have

$$x = p_1 + \cdots + p_k,$$

where the p_i are distinct non-zero irreducibles. If y is irreducible, y can cover no element other than x; y then contains itself, x, and all that x contains, and nothing else; hence y contains and is the join of just $k + 1$ distinct non-zero irreducibles:

$$y = y + p_1 + \cdots + p_k.$$

If y is reducible, y covers at least one element $z \neq x$; z like x is of height k; hence

$$z = q_1 + \cdots + q_k,$$

where the q_j are all the distinct non-zero irreducibles contained in z. By Th. 145 the condition C4 is satisfied in L; but $y = x + z$ covers x and z; therefore x and z cover xz. If $xz = o$, x and z are atoms, y of height 2 contains and is the join of these two distinct non-zero irreducibles and, as proved earlier, cannot contain more than two such elements; therefore in this case $k + 1$ belongs to H. If $xz > o$, xz is of height $k - 1 \geqq 1$ and $k - 1$ belongs to H; hence xz contains $k - 1$ distinct non-zero irreducibles, all of which are contained in x and in z; therefore the sets $\{p_1, \ldots, p_k\}$, $\{q_1, \ldots, q_k\}$ must differ in just one item, say

$$p_1 = q_1, \ldots, \quad p_{k-1} = q_{k-1}, \quad p_k \neq q_k.$$

It follows that y contains the $k + 1$ distinct non-zero irreducibles $p_1, \ldots, p_k, q_k$, equals their join, and, as proved earlier, cannot contain more than this number of such elements; therefore $k + 1$ belongs to H. Thus the set H consists of all integers from 1 to n, and the first part of the theorem is proved for any fixed n.

To complete the proof, we observe that the unity element u of L is of height n, and therefore contains and is the join of just n distinct non-zero irreducibles; but u contains all elements of L; hence the lattice contains just n such elements.

It is to be noted that each element of L has a unique representation as join of irreducibles, but the number of components in such a representation may well be less than the height of the element.

A process of considerable interest in lattice theory is that of embedding one lattice in another; what this phrase means is made precise in the following definition:

Definition 60. If a lattice A can be shown to be isomorphic with a sublattice B of a lattice C, we say that A can be embedded in C. With the help of Th. 147 we are going to prove two embedding theorems for distributive lattices of finite length.

THEOREM 148. A distributive lattice L of finite length $n > 0$ can be embedded in the lattice F of the 2^n subsets of a set of n objects, ordered by set-inclusion. Consequently, a distributive lattice of finite length n is finite, and the number of its elements cannot exceed 2^n.

Proof. By Th. 147 L contains just n non-zero join-irreducibles

$$s_1, \dots, s_n.$$

Denote the set of these elements by S; as we know, there are 2^n subsets of S, which ordered by set-inclusion constitute a lattice with intersection for meet and union for join; this is the lattice F in which we embed L; the elements of F are the subsets of S, and by (3) of § 1 F is distributive. By Th. 147 each non-zero element x of L contains and is the join of a subset $S(x)$ of S; if x is of height k, $S(x)$ consists of just k of the s_i; clearly $S(u) = S$, and $S(o)$ can appropriately be defined as the empty subset of S. Consider the correspondence associating $S(x)$ in F with x in L. To each x in L there corresponds just one $S(x)$ in F; if T is a subset of S such that $S(x) = T = S(y)$ for x, y in L, then x is join of the elements of T and so is y, so that $x = y$; thus every consequent in the correspondence has just one antecedent. Therefore we have a one-to-one correspondence between the elements of L and certain subsets of S. But not every subset of S need be a consequent in the correspondence, for if $S(x) = \{s_1, \dots, s_k\}$ where $x = s_1 + \cdots + s_k$ but s_1 is redundant, then $x = s_2 + \cdots + s_k$ and the set $\{s_2, \dots, s_k\} \neq S(x)$ has no antecedent in L. Thus the correspondence is a one-to-one mapping of L *into* F; let R be the subset of elements of F which appear as consequents in the mapping. If $x \leqq y$ in L, then $S(x)$ is contained in $S(y)$ in R; if $S(x)$ is contained in $S(y)$ in R, then the join of the members of $S(x)$ is contained in the join of the members of $S(y)$, that is, $x \leqq y$ in L. Therefore the set R ordered by set-inclusion and the lattice L are isomorphic partially ordered sets; the detail of the proof of Th. 77 shows that R is a lattice isomorphic with L if we define the meet $S(a) \wedge S(b)$ of $S(a)$, $S(b)$ in R as $S(ab)$, and the join $S(a) \vee S(b)$ as $S(a + b)$. It remains to show that R is a sublattice of F. If s_i belongs to $S(ab)$, then $s_i \leqq ab \leqq a$, $s_i \leqq ab \leqq b$ entail that s_i belongs to $S(a)$ and to $S(b)$ and consequently to their intersection; hence $S(ab) \leqq S(a)\, S(b)$. If s_j belongs to the intersection

$S(a)\,S(b)$, then $s_j \leqq a$, $s_j \leqq b$ so that $s_j \leqq ab$, s_j belongs to $S(ab)$, and we have $S(a)\,S(b) \leqq S(ab)$; it follows that $S(ab) = S(a)\,S(b)$. If s_i belongs to $S(a + b)$, then $s_i \leqq a + b$ and $s_i = s_i(a + b) = s_i a + s_i b$ by VII; but s_i is irreducible; hence by Th. 101 $s_i = s_i a$ or $s_i = s_i b$; in the first case $s_i \leqq a$, in the second $s_i \leqq b$; thus s_i belongs to $S(a)$ or to $S(b)$ and consequently to the union $S(a) + S(b)$; we have $S(a + b) \leqq S(a) + S(b)$. If s_j belongs to the union $S(a) + S(b)$ then s_j belongs to $S(a)$ with $s_j \leqq a$, or to $S(b)$ with $s_j \leqq b$; in any case $s_j \leqq a + b$ so that s_j belongs to $S(a + b)$; hence $S(a) + S(b) \leqq S(a + b)$; it follows that $S(a + b) = S(a) + S(b)$. Therefore R is a sublattice of F.

In the next theorem an alternative embedding procedure is described.

THEOREM 149. A distributive lattice of finite length $n > 0$ can be embedded in the direct product P of n two-element chains.

Proof. We give a demonstration which is independent of the last result, although in point of fact P and F are isomorphic.

By Th. 147 L possesses just n distinct non-zero join-irreducibles; let these be $s_1, \ldots, s_n$. Since $os_i = o$ and $us_i = s_i$, each element x by the same theorem can be displayed as

$$x = e_{x1}s_1 + \cdots + e_{xn}s_n,$$

where $e_{xi} = u$ if $s_i \leqq x$, $e_{xi} = o$ if $s_i \nleqq x$. We write $x = \bigvee e_{xi}s_i$. Then corresponding to each x of L there is a sequence

$$e_{x1}, \ldots, e_{xn}$$

where each of the n terms is either o or u.

Consider the direct product

$$P = [0, 1] \times \cdots \times [0, 1] \quad \text{to } n \text{ factors,}$$

where [0, 1] is the two-element chain of the integers 0, 1 in their usual order. From Example 89 and Th. 143 P is distributive. Each element of P is in the form of an n-termed sequence

$$[e_1, \ldots, e_n]$$

where each e_i is either 0 or 1. To each element x of L we now make correspond the element $p(x)$ of P

$$p(x) = [e_1, \ldots, e_n]$$

where $e_i = 0$ if $e_{xi} = o$, $e_i = 1$ if $e_{xi} = u$. Each element x of L is mapped on just one element of P; if q is an element of P such that $p(x) = q = p(y)$ for x, y in L, then x and y are identical joins; thus every consequent in the correspondence has just one antecedent. Not every element of P need be a consequent, however; if $x = \bigvee e_{xi}s_i$ where for one particular subscript k we have $e_{xk} = u$ but s_k is redundant, we may write e^*_{xi} for e_{xi}, $i \neq k$, and replace e_{xk} by $e^*_{xk} = o$, obtaining $x = \bigvee e^*_{xi}s_i$; the sequence of the e^*_{xi} differs from that of the e_{xi} in the kth place and gives an element of P without antecedent in L. Thus the correspondence is a one-to-one mapping of L *into* P; let Q denote the subset of elements of P appearing as consequents in the mapping. If $x \leqq y$ in L, then $e_{xi} \leqq e_{yi}$ for every i; hence $p(x) \leqq p(y)$ in Q; if $p(x) \leqq p(y)$ in Q, then $e_{xi} \leqq e_{yi}$ for every i; hence $x \leqq y$ in L. Therefore Q and L are isomorphic partially ordered sets. The proof of Th. 77 shows that Q is a lattice isomorphic with L if we take $p(ab)$ for meet of $p(a)$, $p(b)$ in Q, and $p(a + b)$ as their join.

It remains to show that Q is a sublattice of P. Let a, b be elements of L where

$$a = \bigvee e_{ai}s_i, \quad b = \bigvee e_{bi}s_i.$$

The meet of $p(a)$, $p(b)$ in P is $[m_1, \ldots, m_n]$ where $m_i = 0$ or 1 according as min $(e_{ai}, e_{bi}) = o$ or u. We observe that e_{ai}, e_{bj} are members of a chain so that for any i, j

$$e_{ai}e_{bj} = \min(e_{ai}, e_{bj}), \quad e_{ai} + e_{bj} = \max(e_{ai}, e_{bj}).$$

Then

$$\begin{aligned} ab &= \bigvee e_{ai}s_i \cdot \bigvee e_{bi}s_i \\ &= \bigvee e_{ai}e_{bj}s_is_j \quad (i = 1, \ldots, n; j = 1, \ldots, n) \end{aligned}$$

as a consequence of VII, the join being taken over all combinations of values of i, j.

Thus

$$\begin{aligned} ab &= \bigvee \min(e_{ai}, e_{bj})\, s_is_j \\ &= \bigvee_{i=j} \min(e_{ai}, e_{bj})\, s_is_j + \bigvee_{i \neq j} \min(e_{ai}, e_{bj})\, s_is_j \\ &\geqq \bigvee_{i=j} \min(e_{ai}, e_{bj})\, s_is_j \quad (i = 1, \ldots, n) \\ &= \bigvee \min(e_{ai}, e_{bi})\, s_i \qquad \text{by idempotence.} \end{aligned}$$

On the other hand, let $ab = c = \bigvee e_{ci}s_i$.

If $\min(e_{ai}, e_{bi}) = u$, both a and b contain s_i; hence ab contains s_i so that $e_{ci} = u$; if $\min(e_{ai}, e_{bi}) = o$, then at least one of a, b does not contain s_i and consequently ab cannot contain s_i so that $e_{ci} = o$. In any case $e_{ci} \leqq \min(e_{ai}, e_{bi})$ for every i. Therefore

$$ab = \bigvee e_{ci}s_i \leqq \bigvee \min(e_{ai}, e_{bi})\, s_i.$$

The two inequalities proved yield

$$ab = \bigvee \min(e_{ai}, e_{bi})\, s_i$$

and hence

$$p(ab) = [m_1, \ldots, m_n],$$

which is the meet of $p(a)$, $p(b)$ in P.

Again, the join of $p(a)$, $p(b)$ in P is

$$[M_1, \ldots, M_n]$$

where $M_i = 0$ or 1 according as $\max(e_{ai}, e_{bi}) = o$ or u. Now

$$a + b = \vee e_{ai} s_i + \vee e_{bi} s_i$$

$$= \vee (e_{ai} + e_{bi})\, s_i$$

$$= \vee \max(e_{ai}, e_{bi})\, s_i .$$

Hence

$$p(a + b) = [M_1, \dots, M_n]$$

which is the join of $p(a)$, $p(b)$ in P. Therefore Q is a sublattice of P, and the theorem is proved. In the notation of Example 42, § 9, we have embedded the lattice L in the direct product K_2^n.

Example 93. The lattice of the eight factors of 24 ordered by divisibility has the diagram of Fig. 12b. The non-zero join-irreducibles are the prime powers 2, 3, 4, 8. The chain (2) of Th. 147 for $x = 24$ is as follows:

$$1 < 2 < 2 \cup 3 < 2 \cup 3 \cup 4 < 2 \cup 3 \cup 4 \cup 8 = 24;$$

but the unique irredundant representation of 24 is $24 = 3 \cup 8$. The table below gives the details required for illustration of Ths. 147–9.

x	$h(x)$	$S(x)$	$p(x)$
24	4	2 3 4 8	1 1 1 1
12	3	2 3 4	1 1 1 0
8	3	2 4 8	1 0 1 1
6	2	2 3	1 1 0 0
4	2	2 4	1 0 1 0
3	1	3	0 1 0 0
2	1	2	1 0 0 0
1	0	empty	0 0 0 0

The lattice F is that of the 2^4 subsets of $\{2, 3, 4, 8\}$ ordered by set-inclusion; the lattice P is the direct product of four two-element chains; Fig. 10e gives the diagram of these isomorphic lattices.

Special interest attaches to the second embedding theorem, for Q is something more than a sublattice of P.

Definition 61. If Q is a sublattice of a direct product P of n lattices $L_1, \ldots, L_n$:

$$P = L_1 \times \cdots \times L_n$$

such that every element x_r of every component lattice L_r appears at least once in the rth place in an element of Q, we say that Q is a sub-direct product of P.

Example 94. In Fig. 15 (Example 41, § 9) we have the direct product of lattices with elements O, L, M, N, U and 1, 2 respectively. In the product

the elements $O1, L1, M1, N1, U1$ form a sublattice but not a subproduct, for 2 does not appear;

the set $O1, L1, M1, N1, U2$ has every one of O, L, M, N, U and 1, 2 on view but is not a subproduct, for it is not a sublattice;

the elements $O1, L1, M1, N1, U1, U2$ fulfil both requirements and therefore form a subproduct.

It is easy to check that Q in Th. 149 is a sub-direct product of P, and the theorem may be rephrased:

Any finite distributive lattice containing more than one element may be represented as a sub-direct product of two-element chains.

Exercises

132. Find a small finite lattice to show that a lattice may have the unique representations of Th. 146 without being distributive.

133. Embed the lattices given below, giving details as in Example 93:
   (i) the five-element lattice of Fig. 9c;
   (ii) the sixteen-element factorization lattice of the number 120.
   Further
   (iii) show that $K_2 \times K_4$ (Fig. 16) can be embedded in K_2^4;
   (iv) embed K_4^2 and K_2^4 in the same lattice;
   (v) embed the lattice of Fig. 35 (see Exercise 131) in a suitable Boolean lattice.

134. Consider the singular partitions of $\Pi(5)$ which contain a fixed atom A. Is this subset a lattice embedded in $\Pi(5)$? Interpret this subset with respect to Fig. 37 (p. 280).

27. Boolean Algebras

(1) *Complements*

We come now to complements in distributive lattices.

THEOREM 150. If an element of a distributive lattice has a complement, that complement is unique.

Proof. Let a and b be complements of c in a distributive lattice; then $ac = o = bc$, $a + c = u = b + c$; hence $a = b$ by Th. 142.

Complemented distributive lattices are the oldest of all, for they emerged from the pioneer work of George Boole (1847). Therefore we have:

Definition 62. A complemented distributive lattice is called a Boolean lattice.

Since in a Boolean lattice each element a has a unique complement, generally written a', complementation is a unary operation with respect to which the lattice is closed. Hence we lay down

Definition 63. A Boolean lattice considered as an algebra closed with respect to the three operations of complementation, formation of meet, formation of join, is called a Boolean algebra.

Boolean algebras are very rich systems and have been extensively studied, notably by Schröder, E.V. Huntington and M.H. Stone. Our definition—"complemented distributive lattice"—consists of only three words but involves some ten postulates, namely IA–IVA, IB–IVB, VII, and the requirement that there exist o, u and complements for all elements. Numerous other postulate sets have been determined, some of them making no mention at all of the lattice structure, though of course necessarily entailing such a structure. One consequence of the attention given to Boolean algebras is that there are available several books devoted to this special class of lattice; hence we are free to concentrate on those aspects of Boolean theory more particularly relevant to lattice theory as a whole.

Example 95. The subsets of a set S ordered by set-inclusion give the classic example of a Boolean algebra. See § 1, Example 2 of § 3, § 9 (2). If X is a subset of S, the complement of X is the set X' consisting of all members of S not in X; then XX' is empty, for X and X' have nothing in common, $X + X' = S$, for together they exhaust S. Note that if S contains only one object, the Boolean algebra of its subsets is the two-element chain; if S is empty, the Boolean algebra of its subsets consists of one element, namely S itself. The smallest lattice of all then is the one-element Boolean algebra.

Example 96. We have referred to the arithmetic product n of m distinct primes as a square-free natural number. The factors of such a number, ordered by divisibility, form a Boolean algebra. See § 9 (3). The complement of 1 (zero element) is n (unity element); the complement of a number with r $(1 \leqq r < m)$ of the primes as factors is the arithmetic product of the remaining $m - r$ primes; in all cases $x' = n \div x$.

Example 97. Here is an example of an infinite Boolean algebra. Let S denote an infinite sequence $[s_1, s_2, \ldots, s_n, \ldots]$ where each term is either 0 or 1. If $T = [\ldots, t_n, \ldots]$ is another such sequence, we define $S = T$ to mean $s_n = t_n$ for every n. Define binary operations

$$ST = [\ldots, \min(s_n, t_n), \ldots],$$

$$S + T = [\ldots, \max(s_n, t_n), \ldots].$$

It is left to the reader to prove that these operations are commutative, associative, mutually absorptive, and each distributive over the other. See Exercise 9 and formulae (5)–(8) of § 2. The sequences S will then constitute an infinite distributive lattice L. Defining $S \leqq T$ by $S = ST$, it follows from $S \leqq T$ that $s_n = \min(s_n, t_n)$ for every n. Then for every S in L

$$O = [0, 0, 0, \ldots] \leqq S,$$

$$U = [1, 1, 1, \ldots] \geqq S.$$

Let $s_n' = 0$ if $s_n = 1$, $s_n' = 1$ if $s_n = 0$; then $\min(s_n, s_n') = 0$, $\max(s_n, s_n') = 1$, for every n; hence if $S = [\ldots, s_n, \ldots]$ and $S' = [\ldots, s_n', \ldots]$, we have $SS' = O$, $S + S' = U$. Thus L is a Boolean algebra, and could be described as an infinite product of two-element chains.

THEOREM 151. A sublattice of a Boolean algebra need not be a subalgebra.

Proof. A subalgebra of a Boolean algebra L must contain with a, b not only ab and $a + b$, but also a', b' and consequently the o and u of L; a sublattice need contain only ab and $a + b$.

THEOREM 152. The dual of a Boolean algebra is a Boolean algebra.

Proof. Distributivity is secured by Th. 134; complementation by the duality of $xx' = o$, $x + x' = u$.

THEOREM 153. The direct product of two Boolean algebras is a Boolean algebra. Conversely, if a product of two lattices is a Boolean algebra, so is each constituent.

Proof. By Ths. 143 and 55. Note that in particular K_2^n is a Boolean algebra.

THEOREM 154. Any homomorphic image of a Boolean algebra is itself a Boolean algebra.

Proof. By Ths. 144 and 83.

We conclude these general remarks about Boolean algebras by indicating their place in the broad classification of lattices sketched at the beginning of § 16. All Boolean algebras are by definition distributive; we note that the smallest non-Boolean distributive lattice is the three-element chain, where the middle element lacks a complement. All distributive lattices are modular; all modular lattices are semi-modular; but lattices in general need enter into none of these categories. Figure 36 shows this classification; each rectangle represents a class of lattices and is illustrated by the smallest appropriate representative of the class; as we proceed inwards the classes become more and more specialized.

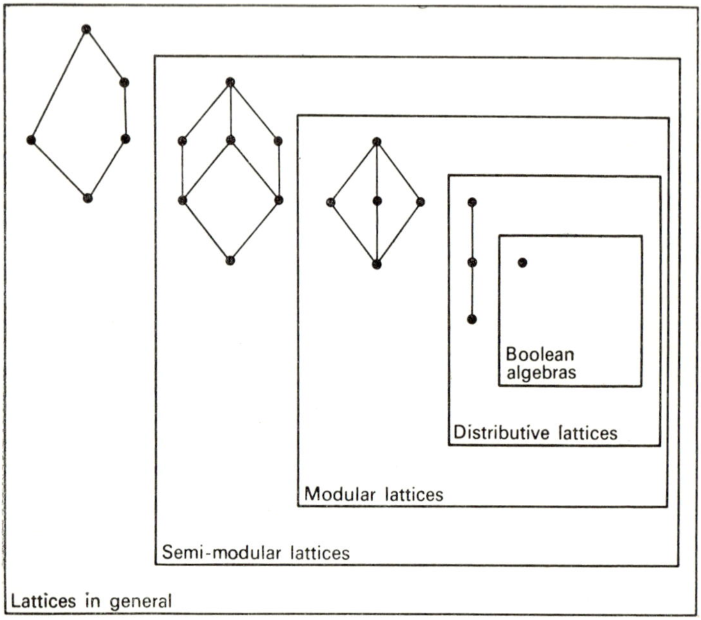

FIG. 36.

Some properties of Boolean complements are detailed in the following theorem:

THEOREM 155. Let a' denote the unique complement of element a in a Boolean algebra L. Then

(1) writing a'' for $(a')'$, we have $a'' = a$;
(2) $(ab)' = a' + b'$;
(3) $(a + b)' = a'b'$;
(4) if $a \leqq b$, then $b' \leqq a'$, and if $a' \leqq b'$, then $b \leqq a$;

(5) $a \leqq b$ if and only if $ab' = o$; $a \leqq b$ if and only if $a' + b = u$;
(6) the mapping $\varphi(x) = x'$ for x in L is a dual automorphism of L.

Proof.

(1) $(a')'\, a' = o = aa'$; $(a')' + a' = u = a + a'$; hence by Th. 142 $(a')' = a$, that is, $a'' = a$. This small result is of capital importance in the application of lattice theory to logic.

(2) $ab\,(a' + b') = aba' + abb' = ob + oa = o + o = o;$

$$ab + (a' + b') = (a + a' + b')\,(b + a' + b') \text{ by Th. 132}$$

$$= (u + b')\,(u + a') = uu = u;$$

hence $a' + b'$ is a complement of ab, by Th. 150 unique; that is, $(ab)' = a' + b'$.

(3) Dualize the proof of (2). Results (2) and (3) are called de Morgan's formulae, after Augustus de Morgan, an English contemporary of Boole. They can be extended in the obvious way; thus if

$$(a_1 \cdots a_k)' = a_1' + \cdots + a_k'$$

for some k, then

$$a_1' + \cdots + a_k' + a_{k+1}' = (a_1 \cdots a_k)' + a_{k+1}'$$

$$= (a_1 \cdots a_{k+1})' \quad \text{by (2);}$$

hence we have for any n

$$(a_1 \cdots a_n)' = a_1' + \cdots + a_n',$$

and similarly we may obtain

$$(a_1 + \cdots + a_n)' = a_1' \cdots a_n'.$$

(4) If $a \leqq b$, $a = ab$; then by (2) $a' = (ab)' = a' + b'$; whence $b' \leqq a'$. If $a' \leqq b'$, by what we have just proved $b'' \leqq a''$, that is, $b \leqq a$ by (1).

(5) If $ab' = o$, then $a = au = a(b + b') = ab + ab' = ab + o = ab$; therefore $a \leqq b$.

If $a \leqq b$, then $ab' \leqq bb' = o$; therefore $ab' = o$.

Again, if $a' + b = u$, then

$$b = b + o = b + aa' = (b + a)(b + a') = (b + a)u = b + a;$$

hence $a \leqq b$. Note the use of Th. 132 in the expansion of b.

If $a \leqq b$, then $u = a' + a \leqq a' + b$; hence $a' + b = u$.

(6) We recall that a dual automorphism φ of a lattice L means a one-to-one internal mapping of the elements of L such that

$$\varphi(ab) = \varphi(a) + \varphi(b), \quad \varphi(a + b) = \varphi(a)\,\varphi(b).$$

See Def. 52, § 15. Here each element x of L is mapped by φ on its unique complement x' in L; if y is a consequent in the given mapping φ and $x' = y = z'$, then $x = x'' = y' = z'' = z$; hence φ is one-to-one. Formulae (2) and (3) above complete the proof, whilst (4) confirms that φ inverts order.

By Th. 150 in a complemented distributive lattice complements are unique; the converse assertion that a complemented lattice in which complements are unique is distributive is in general false. With regard to relative complementation we have the following:

THEOREM 156. If an element x of a distributive lattice belongs to an interval $[a, b]$ and has a complement y relative to that interval, then x has no other complement relative to that interval. Briefly, in a distributive lattice relative complements are unique.

Proof. If y and z are complements of x relative to the interval $[a, b]$, then $xy = a = xz$ and $x + y = b = x + z$; hence $y = z$ by Th. 142.

THEOREM 157. A lattice in which relative complements are unique is distributive.

Proof. Such a lattice contains no sublattice isomorphic with the "pentagonal" lattice or with the five-element partition lattice $\Pi(3)$; therefore by Th. 140 the lattice is distributive.

THEOREM 158. A Boolean algebra is relatively complemented, the relative complements being unique in the sense of Th. 156.

Proof. A Boolean algebra is complemented and modular, and hence relatively complemented by Th. 107; then by Th. 156.

THEOREM 159. Every interval of a Boolean algebra is itself a Boolean algebra.

Proof. Every interval is a distributive lattice (Ths. 56, 137) which is complemented by the theorem just proved. Note that the only interval which is a subalgebra is $[o, u]$, for a subalgebra must contain o and u.

Definition 64. A relatively complemented distributive lattice which possesses a zero element is called a generalized Boolean algebra.

Example 98. The totality of the square-free natural numbers with 1 adjoined, ordered by divisibility, furnishes an example of a generalized Boolean algebra. Thus relative to the interval [6, 210] the number 30 has the unique complement 42.

Theorems corresponding to Ths. 153 and 154 are easily proved for generalized Boolean algebras.

(2) *Atoms*

We turn now to the consideration of the role of the atoms in a finite Boolean algebra. First a preparatory theorem:

THEOREM 160. If in a distributive lattice we have a representation

$$x = s_1 + \cdots + s_k$$

where the s_i are join-irreducibles and s_1 is redundant, then

$$s_1 \leqq s_j$$

for some j,

$$2 \leqq j \leqq k.$$

Proof. If $s_1 + \cdots + s_k = s_2 + \cdots + s_k$,
then

$$\begin{aligned} s_1 &= s_1 (s_2 + \cdots + s_k) \\ &= s_1 s_2 + \cdots + s_1 s_k \quad \text{by VII.} \end{aligned}$$

But s_1 is irreducible; hence by Th. 101

$$s_1 = s_1 s_j \quad \text{for some } j, \quad 2 \leqq j \leqq k;$$

therefore

$$s_1 \leqq s_j.$$

A finite Boolean algebra is relatively complemented (Th. 158); therefore its atoms and zero are the only join-irreducibles (Th. 110).

A Boolean algebra of length $n > 0$ contains then just n atoms, and each element contains and is the join of just k distinct atoms, where k is the height of the element (Th. 147). Let

$$x = p_1 + \cdots + p_k$$

be such a representation. No redundancy is possible here: for if, say, p_1 were redundant, we should have $p_1 \leqq p_j$ for some j, $2 \leqq j \leqq k$ (Th. 160); but $p_1 < p_j$ is impossible since p_1, p_j are atoms, and $p_1 = p_j$ is ruled out since p_1, p_j are distinct. It follows that the correspondence set up in the proof of Th. 148 between each element x of a finite distributive lattice and the subset $S(x)$ of join-irreducibles contained by x becomes in the case where L is a finite Boolean algebra a one-to-one mapping of L *onto* the lattice F of all the subsets of the set of atoms of L, for now every subset has an antecedent in L. We have proved:

THEOREM 161. Each non-zero element of a finite Boolean algebra contains and is the irredundant join of just k atoms, where k is the height of the element. Every finite Boolean algebra of length n possesses just n atoms and 2^n elements, being isomorphic with the lattice of the 2^n subsets of the set of its atoms, ordered by set-inclusion. And dually.

Applying Th. 149 to the case of a finite Boolean algebra L, we see that in the join

$$x = e_{x1}p_1 + \cdots + e_{xk}p_k$$

$e_{xi}p_i$ cannot now be redundant if $e_{xi} = u$. In the correspondence every element of the direct product P now has a unique antecedent in L, and the sub-direct product Q now coincides with P. We have:

THEOREM 162. Every finite Boolean algebra of 2^n elements is isomorphic with the direct product K_2^n of n two-element chains.

Example 99. Consider the lattice of the numbers 1, 2, 3, 5, 6, 10, 15, 30 ordered by divisibility. This Boolean algebra is of length 3, has 3 atoms (prime numbers) and 2^3 elements; each number other than 1 is the arithmetic product of the unique set of its prime factors; if each number is written as the arithmetic product of all the atoms with appropriate exponents, the isomorphism with the direct product of three two-element chains [0, 1] is plainly on view.

x	$h(x)$	$S(x)$	$p(x)$	x
30	3	2 3 5	1 1 1	$2^1 \times 3^1 \times 5^1$
15	2	3 5	0 1 1	$2^0 \times 3^1 \times 5^1$
10	2	2 5	1 0 1	$2^1 \times 3^0 \times 5^1$
6	2	2 3	1 1 0	$2^1 \times 3^1 \times 5^0$
5	1	5	0 0 1	$2^0 \times 3^0 \times 5^1$
3	1	3	0 1 0	$2^0 \times 3^1 \times 5^0$
2	1	2	1 0 0	$2^1 \times 3^0 \times 5^0$
1	0	empty	0 0 0	$2^0 \times 3^0 \times 5^0$

It was stated above—in the remarks prefacing Th. 156—that a complemented lattice in which complements are unique need not be a Boolean algebra; this was proved by R.P. Dilworth in 1945 with a demonstration that *any* lattice could be embedded in a suitable uniquely complemented lattice. Thus unique complementation is a necessary but not a sufficient condition for a lattice to be Boolean. However, it has been shown that if a uniquely complemented lattice is atomic in the sense that every non-zero element contains at least one atom, then the lattice is Boolean. This might suggest that atomicity is a necessary condition for a lattice to be Boolean, and the emphatic part played by the atoms in Th. 161 might appear to support this conjecture: as a matter of fact a Boolean algebra need have no atoms at all.

Example 100. This example is due to H. Hermes. We begin by noting that if A, B are subsets of a set U, the set AB' consists of those members of A which are not in B; AB' is called the difference between A, B (in that order) and is usually written $A - B$. The set $(A - B) + (B - A) = AB' + A'B$ is called the symmetric difference of A and B (in any order); in books where set-union of A and B is denoted always by $A \cup B$ symmetric difference is written $A + B$, for the very good reason that a Boolean algebra viewed as a set closed with respect to formation of symmetric difference $xy' \cup x'y$ is an Abelian group; we shall, however, continue to use the plus sign to indicate lattice-join in general and set-union in particular. The symmetric difference of A, B consists of those members of A not in B and those members of B not in A, that is, it consists of those elements which do not belong to both sets.

Let the set U now be some fixed infinite set such as the set of the natural numbers, or the set of the rational numbers between 0 and 1; let L be the Boolean algebra of all the subsets of U, ordered by set-inclusion. Define a dyadic relation r in L thus: for A, B in L ArB if and only if their symmetric difference is a finite set or empty. Clearly ArA for every A; if ArB, then BrA; hence r is over L, reflexive and symmetric. To show r transitive we observe that $AC' = AC'(B' + B) = AC'B' + AC'B = (AB' + BC')AC'$; hence $AC' \leqq AB' + BC'$; similarly $CA' \leqq CB' + BA'$; therefore

$$\begin{aligned} AC' + A'C &\leqq AB' + BC' + B'C + A'B \\ &= (AB' + A'B) + (BC' + B'C). \end{aligned}$$

Then if ArB and BrC, the sets in parentheses are finite or empty, their union is finite or empty, the contained set $AC' + A'C$ is finite or empty, and ArC. We have proved r to be an equivalence relation, and the elements of L (the subsets of U) fall into classes of equivalent elements. If O is the empty subset of U and F any finite subset, we have $FO' + F'O = FU + O = FU = F$, so that FrO; if I

is any infinite subset of U, $IO' + I'O = I$ so that I, O are not equivalent. Suppose ArB and CrD; then

$$AC(BD)' + (AC)'BD = AC(B' + D') + (A' + C')BD \quad \text{by Th. 155 (2)}$$
$$= ACB' + ACD' + A'BD + C'BD$$
$$\leqq AB' + CD' + A'B + C'D$$
$$\text{which by hypothesis is finite or empty;}$$

it follows that $ACrBD$; the reader will verify that $(A + C)r(B + D)$; therefore r is a congruence relation. The classes of equivalent subsets of U accordingly constitute the quotient lattice L/r, which we will denote by H. By Th. 80 H is a homomorphic image of L; by Th. 154 H is a Boolean algebra. Let ω be the class in H which comprises O and all finite subsets of U; since $O \leqq A$ for any A in L, $\omega \leqq \alpha$ for any class α in H; ω is the zero element of H. If α includes an infinite subset I, $\omega < \alpha$ in H; split I into disjoint infinite subsets J, K; $I - J = K$, $J - I = O$, whence

$$(I - J) + (J - I) = K + O = K,$$

so that I, J are not equivalent. Let J belong to the class β in H; since J is infinite, $\omega < \beta$; since $J < I$, $\beta \leqq \alpha$; but we have just proved that $\beta \neq \alpha$; therefore we have

$$\omega < \beta < \alpha.$$

Thus no class $\alpha > \omega$ can cover ω, and H is without atoms.

(3) *Subalgebras*

We set ourselves the following problem: Let a, b be elements of a Boolean algebra B which is such that no *equalities* hold between elements of the lattice save those entailed by Postulates I–IV, VII, and Def. 62. Determine the smallest subalgebra of B containing a, b, if such exists.

The property stipulated means, for instance, that $a = a + ab$, $a + a' = u$, but $ab < a$, for $ab = a$ is ruled out. Therefore in our subalgebra we have a, b, a', b' distinct and incomparable in pairs, and likewise

$$ab, \quad ab', \quad a'b, \quad a'b' \tag{1}$$

distinct and incomparable in pairs.

Let x stand for a or a', y for b or b'; then for every combination of values of x and y we have

$$o < xy < x < x + y < u, \tag{2}$$

$$o < xy < y < x + y < u. \tag{3}$$

This means that our subalgebra must contain fourteen distinct elements: o, four of type xy, four of type x, four of type $x + y$, u. Hence the smallest feasible subalgebra is one of 2^4 elements, with four atoms. Since

$$x = x(y + y') = xy + xy', \tag{4}$$

$$y = y(x + x') = xy + x'y, \tag{5}$$

we see that the elements (1) will serve very well as atoms. If we denote these elements by p_1, p_2, p_3, p_4, from (2)–(5) we have the lattice:

$u = p_1 + p_2 + p_3 + p_4,$

$p_1 + p_2 + p_3, \quad p_1 + p_2 + p_4, \quad p_1 + p_3 + p_4, \quad p_2 + p_3 + p_4,$

$a = p_1 + p_2, \quad b = p_1 + p_3, \quad p_2 + p_3, \quad p_1 + p_4,$

$b' = p_2 + p_4, \quad a' = p_3 + p_4,$

$p_1, p_2, p_3, p_4,$

$o.$

As in Th. 149, each element x of this lattice can be exhibited in the form

$$x = e_{x1}p_1 + e_{x2}p_2 + e_{x3}p_3 + e_{x4}p_4$$

$$= e_{x1}ab + e_{x2}ab' + e_{x3}a'b + e_{x4}a'b'$$

where each $e_{xi} = u$ or o according as x does or does not contain p_i. Dually, if we denote the dual atoms

$$a + b, \quad a + b', \quad a' + b, \quad a' + b',$$

respectively, by d_1, d_2, d_3, d_4, we have

$$x = (f_{x1} + d_1)(f_{x2} + d_2)(f_{x3} + d_3)(f_{x4} + d_4),$$

where each $f_{xi} = o$ or u according as x is or is not contained by d_i. We return to this solution of our problem below.

Let B_n denote a Boolean algebra of 2^n elements, with n atoms

$$p_1, \ldots, p_n.$$

A subalgebra of B_n is a sublattice which contains with any x its complement x'; consequently every subalgebra must contain $xx' = o$ and $x + x' = u$. The elements o, u constitute what is obviously the smallest subalgebra of B_n; B_n itself constitutes the largest. If $n > 2$, does B_n contain subalgebras other than these?

Let

$$\pi = Q_1 / \cdots / Q_n \quad (1 \leqq k \leqq n)$$

be any partition of the set of atoms $\{p_1, \ldots, p_n\}$ into k blocks Q_i; we recall that in a partition the blocks are mutually disjoint and that collectively they exhaust the set partitioned. Let T be the collection of k blocks Q_i; then the subcollections of T ordered by set-inclusion constitute a Boolean algebra A_k of 2^k elements; each non-zero element of A_k is a set of blocks, and each of the k atoms of A_k

comprises just one block. For an example take B_4 displayed above; let π be the partition

$$(p_1 p_2 / p_3 / p_4)$$

so that $Q_1 = \{p_1, p_2\}$, $Q_2 = \{p_3\}$, $Q_3 = \{p_4\}$. T is the set $\{Q_1, Q_2, Q_3\}$; A_3 is the Boolean algebra of the 2^3 subsets of T, ordered by set-inclusion. The eight elements of A_3 are: the empty set, three one-block sets $\{Q_i\}$, three two-block sets $\{Q_i, Q_j\}$, and T itself.

To continue: Let O be the zero element of A_k (the empty set) and X any non-zero element; then X consists of one or more parcels of atoms of B_n; let x be the join in B_n of these atoms; then the mapping φ:

$$\varphi(X) = x, \quad \varphi(O) = o,$$

maps A_k into B_n. In the example, if X is $\{Q_1, Q_2\}$, $x = p_1 + p_2 + p_3$. If $\varphi(X) = x = \varphi(Y)$, then since x is join of a unique set of atoms and the Q_i are disjoint we must have the same Q_i in X and Y, that is, $X = Y$. If $x = \varphi(X) = y$, then x and y are identical joins. An element z of B_n will have no antecedent in A_k if the atoms of which z is the join do not fill entire blocks of π. In the example, the eight elements $p_1, p_1 + p_3, p_1 + p_4, p_2, p_2 + p_3, p_2 + p_4, p_1 + p_3 + p_4, p_2 + p_3 + p_4$ cannot be consequents in the correspondence.

Let the subset of elements of B_n which do appear as consequents in the mapping be denoted by C_k. We have proved that the mapping is one-to-one from A_k to C_k. If $X \leqq Y$ in A_k, then the atoms within X are within Y, and $x \leqq y$ in B_n and so in C_k; if $x \leqq y$ in B_n and so in C_k, y contains all the atoms contained by x, so that Y includes all the blocks included by X, and $X \leqq Y$ in A_k. Therefore the lattice A_k and the partially ordered set C_k are isomorphic partially ordered sets; hence (from the proof of Th. 77) C_k is a lattice isomorphic with A_k if we define the meet of x, y in C_k as $\varphi(XY)$, their join as $\varphi(X + Y)$. With these definitions C_k is a Boolean algebra of 2^k elements lying in B_n. We proceed to show that C_k is a subalgebra of B_n.

If $x = \bigvee p_i$, $y = \bigvee p_j$, where each of i, j runs through some subset of the sequence $1, \ldots, n$, then in B_n we have

$$\begin{aligned} xy &= (\bigvee p_i)(\bigvee p_j) \\ &= \bigvee p_i p_j \qquad \text{by VII} \\ &= \bigvee_{i=j} p_i p_j + \bigvee_{i \neq j} p_i p_j . \end{aligned}$$

But $p_i p_j = o$ if p_i, p_j are distinct atoms; hence xy is the join of those atoms common to x and y. If p is such an atom, then we have $p \leqq xy \leqq x = \varphi(X)$, so that p belongs to some block Q in X, and $p \leqq xy \leqq y = \varphi(Y)$, which entails that the block Q is also in Y; hence Q belongs to the intersection XY; it follows that $p \leqq \varphi(XY)$. On the other hand, if an atom $p \leqq \varphi(XY)$, then p belongs to some block Q in XY; Q belongs to both X and Y; hence $p \leqq \varphi(X) = x$ and $p \leqq \varphi(Y) = y$, and thus $p \leqq xy$. Therefore the meet $\varphi(XY)$ of x, y in C_k coincides with the meet xy in B_n.

Again, since $x + y = \varphi(X) + \varphi(Y)$, if p is an atom such that $p \leqq x + y$, then p belongs to some block Q in X or in Y; this block Q belongs to the union $X + Y$; hence $p \leqq \varphi(X + Y)$. Conversely, if an atom $p \leqq \varphi(X + Y)$, then p belongs to some block in X or in Y; hence $p \leqq \varphi(X) = x$ or $p \leqq \varphi(Y) = y$; in any case $p \leqq x + y$. Thus the join $\varphi(X + Y)$ of x, y in C_k coincides with the join $x + y$ in B_n.

We have shown C_k to be a sublattice of B_n; to prove C_k a subalgebra, we must prove that if x is in C_k, then so is x'. Let X' be the complement of X in A_k; the isomorphism φ preserves complements (Th. 83); therefore $\varphi(X')$ is the complement in C_k of $\varphi(X) = x$. All the atoms of B_n lie within T; hence $\varphi(T) = u$. It follows that

$$x \cdot \varphi(X') = \varphi(O) = o, \quad x + \varphi(X') = \varphi(T) = u;$$

but complements are unique in B_n; hence $\varphi(X') = x'$.

The proof is complete; we have shown that corresponding to every partition π of the set of n atoms of B_n there is a subalgebra B_k of B_n, where k is the number $1 \leqq k \leqq n$ of blocks in π.

Now let B_m be a subalgebra of B_n (with $n \geqq m \geqq 1$); B_m must possess m elements

$$q_1, \cdots, q_m$$

which serve as its own atoms; to avoid confusion with the atoms

$$p_1, \cdots, p_n$$

of B_n call these q_i the minimal elements of B_m. For these minimal elements we have

$$q_i q_j = o \quad \text{if} \quad i \neq j, \quad q_1 + \cdots + q_m = u;$$

each q_i by Th. 161 is the join of a unique subset Q_i of the atoms of B_n; therefore no two Q_i have an atom in common, but collectively the Q_i exhaust the set of atoms of B_n; thus corresponding to every subalgebra B_m of B_n there is a unique partition

$$Q_1 / \cdots / Q_m$$

of the set of n atoms of B_n, the partition having m blocks. This with what we proved above shows that the number of subalgebras in a Boolean algebra of 2^n elements is $p(n)$, where $p(n)$ is the number of ways of partitioning a set of n objects.

Let B_k, B_m be subalgebras of B_n ($n \geqq k \geqq 1, n \geqq m \geqq 1$). If x, y belong to the set-intersection $B_k B_m$, then x, y both belong to B_k, and consequently xy, $x + y$, x', y' belong to B_k; likewise all these elements belong to B_m, and therefore to the intersection; thus the intersection of two subalgebras is a subalgebra. Consider the set S of all subalgebras of B_n which contain B_k and B_m; S is not empty, for B_n belongs to it; S is finite, for $p(n)$ is finite; therefore the intersection of the subalgebras in S exists and by what has just been proved is a subalgebra of B_n. Clearly this subalgebra derived from

S is the smallest subalgebra of B_n which contains B_k and B_m. Therefore the subalgebras of B_n, ordered by set-inclusion, constitute a lattice: call this lattice B. The preceding discussion shows that the correspondence

$$\pi(B_k) = Q_1/ \cdots /Q_k,$$

where the k minimal elements of B_k are the joins of the atoms in the respective blocks, is one-to-one between B and $\Pi(n)$. We prove this correspondence to be a dual isomorphism. Let

$$\pi(B_k) = Q_1/ \cdots /Q_k \quad \text{and} \quad \pi(B_m) = R_1/ \cdots /R_m.$$

If B_k contains B_m, then $m \leqq k$, and each minimal element of B_m is the join of a unique subset of the minimal elements of B_k; hence each block R_i is the union of some blocks Q_j; therefore if

$$B_k \geqq B_m, \quad \pi(B_k) \leqq \pi(B_m).$$

Conversely, if $\pi(B_m) \geqq \pi(B_k)$, each block R_i is union of some blocks Q_j; hence each minimal element of B_m is join of some minimal elements of B; therefore if

$$\pi(B_m) \geqq \pi(B_k), \quad B_m \leqq B_k.$$

We have proved:

THEOREM 163. The lattice of the subalgebras of a finite Boolean algebra of 2^n elements, ordered by set-inclusion, is dually isomorphic with the lattice of the partitions of a set of n objects, ordered by refinement.

Example 101. Let the four atoms of B_4 be p, q, r, s.
If B_2 is the set $\{o, p + q, r + s, u\}$, $\pi(B_2) = (pq/rs)$;
if B_3 is the set $\{o, p + q, r, s, p + q + r, p + q + s, r + s, u\}$,

$$\pi(B_3) = (pq/r/s);$$

we have:

$$B_3 \text{ contains } B_2,$$

but

$$\pi(B_3) \text{ is contained by } \pi(B_2).$$

The algebra B_4 has sixteen elements; B_4 contains six subalgebras of eight elements, seven of four elements (four with an atom of B_4, three without), and one of two elements.

Returning to the problem solved earlier we lay down:

Definition 65. If S is a set of elements of a lattice, the smallest sublattice containing S is said to be generated by S.

Definition 66. Let a Boolean algebra L be such that no equalities hold between the elements of L save those entailed by Postulates I–IV, VII, and Def. 62; let S denote a set of elements

$$x_1, \ldots, x_n$$

of L; then the smallest subalgebra of L generated by S is called the free Boolean algebra with n generators. Denote this algebra by $FB(n)$.

We shall endeavour to find the number of elements in $FB(n)$.

Case (i). Let S consist of one element a. Then $o < a < u$, $o < a' < u$ immediately give the result: $FB(1)$ has four elements.

Case (ii). The case with two generators a, b was our problem: $FB(2)$ has sixteen elements. Let the set of atoms of $FB(2)$ contained in a be denoted by A, those contained in a' by A'; the lattice of subalgebras of $FB(2)$ will contain the $FB(1)$ generated by a; the partition corresponding to this $FB(1)$ will be

$$\pi\,[FB(1)] = A/A'$$

where each block contains two atoms:

$$A = \{ab, ab'\}, \quad A' = \{a'b, a'b'\}.$$

Case (iii). Let the generators be a, b, c. The lattice of subalgebras of $FB(3)$ will contain the $FB(2)$ generated by a, b; the corresponding partition will be

$$\pi\,[FB(2)] = AB/AB'/A'B/A'B'$$

where AB denotes set-intersection as usual; since in $FB(3)$

$$o < abc < ab,$$

ab is the join of at least two atoms of $FB(3)$; hence AB must contain at least two atoms, and the same is true for the other blocks; therefore $FB(3)$ must have at least eight atoms; the eight elements such as abc will serve very well for atoms: for instance,

$$\begin{aligned} c = cu &= c\,(ab + ab' + a'b + a'b') \\ &= abc + ab'c + a'bc + a'b'c; \end{aligned}$$

the number of atoms in $FB(3)$ is therefore eight, and $FB(3)$ has 256 elements.

Case (iv). We note that the number of atoms for the cases $n = 1, 2, 3$ is $2^1, 2^2, 2^3$, respectively. Let N be the set of natural numbers n for which it is true that $FB(n)$ has 2^n atoms. N is not empty, for 1, 2, 3 belong to it. Let $k - 1$ belong to N. Then if $FB(k)$ has the k generators $x_1, \ldots, x_k$, the lattice of subalgebras of $FB(k)$ contains the lattice $FB(k-1)$ generated by $x_1, \ldots, x_{k-1}$; the partition corresponding will be

$$\pi\,[FB(k-1)] = X_1 \cdots X_{k-1}/ \cdots /X_1' \cdots X_{k-1}',$$

where the number of blocks is 2^{k-1}. Since in $FB(k)$

$$o < x_1 \cdots x_k < x_1 \cdots x_{k-1},$$

the element $x_1 \cdots x_{k-1}$ must contain at least two atoms; hence the intersection $X_1 \cdots X_{k-1}$ must contain at least two atoms, and the same is true for each of the remaining blocks; hence $FB(k)$ must have at least 2^k atoms. The generalized form of (4) shows that the 2^k elements

$$y_1 \cdots y_k$$

where each $y_i = x_i$ or x_i', will serve very well; for instance,

$$x_k = x_k u = x_k (\vee y_1 \cdots y_{k-1}).$$

Therefore k belongs to N, which thus contains all natural numbers.
We have:

THEOREM 164. The free Boolean algebra with n generators has 2^{2^n} elements.

(4) *Ideals*

In § 15 it was shown that a congruence relation C over a lattice L induces a homomorphism γ from L onto the quotient lattice L/C (Th. 80). If L has a zero element o, then L/C has a zero element $\gamma(o)$ (from Th. 78). If L/C has a zero element z, then the set Z of elements of L mapped by γ on z constitute an ideal of L called the kernel of γ; by a natural transference we shall speak of the kernel of C.

THEOREM 165. Every ideal of a distributive lattice L possessing a zero element o is the kernel of at least one congruence relation over L.

Proof. Let J be an ideal of L. Define the dyadic relation C: for a, b in L, aCb, if and only if there exists x in J such that $a + x = b + x$.

Clearly aCa for every a in L; and if aCb, then bCa. If aCb and bCc, then there exist x and y in J such that

$$a + x = b + x \quad \text{and} \quad b + y = c + y;$$

hence

$$\begin{aligned} a + (x + y) &= (a + x) + y = (b + x) + y = (b + y) + x \\ &= (c + y) + x = c + (x + y). \end{aligned}$$

But by J1, Def. 39, $x + y$ is in J; therefore aCc. Hence C is an equivalence relation.

If pCq and rCs, then there exist x and y in J such that

$$p + x = q + x \quad \text{and} \quad r + y = s + y.$$

Hence

$$(p + x)(r + y) = (q + x)(s + y),$$

that is,

$$pr + (py + xr + xy) = qs + (qy + xs + xy) \quad \text{by VII},$$

where by J2, Def. 39, the six meets in the parentheses are all in J; then by J1, Def. 39, each of $py + xr + xy$ and $qy + xs + xy$ is in J; but

$$\begin{aligned} py + xr + xy &= py + xy + xr + xy \\ &= y(p + x) + x(r + y) \\ &= y(q + x) + x(s + y) \\ &= qy + xy + xs + xy \\ &= qy + xs + xy; \end{aligned}$$

therefore $prCqs$. Also we have

$$p + x + r + y = q + x + s + y$$

or

$$(p + r) + (x + y) = (q + s) + (x + y),$$

where by J1 $x + y$ is in J; therefore $(p + r)\,C\,(q + s)$. Thus C is a congruence relation over L.

By hypothesis L has a zero element o; hence L/C has a zero element on which o is mapped, and the elements of L congruent to o constitute the kernel Z which is an ideal of L. We prove that J and Z are identical. If a belongs to Z, then aCo; hence there exists x in J such that $a + x = o + x = x$; consequently $a \leqq x$ so that by J3, Th. 59, a is in J. If b belongs to J, then $b + b = o + b$, and therefore bCo, which means that b belongs to Z. Thus $J = Z$.

THEOREM 166. An ideal of a relatively complemented lattice L which possesses a zero element o is the kernel of at most one congruence relation.

Proof. We have to prove that if an ideal of L is kernel of congruence relations C_1, C_2, then $C_1 = C_2$.

Let C be a congruence relation over L. If aCb, then from bCb we have $(a + b)\,C\,(b + b)$ and $abCbb$, that is, $(a + b)\,Cb$ and $abCb$, whence by transitivity $(a + b)\,Cab$. If, on the other hand, $(a + b)\,Cab$, from aCa we have $[a + (a + b)]\,C\,(a + ab)$, that is, $(a + b)\,Ca$; similarly from bCb we have $(a + b)\,Cb$; hence aCb. We have proved

$$aCb \Longleftrightarrow (a + b)\,Cab.$$

Since L has a zero element o, C has a kernel Z consisting of the elements of L which are congruent to o. Since L is relatively complemented and $o \leqq ab \leqq a + b$, the element ab has at least one complement relative to the interval $[o, a + b]$. Let p be *any* such complement; then

$$abp = o, \quad p \leqq ab + p = a + b. \tag{1}$$

If $(a + b)\, Cab$, from pCp we have $[p\,(a + b)]\, Cpab$, that is, from (1) pCo; therefore p belongs to Z. If on the other hand p belongs to Z, then pCo, which with $abCab$ yields $(p + ab)\, Cab$; then from (1) $(a + b)\, Cab$. We have proved

$$(a + b)\, Cab \Longleftrightarrow p \text{ belongs to } Z.$$

Then from the implication proved above

$$aCb \Longleftrightarrow p \text{ belongs to } Z.$$

It follows that if an ideal of L is the kernel Z of congruence relations C_1, C_2, then

$$aC_1b \Longrightarrow \quad p \text{ belongs to } Z \quad \Longrightarrow aC_2b$$

and

$$aC_2b \Longrightarrow \quad p \text{ belongs to } Z \quad \Longrightarrow aC_1b;$$

therefore $C_1 \leqq C_2$ and $C_2 \leqq C_1$, that is, $C_1 = C_2$.

THEOREM 167. Every ideal of a Boolean algebra is the kernel of just one congruence relation over the algebra.

Proof. A Boolean algebra is distributive, possesses a zero element and is relatively complemented (Def. 62, Def. 34, Th. 158).

Exercises

135. Let L be a distributive lattice with zero and unity elements. Show that the complemented elements form a sublattice of L.
136. Check the details of Examples 97 and 100.
137. Determine the free distributive lattice with three generators. Cf. Exercise 131 and Fig. 35.
138. A ring was defined in § 20. Show that a Boolean algebra is a ring if symmetric difference is taken for ring sum, lattice meet for ring product. (Write $x + y$ for $xy' \cup x'y$, xy for $x \cap y$.) What is the additive zero of the ring? Determine the form of x' in ring notation.
139. Show that the lattice of ideals (Th. 65) of a distributive lattice is itself distributive.
140. Taking the wider definition of join of two equivalence relations (see § 24, before Th. 131), prove that the lattice of congruence relations over *any* lattice is distributive.
141. Prove that the lattice of congruence relations over a finite distributive lattice is a Boolean algebra.

28. Skolem Algebras

Let a, b be elements of a lattice L and let X be the subset of elements x of L such that $ax \leqq b$; X is not empty, for b belongs to X. Suppose now that X has a greatest member c so that

(i) $ac \leqq b$;
(ii) if $ax \leqq b$, then $x \leqq c$.

If such an element c exists it is unique; for if c, c_1 satisfy (i) and (ii), we have $ac \leqq b$ and $ac_1 \leqq b$, whence $c_1 \leqq c$ and $c \leqq c_1$ so that $c_1 = c$. If this unique element c exists for the given ordered pair a, b, we write $c = a \to b$.

Dually, there may exist in the lattice an element d such that

(iii) $a + d \geqq b$;
(iv) if $a + y \geqq b$, then $y \geqq d$.

These conditions require d to be the least element of the subset Y of elements y such that $a + y \geqq b$. If this element d exists, it is unique; for the given ordered pair a, b we write $d = b - a$.

Example 102. Let L be the lattice of the partitions of the set $\{p, q, r, s\}$, ordered by refinement; let a, b, f, g, u be these partitions:

$$a = (pq/r/s), \quad b = (pqr/s), \quad f = (pq/rs), \quad g = (pqs/r), \quad u = (pqrs).$$

To determine $a \rightarrow b$ is easy, since $a < b$; thus $ax \leqq a < b$ for every x in the lattice including its greatest element u; hence

$$a \rightarrow b = u.$$

To determine $b \rightarrow a$ is impossible, since we have

$$bf = a, \quad bg = a, \quad \text{but} \quad bu = b > a,$$

so that the set X contains the incomparable dual atoms f, g but does not contain u; therefore X has no greatest member and $b \rightarrow a$ does not exist. If we now consider a and b to be the equivalence relations associated with the partitions $(pq/r/s)$ and (pqr/s) and if we recall that equivalence relations were partially ordered in § 4 as follows: $E_1 \leqq E_2$ if and only if xE_1y *implies* xE_2y, we have three curiously parallel statements:

If $a \leqq b$, then it is true that a implies b.
If $a \leqq b$, then $a \rightarrow b = u$.
If $a \leqq b$, then "a implies b" is true.

Example 103. Let L be the Boolean algebra of the subsets of a set U, ordered by set-inclusion. Given the subsets A, B, we seek the element $B - A$. Consider the element BA'. We see that

$$A + BA' = A + AB + BA' = A + B(A + A')$$
$$= A + BU = A + B;$$

also if Y is an element such that $A + Y \geqq B$, then $A + Y \geqq A + B$. Therefore BA' is the least element Y such that $A + Y$

$\geqq B$; that is to say, $B - A = BA'$. This is the set-difference of B, A as in Example 100. We note that $A + (B - A) = A + B$, $A - A = AA' = O$.

Definition 67. A lattice in which $a \to b$ exists for every pair of elements is called an implicative lattice. Dually, a lattice in which $b - a$ exists for every pair of elements is called a subtractive lattice.

Thus the partition lattice of Example 102 is not implicative; the Boolean algebra of Example 103 is subtractive. The names are due to H. B. Curry (1952); these lattices were introduced by Th. Skolem in 1919, and on this account we may call them Skolem lattices.

Definition 68. A Skolem lattice considered as a set closed with respect to formation of meet, formation of join, and either implication or subtraction may be termed a Skolem algebra; if closed with respect to all four operations, the lattice may be termed a double Skolem algebra.

The ascription is that advocated by Curry (1963); in the literature "Brouwer algebra" is a more usual but seemingly less just appellation.

To emphasize the nature of these new binary operations we state the obvious theorem:

THEOREM 168.

In an implicative lattice

(1) if $ax \leqq b$,
then $x \leqq a \to b$;

(2) if $x \leqq a \to b$,
then $ax \leqq b$.

In a subtractive lattice

(3) if $a + y \geqq b$,
then $y \geqq b - a$;

(4) if $y \geqq b - a$,
then $a + y \geqq b$.

THEOREM 169. An implicative lattice has a unity element; a subtractive lattice has a zero element.

Proof. Let a be any element of an implicative lattice L; then $a \to a$ exists; hence $a(a \to a) \leqq a$, and if $ax \leqq a$, then $x \leqq a \to a$. But $ax \leqq a$ for every x in L; therefore $a \to a$ is greatest element of L. We have $a \to a = b \to b = u$. Dually, in a subtractive lattice $a - a = b - b = o$.

THEOREM 170. Every Skolem algebra is distributive.

Proof. Let a, b, c be any elements of an implicative lattice L; in view of Th. 41 we need prove only that $a(b + c) \leqq ab + ac$. Let $ab + ac = d$; by hypothesis $a \to d$ exists so that $a(a \to d) \leqq d$; now $ab \leqq d$, $ac \leqq d$; hence by Th. 168 $b \leqq a \to d$ and $c \leqq a \to d$; it follows that $b + c \leqq a \to d$, whence

$$a(b + c) \leqq a(a \to d) \leqq d = ab + ac.$$

Dualize for a subtractive lattice.

Example 104. A chain with a greatest element is implicative; a chain with a least element is subtractive. We prove the latter assertion for the chain of integers $\geqq 0$. Let a, b be integers, positive or zero. If $a \geqq b$, then the least y such that $\max(a, y) \geqq b$ is 0; if $a < b$, the least such y is b. In all cases there exists an integer d such that $\max(a, d) \geqq b$ and if $\max(a, y) \geqq b$, then $y \geqq d$.

Example 105. The lattice L of the natural numbers ordered by divisibility is subtractive. With the notation of § 2 let

$$a = \prod p_i^{\alpha_i}, \quad b = \prod p_i^{\beta_i}$$

where the p_i include all the prime factors of both a and b, and where the exponents are the integers of the last example. We have just shown that for any pair of exponents α_i, β_i there exists a smallest exponent δ_i such that $\max(\alpha_i, \delta_i) \geqq \beta_i$ in the chain of integers $\geqq 0$. Then if

$$d = \prod p_i^{\delta_i},$$

we assert that $d = b - a$, in the new sense. The proof is left as an exercise for the reader. Here is an illustration with $a = 12$, $b = 15$.

$$a = 2^2 \times 3^1 \times 5^0 = 12$$

$$b = 2^0 \times 3^1 \times 5^1 = 15$$

$$\alpha: \quad 2 \quad 1 \quad 0$$

$$\beta: \quad 0 \quad 1 \quad 1$$

$$\delta: \quad 0 \quad 0 \quad 1$$

$$d = 2^0 \times 3^0 \times 5^1 = 5.$$

The l.c.m. of 12 and 5 is 60, which is divisible by 15. If the l.c.m. of 12 and y is divisible by 15, then y is divisible by 5.

THEOREM 171. A finite distributive lattice is both implicative and subtractive, that is to say, a double Skolem algebra.

Proof. Let a, b be any two elements of a finite distributive lattice L. Let X be the set of elements x of L such that $ax \leqq b$; X is not empty, for b belongs to X; X is finite, for L is finite; let X consist of the elements $x_1, \ldots, x_n$. Then

$$a \to b = x_1 + \cdots + x_n,$$

for

$$\begin{aligned} a(x_1 + \cdots + x_n) &= ax_1 + \cdots + ax_n \quad \text{by VII} \\ &\leqq b + \cdots + b \qquad \text{by definition of } X \\ &= b; \end{aligned}$$

whilst if $ax \leqq b$, then for some i, $x = x_i \leqq x_1 + \cdots + x_n$.

Thus L is implicative. To prove L subtractive, dualize this proof.

THEOREM 172. Every Boolean algebra is a double Skolem algebra.

Proof. If a, b are any elements of a Boolean algebra, take

$$a' + b \quad \text{for} \quad a \to b,$$

$$ba' \quad \text{for} \quad b - a.$$

The second of these choices was justified in Example 103. Dualize to justify the first.

Note that in view of Th. 171 the converse assertion is false.

We proceed to note in a sequence of theorems some properties of implication; the dual theorems for subtraction are all valid. Let a, b, c be any elements of an implicative lattice L.

THEOREM 173. $b \leqq a \to b$.

Proof. Since $ab \leqq b$, by Th. 168 (1) $b \leqq a \to b$.

THEOREM 174. If $a \leqq b$, then for any c, $b \to c \leqq a \to c$.

Proof. If $a \leqq b$, then

$$a(b \to c) \leqq b(b \to c)$$
$$\leqq c \qquad \text{by Th. 168 (2);}$$

hence

$$b \to c \leqq a \to c \qquad \text{by Th. 168 (1).}$$

THEOREM 175. If $a \leqq b$, then for any c, $c \to a \leqq c \to b$.

Proof. Since $c(c \to a) \leqq a \leqq b$, we have $c \to a \leqq c \to b$ by Th. 168 (1).

THEOREM 176. $(a \to b)(a \to c) = a \to bc$.

Proof. Since $bc \leqq b$, by Th. 175

$$a \to bc \leqq a \to b,$$

and since $bc \leqq c$, by the same

$$a \to bc \leqq a \to c;$$

therefore

$$a \to bc \leqq (a \to b)(a \to c).$$

Also from

$$a(a \to b) \leqq b \quad \text{and} \quad a(a \to c) \leqq c$$

we have

$$a(a \to b)(a \to c) \leqq bc;$$

therefore

$$(a \to b)(a \to c) \leqq a \to bc \quad \text{by Th. 168 (1).}$$

By anti-symmetry

$$(a \to b)(a \to c) = a \to bc.$$

THEOREM 177. $a \to (b \to c) \leqq (a \to b) \to (a \to c)$.

Proof. From
$$b\,(b \to c) \leqq c$$
we have
$$a \to [b\,(b \to c)] \leqq a \to c \qquad \text{by Th. 175;}$$
but
$$(a \to b)\,[a \to (b \to c)] = a \to [b\,(b \to c)] \qquad \text{by Th. 176;}$$
hence
$$(a \to b)\,[a \to (b \to c)] \leqq a \to c;$$
it follows that
$$a \to (b \to c) \leqq (a \to b) \to (a \to c) \quad \text{by Th. 168 (1).}$$

THEOREM 178. $a \leqq b \to ab$.

Proof. From $b\,(b \to a) \leqq a$ we have
$$b\,(b \to a) \leqq ab;$$
hence by Th. 168 (1)
$$b \to a \leqq b \to ab;$$
then by Th. 173
$$a \leqq b \to a \leqq b \to ab.$$

THEOREM 179. $(a \to c) \leqq (b \to c) \to [(a + b) \to c]$.

Proof. From
$$a\,(a \to c) \leqq c$$

we have
$$a(a \to c)(b \to c) \leqq c(b \to c) \leqq c;$$
and from
$$b(b \to c) \leqq c$$
we have
$$b(b \to c)(a \to c) \leqq c(a \to c) \leqq c;$$
hence
$$a(b \to c)(a \to c) + b(b \to c)(a \to c) \leqq c + c = c.$$

Now by Th. 170 the lattice L is distributive; therefore by VII

$$(a + b)(b \to c)(a \to c) = a(b \to c)(a \to c) + b(b \to c)(a \to c) \leqq c.$$

Hence
$$(b \to c)(a \to c) \leqq (a + b) \to c \quad \text{by Th. 168 (1).}$$

By the same theorem it follows that

$$(a \to c) \leqq (b \to c) \to [(a + b) \to c].$$

It was shown in Th. 169 that an implicative lattice must have a unity element u; if the lattice also has a zero element o, the elements of the form $x \to o$ are of particular interest. Dually, if a subtractive lattice possesses a unity element u in addition to its obligatory zero element o, special interest attaches to elements of the form $u - x$. For such elements we define a new notation.

Definition 69. In an implicative lattice with o the element

$x \to o$ will be written x^*.

In a subtractive lattice with u the element

$u - x$ will be written $x\dagger$.

Some authors use $\urcorner x$ for one or the other. The reason for the interest and for the notation is not far to seek:

THEOREM 180.

In an implicative lattice with o we have

$$aa^* = o$$

for every element a in the lattice.

In a subtractive lattice with u we have

$$a + a\dagger = u$$

for every element a in the lattice.

Proof.

$$aa^* = a(a \to o)$$
$$\leqq o \quad \text{by Th. 168;}$$

hence

$$aa^* = o.$$

a^* is then the greatest element x such that $ax = o$.

$$a + a\dagger = a + (u - a)$$
$$\geqq u \quad \text{by Th. 168;}$$

hence

$$a + a\dagger = u.$$

$a\dagger$ is then the least element y such that $a + y = u$.

We note that a double Skolem algebra, being implicative and subtractive at the same time, must possess both o and u; hence in such a lattice x^* and $x\dagger$ exist for every x; these elements x^* and $x\dagger$ may coincide or differ. In the lattice of the factors of 120, ordered by divisibility, we have $3^* = 40 = 3\dagger$ but $10^* = 3 \neq 24 = 10\dagger$.

THEOREM 181.

(i) An implicative lattice L with o is Boolean if and only if $x + x^* = u$ for every x in L.

(ii) A subtractive lattice L with u is Boolean if and only if $xx\dagger = o$ for every x in L.

(iii) A double Skolem algebra L is a Boolean algebra if and only if $x^* = x\dagger$ for every x in L.

Proof.

(i) By Th. 180 for every x in L, $xx^* = o$; if also $x + x^* = u$, then x^* is a complement of x in L; but L is distributive; hence L is Boolean. Complements being unique, we have $x^* = x'$.

Let L be Boolean. In general, if $ax = o$, then $x \leqq a^*$; here $xx' = o$, whence $x' \leqq x^*$. It follows that

$$u = x + x' \leqq x + x^*,$$

that is, $u = x + x^*$. Since also $xx^* = o$, we have $x^* = x'$. (This proof is independent of Th. 172; if we assume that $a \rightarrow b = a' + b$, we have immediately $x^* = x'$, whence $x + x^* = u$.)

(ii) The proof of (ii) is dual to that of (i). In this case we have $x\dagger = x'$.

(iii) In this case L is implicative with o so that $xx^* = o$ for every x, and at the same time subtractive with u so that $x + x\dagger = u$ for every x; therefore if $x^* = x\dagger$, L is complemented and so Boolean.

If on the other hand L is Boolean, from the second part of (i) $x^* = x'$, and from the second part of (ii) $x\dagger = x'$; hence $x^* = x\dagger$, and this for every x in L.

We now consider some of the properties of the element x^*, which from Th. 180 we see is a half-complement to x. First we define x^{**} to mean $(x^*)^*$, x^{***} to mean $(x^{**})^*$, and so on.

Example 106. The sixteen factors of 120, ordered by divisibility, form an implicative lattice with zero element 1. If m, n are natural numbers and h.c.f. $(m, n) = 1$, we say m, n are co-prime. In this lattice therefore x^* is the number co-prime to x which is divisible by all the numbers co-prime to x, that is, x^* is the greatest number co-prime to x; x^{**} is the greatest number co-prime to x^*. We tabulate these elements below.

x	1	2	3	4	5	6	8	10	12	15	20	24	30	40	60	120
x^*	20	15	40	15	24	5	15	3	5	8	3	5	1	3	1	1
x^{**}	1	8	3	8	5	24	8	40	24	15	40	24	120	40	120	120

Next we notice the simplification of Th. 168 (1), (2) if $b = o$:

(1*) If $ax = o$, then $x \leqq a^*$.

(2*) If $x \leqq a^*$, then $ax = o$.

We proceed to a sequence of theorems on x^*. Let a, b, c be any elements of an implicative lattice with o.

THEOREM 182. $a \leqq a^{**}$.

Proof. By Th. 180 $aa^* = o$; hence $a \leqq a^{**}$.

It must be emphasized that we may have either $a < a^{**}$ or $a = a^{**}$.

In Example 106 $3 = 3^{**}$ but 4 properly divides $4^{**} = 8$.

THEOREM 183. If $a \leqq b$, then $b^* \leqq a^*$.

Proof. Take $c = o$ in Th. 174.

THEOREM 184. $a^* = a^{***}$.

Proof. By Th. 182 $a^* \leqq (a^*)^{**} = [(a^*)^*]^*$.
Also Ths. 182 and 183 taken together give $a^* \geqq (a^{**})^* = [(a^*)^*]^*$. By anti-symmetry $a^* = a^{***}$.

THEOREM 185. $(a + b)^* = a^*b^*$; $(ab)^* \geqq a^* + b^*$.

Proof. Theorem 179 asserted that

$$(a \to c) \leqq (b \to c) \to [(a \to b) \to c].$$

Taking $c = o$, we have

$$a^* \leqq b^* \to (a + b)^*;$$

hence by Th. 168 (2)

$$a^*b^* \leqq (a + b)^*.$$

Also, from $a \leqq a + b$ and $b \leqq a + b$ we have by Th. 183

$$a^* \geqq (a + b)^* \quad \text{and} \quad b^* \geqq (a + b)^*,$$

from which we obtain

$$a^*b^* \geqq (a + b)^*.$$

By anti-symmetry

$$(a + b)^* = a^*b^*.$$

For the second formula, from $ab \leqq a$ follows $(ab)^* \geqq a^*$ by Th. 183; similarly $(ab)^* \geqq b^*$; therefore $(ab)^* \geqq a^* + b^*$. It must be emphasized that either alternative is possible here.

THEOREM 186. $a \to b^* \leqq b \to a^*$.

Proof. Theorem 177 asserted that

$$a \to (b \to c) \leqq (a \to b) \to (a \to c);$$

taking $c = o$ we have

$$a \to b^* \leqq (a \to b) \to a^*.$$

By Th. 173 $b \leqq a \to b$; applying Th. 174 to this inequality we obtain

$$(a \to b) \to c \leqq b \to c,$$

which with a^* for c yields

$$(a \to b) \to a^* \leqq b \to a^*.$$

Thus

$$a \to b^* \leqq (a \to b) \to a^* \leqq b \to a^*.$$

THEOREM 187. $a \leqq a^* \to b$; $a^* \leqq a \to b$.

Proof. $aa^* = o \leqq b$; hence by Th. 168 (1) $a \leqq a^* \to b$, $a^* \leqq a \to b$.

THEOREM 188. $u^* = o$; $o^* = u$.

Proof. By Th. 180 $u^* = u^*u = o$. Then by Th. 182 $u = u^{**} = (u^*)^* = o^*$. We note that $o = o^{**}$, $u = u^{**}$.

THEOREM 189. $(ab)^{**} = a^{**}b^{**}$.

Proof. By Th. 183 from $ab \leqq a$ we have $a^* \leqq (ab)^*$, then $(ab)^{**} \leqq a^{**}$; in the same way from $ab \leqq b$ we obtain $(ab)^{**} \leqq b^{**}$; hence

$$(ab)^{**} \leqq a^{**}b^{**}.$$

Since

$$a\,[b\,(ab)^*] = (ab)\,(ab)^* = o,$$

$$b\,(ab)^* \leqq a^* = a^{***} = (a^{**})^*;$$

hence

$$a^{**}b\,(ab)^* = o.$$

It follows that

$$a^{**}\,(ab)^* \leqq b^* = b^{***} = (b^{**})^*,$$

from which we have

$$a^{**}b^{**}\,(ab)^* = o$$

so that

$$a^{**}b^{**} \leqq (ab)^{**}.$$

Consequently,

$$(ab)^{**} = a^{**}b^{**}.$$

Corresponding to Ths. 182–9 there are the dual theorems on $x\dagger$ in a subtractive lattice with u; we can now make the following comparison:

Implicative lattice with zero	Boolean algebra	Subtractive lattice with unity
$a \leqq a^{**}$	$a = a''$	$a \geqq a\dagger\dagger$
$a^* = a^{***}$	$a' = a'''$	$a\dagger = a\dagger\dagger\dagger$
$(ab)^* \geqq a^* + b^*$	$(ab)' = a' + b'$	$(ab)\dagger = a\dagger + b\dagger$
$(a + b)^* = a^*b^*$	$(a + b)' = a'b'$	$(a + b)\dagger \leqq a\dagger b\dagger$
$aa^* = o$	$aa' = o$	$aa\dagger \geqq o$
$a + a^* \leqq u$	$a + a' = u$	$a + a\dagger = u$

Exercises

142. Complete the proof required in Example 105.

143. Show that a homomorphic image of an implicative lattice is itself implicative.

144. Let L be an implicative lattice with zero element. Let S be the subset of elements x of L such that $x = x^{**}$. Show that if p, q are elements of S and we define meet and join in S by

$$p \wedge q = pq, \quad p \vee q = (p + q)^{**}$$

where pq, $p + q$ are meet and join in L, with these operations the set S constitutes a Boolean algebra of at least two elements. Illustrate from Example 106.

29. Logic

Since lattice theory began with Boole's systematization of logic it is appropriate to devote some pages to a specimen demonstration of the manner in which lattices may be applied to this subtle discipline.

We shall need a wider class of dyadic relation than that of partial order.

Definition 70. A dyadic relation Q defined in a set S which is

(i) reflexive: aQa for every a in S;
(ii) transitive: if for a, b, c in S aQb and bQc, then aQc, is called a relation of quasi-order.

A relation of quasi-order differs from an equivalence relation (Def.6) in that symmetry is not required; it differs from a relation of partial order (Def. 10) in that no previous relation of equality is supposed and thus anti-symmetry cannot be defined. We note that from (i) Q is over S.

THEOREM 190. If a relation Q of quasi-order is defined over a set S (with elements $a, b, c, \ldots$) and we define a dyadic relation E as follows: aEb if and only if aQb and bQa, then E is an equivalence relation.

Proof. Clearly aEa for every a in S; symmetry is obvious in that if aEb, then bEa. If aEb and bEc, then aQb and bQc; but Q is transitive, and therefore aQc; also cQb and bQa, so that by the transitivity of Q cQa; from aQc and cQa we have aEc. Thus E is over S, reflexive, symmetric and transitive.

THEOREM 191. Let E of the last theorem partition S into classes $X, Y, Z, \ldots$ of equivalent elements. Let T be the set $\{X, Y, Z, \ldots\}$. If we define a dyadic relation written $\leqq$ in T as follows:

$$X \leqq Y \text{ in } T \quad \text{if and only if} \quad xQy \text{ in } S$$

for some x in X and for some y in Y, then T is a partially ordered set with respect to this relation.

Proof. If xEv and yEw and xQy, then vQw. For we have

$$vQx, \quad xQy, \quad yQw,$$

and therefore vQw from the transitivity of Q. Thus the definition of $\leqq$ entails that

$$X \leqq Y \quad \text{if} \quad xQy \text{ for any } x \text{ in } X, \text{ any } y \text{ in } Y,$$

and that

$$\text{if } X \leqq Y, \text{ then } xQy \text{ for every } x \text{ in } X, \text{ every } y \text{ in } Y.$$

Clearly $X \leqq X$ for every X in T, since xQx for every x in S. If $X \leqq Y$ and $Y \leqq X$, then xQy and yQx for every x in X, every y in Y; therefore from the definition of E we have xEy for every x in X, every y in Y; that is to say the sets X, Y have identical membership, and as in § 1 we write $X = Y$. We emphasize that the equality sign signifies absolute identity. Finally, if $X \leqq Y$ and $Y \leqq Z$, then for some x in X, every y in Y, some z in Z we have

$$xQy, \quad yQz,$$

which together give xQz, so that $X \leqq Z$. Thus the relation $\leqq$ is reflexive, anti-symmetric (the equality relation required being set identity), and transitive; that is, the relation is one of partial order; T is partially ordered with respect to this relation.

We are ready now to begin our excursion into logic. Let S be a non-empty set of objects called "sentences" which is closed with respect to three binary operations and one unary operation in the following manner:

For every ordered pair of elements a, b of S there exist three elements in S uniquely determined and denoted by

$$a \to b, \quad ab, \quad a + b,$$

and for every element a in S there exists in S a uniquely determined element denoted by

$$a^*.$$

Next we suppose it possible to attach a distinguishing mark to elements of S thus

$$\vdash s$$

where s is an element of S; this is read

the "sentence" s "is asserted".

Further, we lay down that this distinguishing mark *is* attached to any element of S constructed to one of the following ten patterns:

(1) $\vdash p \to (q \to p)$.

(2) $\vdash [p \to (q \to r)] \to [(p \to q) \to (p \to r)]$.

(3) $\vdash pq \to p$.

(4) $\vdash pq \to q$.

(5) $\vdash p \to (q \to pq)$.

(6) $\vdash p \to (p + q)$.

(7) $\vdash q \to (p + q)$.

(8) $\vdash (p \to r) \to \{(q \to r) \to [(p + q) \to r]\}$.

(9) $\vdash (p \to q^*) \to (q \to p^*)$.

(10) $\vdash p \to (p^* \to q)$.

Lastly, we lay down that all other patterns carrying the distinguishing mark are those derivable from the ten given patterns by the unique rule

if $p \to q$ and p are postulated or proved to carry the mark, then q carries the mark;

in symbols

$$\begin{array}{l} \vdash p \to q \\ \vdash p \\ \hline \qquad \vdash q \end{array} \qquad \text{D}$$

where the letter D indicates that this process of detachment has been completed. In words, for actual elements a, b of S,

if $a \to b$ is an "asserted sentence"
and if a is an "asserted sentence",
then b is an "asserted sentence".

Example 107. Let L be an implicative lattice with zero element o as well as unity element u. To fix ideas, we may think of L as the sixteen-element lattice of Example 106. We show that L is an instance of a set S as postulated above. The lattice L is not empty; it is closed with respect to the three binary operations of implication, formation of meet, formation of join, and the unary operation of half-complementation; the notation for the operations of S was, of course, chosen with this example in mind. For the distinguishing mark $\vdash$ that may be applied to elements of L we direct as follows:

In the first instance the mark $\vdash$ may be applied only to elements of the form $a \to b$ and this may be done if and only if $a \leqq b$. Thus

$$\vdash a \to b \quad \text{means that} \quad a \leqq b.$$

For a given element b of L consider the element $u \to b$. We know that $u \to b$ is the greatest element x such that $ux \leqq b$; but $ux = x$, so that clearly $u \to b = b$. It follows that $\vdash u \to b$ would mean that $u \leqq b$ and therefore $b = u$. Thus we may amplify our directive about the distinguishing mark:

> In the second instance the mark $\vdash$ may be applied to an element x not expressed in the form $a \to b$ if and only if that element x is in fact the unity element u. Briefly,
>
> $$\vdash x \quad \text{means that} \quad x = u.$$

For a, b, c in L we verify that any element of L constructed to any one of the patterns (1)–(10) may carry the mark $\vdash$.

(1) $\vdash b \to (a \to b)$ if and only if $b \leqq a \to b$. The latter assertion was proved as Th. 173.

(2) $\vdash [a \to (b \to c)] \to [(a \to b) \to (a \to c)]$ if and only if

$$a \to (b \to c) \leqq (a \to b) \to (a \to c).$$

This was Th. 177.

Similarly, (3) corresponds to Th. 14, (4) to Th. 16, (5) to Th. 178, (6) to Th. 15, (7) to Th. 16, (8) to Th. 179, (9) to Th. 186, and (10) to Th. 187. The rule D of detachment

$$\text{if } \vdash a \to b \text{ and } \vdash a, \text{ then (we may infer) } \vdash b$$

is valid in L, for in our interpretation D becomes

$$\text{if } a \leqq b \text{ and } a = u, \text{ then (we may infer) } b = u.$$

In our numerical example we notice that $6 \cup 6^* = 6 \cup 5 = 30 \neq 120$; therefore if we consider our set of sixteen numbers as a system on its own, defining the operations by means of tables (like multiplication tables for the binary operations, as in Example 106 for the unary operation), and if we test every possible case of formulae (1)–(10), we shall exhibit a finite arithmetical model of the system S, and thereby demonstrate that

$$\vdash p + p^*$$

cannot be established in that system. Again, we remember that in our model, 4 properly divides $4^{**} = 8$ (see Th. 182), in symbols we have a case of $a^{**} \nleqq a$; therefore

$$\vdash p^{**} \rightarrow p$$

cannot be demonstrated in S. If by mistake we had taken for our model the lattice of the sixteen factors of 210 (instead of 120), we should have seen neither of these serious deficiencies in the system S; 210 is square-free and therefore gives a Boolean algebra, which being implicative with zero would have satisfied all requirements: but in a Boolean algebra $a + a^* = a + a' = u$ and $a^{**} = a'' = a \leqq a$, for every a in the lattice. The reader may wonder why we suddenly treated the first lattice as an apparently arbitrary organization of sixteen numbers, jettisoning all our accumulated theory up to Th. 187 inclusive; and again, why the deficiencies of S were described as serious. The explanation will be given below.

In our specification of S we used quotation marks deliberately so that the reader should not be put off by having a factor of 120 presented to him as a sentence, nor by being directed to read

$$\vdash 3 \cup 40$$

as: the sentence l.c.m. (3, 40) is asserted, when we were intending to have it mean: the l.c.m. of 3 and 40 is 120. Let now the objects in S really be sentences, that is, statements, not commands, questions or exclamations. We are not concerned at all with the meaning of the sentences, but only with the correct inference of one from another. Now

$$\vdash s$$

means that s is asserted, asserted as valid either because it is of valid pattern or because it has been obtained in the only legitimate way, namely by detachment. We are restricted to this automatic rule to guard against the danger of using logical reasoning when the subject matter is itself logical reasoning. The patterns (1)–(10) are technically called axiom-schemes; they were published in 1952 by the Polish logician Jan Łukasiewicz and are designed to axiomatize the logic of the "intuitionist" mathematicians; the intuitionist movement, founded by L. E. J. Brouwer, has a logic of its own, markedly different from the classical logic, in common use, which was the subject of the researches of Boole and Schröder. For sentences s, t in S we take as meanings of the operations:

$$s \to t\colon \ s \text{ implies } t$$

$$st\colon \ s \text{ and } t$$

$$s + t\colon \ s \text{ or } t$$

$$s^*\colon \ \text{negation of } s.$$

In making inferences we must not use these meanings. The import of

$$\vdash s + s^*$$

becomes clear: the alternative "s or not-s" is valid. We proved above that this assertion cannot be established in intuitionist logic. Nor can

$$\vdash s^{**} \to s;$$

we cannot infer (by detachment) the validity of s from the validity of not-not-s. It follows that several familiar forms of indirect reasoning found in mathematical proofs are not permitted in this system; that is why we abruptly abandoned the theory supporting our arithmetical model, theory developed with the aid of ordinary classical logic, which admits indirect proof.

The patterns (1)–(10) clearly have some sort of connexion with theorems about implicative lattices with zero. The question presents itself: can the system S of sentences be exhibited as such a lattice? Since partial order requires a previous definition of equality and each sentence in S is a unique individual entity, S cannot be exhibited as a lattice; the work at the beginning of this section suggests that we look for a relation of quasi-order, then for an equivalence relation.

$$\vdash \{p \to [(q \to p) \to p]\} \to \{[p \to (q \to p)] \to (p \to p)\} \qquad (2)$$

$$\vdash p \to [(q \to p) \to p] \qquad (1)$$

$$\vdash [p \to (q \to p)] \to (p \to p) \qquad \mathrm{D}$$

$$\vdash p \to (q \to p) \qquad (1)$$

(11) $$\vdash p \to p. \qquad \mathrm{D}$$

Thus if a is any actual sentence in S, $a \to a$ is asserted. Let α denote $q \to r$, $\beta : p \to q$, $\gamma : p \to r$, $\delta : p \to (q \to r)$, and s any sentence in S.

$$\vdash [\delta \to (\beta \to \gamma)] \to \{s \to [\delta \to (\beta \to \gamma)]\} \qquad (1)$$

$$\vdash \delta \to (\beta \to \gamma) \qquad (2)$$

(12) $$\vdash s \to [\delta \to (\beta \to \gamma)]. \qquad \mathrm{D}$$

$$\vdash \{s \to [\delta \to (\beta \to \gamma)]\} \to \{(s \to \delta) \to [s \to (\beta \to \gamma)]\} \qquad (2)$$

$$\vdash s \to [\delta \to (\beta \to \gamma)] \qquad (12)$$

(13) $$\vdash (s \to \delta) \to [s \to (\beta \to \gamma)] \qquad \mathrm{D}$$

$$\vdash (\alpha \to \delta) \to [a \to (\beta \to \gamma)] \qquad (13)$$

$$\vdash \alpha \to \delta \qquad (1)$$

(14) $$\vdash \alpha \to (\beta \to \gamma). \qquad \mathrm{D}$$

In full (14) reads $\vdash (q \to r) \to [(p \to q) \to (p \to r)]$.

Continuing in this way we obtain in succession

(15) $\vdash (s \to \alpha) \to [s \to (\beta \to \gamma)]$

(16) $\vdash \delta \to [(q \to \beta) \to (q \to \gamma)]$

(17) $\vdash \delta \to (q \to \beta).$

Then by D with (16) and (17) in turn, we infer from

$\vdash \{\delta \to [(q \to \beta) \to (q \to \gamma)]\} \to$

$\{[\delta \to (q \to \beta)] \to [\delta \to (q \to \gamma)]\}$ (2)

(18) $\vdash [p \to (q \to r)] \to [q \to (p \to r)].$

$\vdash [\alpha \to (\beta \to \gamma)] \to [\beta \to (\alpha \to \gamma)]$ (18)

$\vdash \alpha \to (\beta \to \gamma)$ (14)

(19) $\vdash \beta \to (\alpha \to \gamma).$ D

In full (19) reads

$$\vdash (p \to q) \to [(q \to r) \to (p \to r)].$$

$\vdash (\beta\alpha \to \beta) \to \{[\beta \to (\alpha \to \gamma)] \to [\beta\alpha \to (\alpha \to \gamma)]\}$ (19)

$\vdash \beta\alpha \to \beta$ (3)

$\vdash [\beta \to (\alpha \to \gamma)] \to [\beta\alpha \to (\alpha \to \gamma)]$ D

$\vdash \beta \to (\alpha \to \gamma)$ (19)

(20) $\vdash \beta\alpha \to (\alpha \to \gamma).$

$\vdash [\beta\alpha \to (\alpha \to \gamma)] \to [(\beta\alpha \to \alpha) \to (\beta\alpha \to \gamma)]$ (2)

$\vdash \beta\alpha \to (\alpha \to \gamma)$ (20)

$\vdash (\beta\alpha \to \alpha) \to (\beta\alpha \to \gamma)$ D

$\vdash \beta\alpha \to \alpha$ (4)

(21) $\vdash \beta\alpha \to \gamma.$ D

In full (21) reads $\vdash (p \to q)(q \to r) \to (p \to r)$.

(22) $\vdash (p \to q) \to [(q \to p) \to (p \to q)(q \to p)]$. (5)

(23) $\vdash (p \to p) \to [(p \to p) \to (p \to p)(p \to p)]$. (22)

Further, from (14) and (5) we may infer

(24) $\vdash (r \to p) \to [r \to (q \to pq)]$

which applied to (13) yields

(25) $\vdash (r \to p) \to [(r \to q) \to (r \to pq)]$.

Thus we have

(26) $\vdash (pq \to q) \to [(pq \to p) \to (pq \to qp)]$ (25)

from which with the aid of (4) and (3) in succession we infer

(27) $\vdash pq \to qp$.

(28) $\vdash (p \to q)(q \to p) \to (q \to p)(p \to q)$. (27)

Let a, b be actual sentences in S. If $\vdash a \to b$, then and only then we write

$$aQb.$$

By (11) aQa for every a in S.

Suppose aQb, bQc; then by definition $\vdash a \to b$, $\vdash b \to c$.

$\vdash (a \to b) \to [(b \to c) \to (a \to c)]$ (19)

$\vdash a \to b$ by hypothesis

$\vdash (b \to c) \to (a \to c)$ D

$\vdash b \to c$ by hypothesis

$\vdash a \to c$. D

Thus aQc; we have Q a relation of quasi-order. It is emphasized that $a \to b$ is a unique sentence in S, whereas aQb means that a appears as antecedent, b as consequent in one particular ordered pair in the totality of ordered pairs of sentences which constitute the relation Q. See Def. 2, § 3. If $\vdash (a \rightarrow b)^*$, we may write $a\bar{Q}b$. Again, if $\vdash (a \rightarrow b)(b \rightarrow a)$, then and only then we write

$$aEb.$$

If $\vdash [(a \rightarrow b)(b \rightarrow a)]^*$, we may write $a\bar{E}b$.

Suppose aQb, bQa; then by definition $\vdash a \rightarrow b$, $\vdash b \rightarrow a$. From

$$\vdash (a \rightarrow b) \rightarrow [(b \rightarrow a) \rightarrow (a \rightarrow b)(b \rightarrow a)] \tag{5}$$

detachment will yield $\vdash (a \rightarrow b)(b \rightarrow a)$, so that aEb. Conversely if we are given aEb, from (3) and (4) we can infer that aQb, bQa. From (22) and (11) we can infer $\vdash (a \rightarrow a)(a \rightarrow a)$ for every a in S; that is, aEa for every a in S. If aEb, then by definition $\vdash (a \rightarrow b)(b \rightarrow a)$. Then we may infer by detachment from (28) that $\vdash (b \rightarrow a)(a \rightarrow b)$; that is, bEa. To prove transitivity we should need first to infer that

$$\vdash (a \rightarrow b)(b \rightarrow a) \rightarrow [(b \rightarrow c)(c \rightarrow b) \rightarrow (a \rightarrow c)(c \rightarrow a)];$$

then from aEb, bEc we could infer by detachment that aEc. Assuming this last step, we have E an equivalence relation over S. It is emphasized that $(a \rightarrow b)(b \rightarrow a)$ is a particular sentence in S, $\vdash (a \rightarrow b)(b \rightarrow a)$ is a statement (outside S) about that particular sentence, whilst aEb puts the statement in a special form, indicating that (a, b) is one of the ordered pairs of the totality of ordered pairs of sentences of S constituting the defined relation E.

We now classify the elements of S, putting a and b in the same class if and only if aEb; then if a and b are classmates, and b and c are classmates, by transitivity of E a and c are classmates. Since aEa for every a in S, every sentence of S enters some class. To determine that we have disjoint classes we could first establish

(29) $\vdash (p \rightarrow q) \rightarrow (q^* \rightarrow p^*)$

and then infer

$$(30) \vdash (p \to q)(q \to p) \to \{[(q \to r)(r \to q)]^* \to [(p \to r)(r \to p)]^*\};$$

thus if we were given aEb, $b\bar{E}c$, we could infer $a\bar{E}c$.

Denote by T the set of these classes; if a is in class A, b in class B, we define an ordering relation

$$A \leqq B \text{ if and only if } aQb, \text{ that is, } \vdash a \to b.$$

Establishing that this relation was one of partial order—notice that it is not one of set-inclusion, for A, B are either disjoint or identical—we could proceed to show that every pair of classes had greatest lower bound and least upper bound, that T had a zero class—the class containing $(a \to a)^*$—and finally the theorems:

(i) $A(A \to B) \leqq B$
(ii) If $AX \leqq B$, then $X \leqq A \to B$.

We end this excursion with a glance at classical logic. Let B be a non-empty set of sentences closed this time with respect to one binary and to one unary operation, written for a, b in B

$$a \to b \quad \text{and} \quad a',$$

respectively; let the assertion mark and rule of detachment be as before; let the axiomatic patterns be the following:

$$(31) \vdash (p \to q) \to [(q \to r) \to (p \to r)],$$

$$(32) \vdash p \to (p' \to q),$$

$$(33) \vdash (p' \to p) \to p.$$

These are again due to Łukasiewicz (1924).

It is found convenient to define two further binary operations

$$ab \text{ defined as an abbreviation for } (a \to b')',$$

$$a + b \text{ similarly an abbreviation for } a' \to b.$$

Proceeding as before, still by detachment, we could form a partially ordered set C, which this time we could show was a Boolean algebra; moreover, we could show that C had only two elements O and U, where O was the class containing $(a \to a)' = (a \to a'')' = aa'$, and U the class containing $a \to a = a'' \to a = a' + a$. In crude terms: in classical logic a sentence can be either true or false and there is no other possibility *(non datur tertium quid)*. Of course, logic is not concerned with truth or falsehood; that is the province of the philosopher or the judge. Logic is concerned with valid inference of sentence from sentence.

Example 108. Let a, b be two sentences of a classical logic B; let F be the subset of B consisting of all sentences built up by a finite number of operations of implication ($\to$) and priming ($'$) from a and/or b. Then every element of F may be shown to be equivalent to some sentence having the form of an element of the free Boolean algebra with two generators a, b; see § 27 (3). Consider the possibilities:

(i) $\vdash ab$: both a and b asserted;
(ii) $\vdash ab'$: a asserted, b' asserted (in fact b not asserted);
(iii) $\vdash a'b$: a' asserted, b asserted (in fact a not asserted);
(iv) $\vdash a'b'$: a' asserted, b' asserted (neither a nor b asserted).

In each case eight of the representative sentences will fall into the equivalence class U, eight into class O; thus F will be partitioned into classes U and O in just four ways. To take a concrete, if trivial, case: let the sentences a, b be respectively

"Speech is silver" and "Silence is golden";

there are really only sixteen things we can say about speech and silence and their metallic properties; and in the different cases: both a and b true, one true and one false, both false, half of our sixteen statements will be true and half false. The reader should consult Example 65, § 16; if a is given the number tag 6, b the tag 10, the different equivalences can easily be checked.

Thus we have seen that distributive lattices are of particular interest to the logicians; the excursion in § 20 was planned to show a little of the importance that the algebraists attach to modular lattices; geometers favour semi-modular lattices, as was hinted in Exercises 124 and 125; as for the topologists, their concern, like that of the logicians, is with distributive lattices, but topology starts with infinite unions or infinite intersections, which are beyond the scope of this book.

Exercises

145. In the system S of intuitionist logic obtain the following inferences:

(i) $\vdash p\,(p \to q) \to q$;

(ii) $\vdash (pq \to r) \to [p \to (q \to r)]$.

146. In the system B of classical logic determine the assertions corresponding to the de Morgan formulae and obtain one of them, by detachment only, from (31)–(33).

LIST OF SOURCES

BIRKHOFF, G. (1) On the structure of abstract algebras. *Proc. Camb. Phil. Soc.* **31** (1935) 433–54; (2) *Lattice Theory*, New York, 1st ed. 1940; 2nd ed. enlarged, 1948; 3rd ed. with minor amendments, 1961.

CULBERTSON, J.T. *Mathematics and Logic for Digital Devices*, Princeton, 1958.

CURRY, H.B. (1) *Leçons de logique algébrique*, Paris, Louvain, 1952. (2) *Foundations of Mathematical Logic*, New York, London, 1963.

DEDEKIND, R. (1) Über Zerlegungen von Zahlen durch ihre größten gemeinsamen Teiler (1897); (2) Über die von drei Moduln erzeugte Dualgruppe (1900); *Ges. Werke* (ed. Fricke, Noether, Ore), II, Braunschweig, 1931.

DILWORTH, R.P. (ed.) *Proceedings of Symposia in Pure Mathematics*. II: *Lattice Theory*, Providence, Rhode Island, 1961.

DUBREIL, P. and DUBREIL-JACOTIN, M.-L. Théorie algébrique des relations d'équivalence. *Jour. de Math.* **18** (1939) 63–95.

DUBREIL-JACOTIN, M.-L., LESIEUR, L. and CROISOT, R. *Leçons sur la théorie des treillis, des structures algébriques ordonnées et des treillis géométriques*, Paris, 1953.

GOODSTEIN, R.L. *Boolean Algebra*, Pergamon Press, 1963.

HERMES, H. *Einführung in die Verbandstheorie*, Berlin, 1955.

KUROSH, A.G. *The Theory of Groups* (trans. from Russian by K.A.Hirsch), II, New York, 1956.

ŁUKASIEWICZ, J. On the intuitionistic theory of deduction. *Koninkl. Nederl. Akad. Wetensch. Proc.*, Series A, **55**, No.3, 1952.

ORE, O. Theory of equivalence relations. *Duke Math. Jour.* **9** (1942) 573–627.

STONE, M.H. Representations of distributive lattices and Brouwerian logics. *Čas. Mat. Fys.* **67** (1937–8) 1–25.

SZÁSZ, G. *Introduction to Lattice Theory*, Budapest (Hungarian) 1959; (German trans.) 1962; English trans. New York, 1963.

Other books consulted:

DAVENPORT, H. *The Higher Arithmetic*, London, 1952. (Number theory.)

HARDY, G.H. and WRIGHT, E.M. *An Introduction to the Theory of Numbers*, 3rd ed., Oxford, 1954. (Number modules.)

LEDERMANN, W. *Introduction to the Theory of Finite Groups*, 5th ed., Edinburgh, London, 1964. (Group theory.)

PRIOR, A.N. *Formal Logic*, 2nd ed., Oxford, 1962. (Logic.)

LOCATION OF NUMBERED ITEMS

Section	Definitions	Theorems	Examples	Exercises	Figures	Pages
1				1–7		1–3
2				8–14		3–8
3	1–5		1–3	15–20		8–12
4	6, 7	1, 2	4–7	21–30		13–22
5	8 9	3	8–10	31–34		22–29
6	10–17	4	11–26	35, 36	1–5	30–38
7	18, 19	5	27–34	37–42	6	38–43
8	20–22	6–30	35	43–48	7	43–53
9	23	31, 32	36–43	49–54	8–17	53–74
10						75–76
11	24	33–44		55–59		77–85
12	25–31	45–54	44–48	60–67	18–23	85–100
13	32–35	55	49–51	68–73		101–104
14	36–44	56–74	52–60	74–83	24, 25	104–116
15	45–53	75–84	61–66	84–91	26	117–133
16	54	85–90	67–72	92–98	27, 28	134–144
17		91–97		99–104		144–148
18	55, 56	98–106	73–75	105–108	29–31	148–159
19		107–114	76	109, 110		159–165
20			77–83	111–114	32	165–176
21	57, 58	115–123	84–86	115–117	33, 34	177–189
22		124–128		118, 119		189–193
23		129, 130	87	120, 121		193–196
24		131		122–127		197–201
25	59	132–145	88–91	128–131	35	202–212
26	60, 61	146–149	92–94	132–134		212–224
27	62–66	150–167	95–101	135–141	36	224–249
28	67–69	168–189	102–106	142–144		249–263
29	70	190, 191	107, 108	145, 146		264–277
At end					37	280

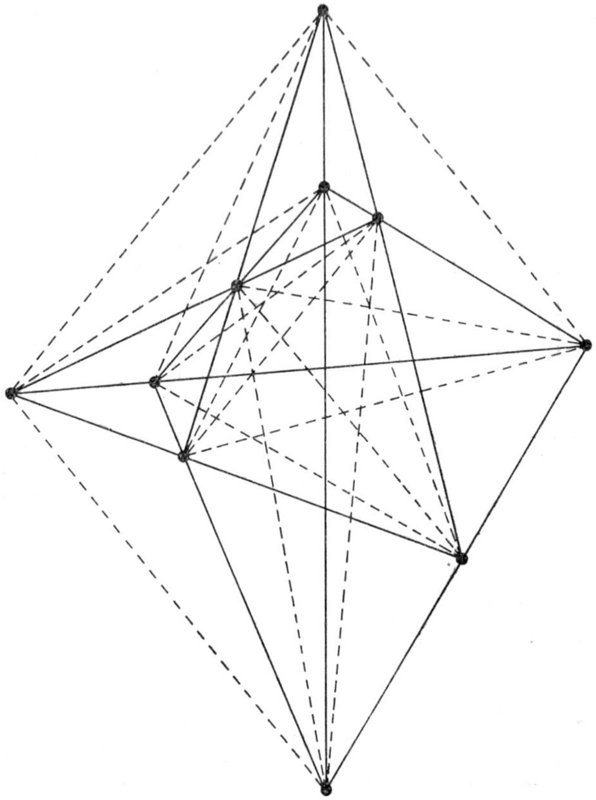

FIG. 37. Solution to Exercise 125.

INDEX

MADE IN GREAT BRITAIN